Operations research
in
management

Operations Research in Management

Edited by

Stephen Littlechild
Director General of Electricity Supply

and

Maurice Shutler
Chief Industrial Adviser, Monopolies and Mergers Commission

PRENTICE HALL

New York   London   Toronto   Sydney   Tokyo   Singapore

First published 1991 by
Prentice Hall International (UK) Ltd
66 Wood Lane End, Hemel Hempstead
Hertfordshire HP2 4RG
A division of
Simon & Schuster International Group

Typeset in 10/12 pt Times
by MHL Typesetting Ltd, Coventry

Printed and bound in Great Britain by
BPC Wheatons Ltd, Exeter

Library of Congress Cataloging-in-Publication Data

Operations research in management/ edited by
  Stephen Littlechild and Maurice Shutler.
    p.   cm.
  Rev. ed. of: Operational research for managers. 1977.
  Includes bibliographical references and index.
  ISBN 0-13-638818-3
  1. Operations research. I. Littlechild, S.C. II. Shutler,
Maurice, 1931– . III. Operational research for managers.
T57.6.06453 1991
658.4′034—dc20   90-27034
                                                CIP

British Library Cataloguing in Publication Data

Operations research in management. — 2nd ed
  1. Operations research
  I. Littlechild, S. C. (Stephen C) II. Littlechild, S.
  C. (Stephen C.
III. Shutler, Maurice, 1931–
  658.403

  ISBN 0-13-638818-3

2 3 4 5   95 94

— Contents —

7 Inventory control   96
C. D. Lewis

— Preface —

to the first edition

There are now many excellent books on operational research. However, these books fall almost entirely into one of two categories: the relatively brief, non-technical appreciation for the manager and intelligent layman (e.g. the book by Duckworth, 1962 or Rivett and Ackoff, 1963) or the more voluminous mathematical treatments of techniques for the specialist (e.g. those by Wagner, 1975, or Hillier and Lieberman, 1967).† There is hardly any choice of text at all for the numerous engineers, economists and accountants, whether undergraduate students or practising managers, who do not intend to become operational research practitioners, but who wish to gain a more thorough introduction to the techniques and practice of operational research than the appreciation books provide. *Operational Research for Managers* [as the first edition of this book was called] is intended to fill this gap.

The book originated in a thirty-hour course of lectures given to young executives attending the six-month Diploma in Business Administration course at the University of Aston Management Centre. Lectures by members of the Centre staff were supplemented by seminars on actual applications led by visitors from industrial operational research groups. In this way, the practical advantages and disadvantages of each operational research technique were communicated, along with a feeling for 'what it is all about'. Since weekly visits from practising operational research managers and consultants are not generally feasible for most lecture courses, it seemed worth trying to embody our experience in a text which could be used much more widely. The present volume is the result. It consists of chapters on theory alternating with case studies illustrating how the theory has been applied in industry.

The emphasis is therefore on techniques which have been repeatedly found to be useful in practice, rather than on techniques which are merely elegant or attractive in theory. This explains the omission of topics such as game theory. Other topics such as reliability, maintenance and dynamic programming have

---

†Hillier, F. and G.J. Lieberman (1967) *Introduction to Operations Research*, Holden Day; Rivett P. and R.L. Ackoff (1963) *A Manager's Guide to Operational Research*, John Wiley; Wagner, H.M. (1975) *Principles of Operations Research*, Prentice Hall.

been omitted partly because of their relatively narrow special interest and partly because of the fairly advanced statistical techniques required.

Reflecting the above philosophy, a unique feature of the book is the emphasis on implementation. For too many students, operational research appears to be nothing more than a collection of theoretical techniques. Such students find great difficulty in usefully relating these techniques to the real-world problems which they subsequently encounter. Our book as a whole is an attempt to show how theoretical techniques are modified when put into practice. The last chapter, entitled 'Putting operational research to work', discusses how operational research groups go about the business of finding problems, what balance of skills is required and what organizational structures within the firm are most conducive to success.

Operations Research for Managers is designed for use by experienced managers and by potential managers still studying for their qualifications (whether diplomas, first degrees or higher degrees). It is suitable for courses ranging from ten to fifty hours in length. At the shorter end of the scale, a brief appreciation of OR can be based on the eight case studies and the introductory and concluding chapters, with the theory chapters available to any manager with an interest in a particular technique. At the longer end of the scale, the theory chapters provide a basic grounding in technique which has been designed in the light of curricula at universities and polytechnics, and the requirements of various professional bodies. For the latter purposes exercises have been provided after each chapter. Following each chapter is a collection of references and suggestions for further reading.

The book requires no mathematical knowledge beyond GCSE or 'O' level. Calculus is used only once, in the derivation of the economic order quantity. However, some familiarity with elementary statistics is assumed — specifically, with the following concepts: subscript and summation notation; mean, standard deviation, frequency distribution, histogram, random variable, percentile; normal and Poisson distributions; significance tests and hypothesis testing; simple and conditional probabilities. It will surely be the case that a suitable introduction to statistics will be given at the same time as, or just before, a course in operational research. The concept of net present value is also used on several occasions without further explanation.

As editor, I have ruthlessly rewritten the contributions of the various authors wherever it seemed necessary in order to achieve a unified level and style. In this, I have been tremendously helped by discussion with the contributing operational research managers, by detailed written comments on the whole book from C.R. Barrett and F.M. Wilkes, and by remarks on particular chapters by P.G. Ascroft, S.I. Katz, H. Nicholls and J.R. Slater.

Any joint effort of this kind also depends upon secretarial help from many people. I should particularly like to thank Kathy Major, Helen Silk and Joy

Tonkin for patiently retyping successive drafts of the whole book and fiercely chasing up laggardly contributors.

S.C. Littlechild
Birmingham, September 1976

— Preface —

to the second edition

After fourteen years a new edition was clearly needed if operations research had changed in that time. Changed it has indeed, and in the process become even more relevant to decision-makers and to the target audience of 'experienced managers and [those] still studying for their qualifications', to quote from the first preface.

With the larger format of this book it has not been necessary to omit very much material from the previous edition in order to accommodate the new. Existing chapters have been revised and up-to-date references added. Three example chapters have been dropped because the applications are now standard and the alternation of theory and practice chapters has only been maintained in part.

Implementation, however, remains just as important. For that reason new chapters have been added which may collectively be thought of as 'soft OR', as distinct from the hard mathematical techniques. Data envelopment analysis is the one new mathematical technique. Operations research scientists are now accustomed to involving themselves much more in the process of decision-making, and these new chapters reflect that. This is also true of the practical use of data envelopment analysis.

One sad event that we have to record since the publication of the first edition is the death in 1979 of Steve Cook, who wrote the first and last chapters in both editions. His final chapter is virtually unchanged; the editors have contributed two new sections to the first. We are very glad to be able to continue to use his wise words.

In many companies these days OR has left the backroom for the boardroom. It is there to support manager's decisions whilst maintaining its role of providing reliable tools for stock and production control, transportation, vehicle routeing and depot location.

Because of the new material, we thought that a new title 'Operations Research in Management' was appropriate, reflecting this increased concern with the decision-making process. As before, the references will encourage readers to read about the topics more deeply.

We would like to thank Professors Glover, Phillips and the late Darwin

Klingman for permission to quote in Chapter 3, applications of network methods
from their unpublished paper 'Netform modelling and applications'.

S.C. Littlechild
M.F. Shutler

List of contributors

J.G. Bright, Company Secretary, Insight Logistics Ltd.

S.L. Cook (d. 1979), formerly Professor of OR, University of Aston.

G.I. Doukidis, Lecturer in OR, London School of Economics and Political Science.

C. Eden, Professor of Management Science and Head of Department, University of Strathclyde Business School.

K.E. Fiddy, Managing Director, Insight Logistics Ltd.

K.J. Johnston, Development Manager, Insight Logistics Ltd.

J.B. Kidd, Lecturer in OR, University of Aston Business School.

A. Land, Professor Emeritus of OR, London School of Economics and Political Science.

C.D. Lewis, Professor of Operations Management, University of Aston Business School.

A.H. Lines, Managing Director, Slimstock Systems Ltd.

S.C. Littlechild, Director General of Electricity Supply and Professor of Commerce, University of Birmingham; formerly a member of the Monopolies and Mergers Commission.

M. Pidd, Senior Lecturer in OR, University of Lancaster Management School.

M.F. Shutler, Chief Industrial Adviser, Monopolies and Mergers Commission and Visiting Professor of OR, London School of Economics and Political Science.

L.B. Sparrow, Corporate Planning Manager, British Gas, West Midlands.

– 1 –

The history of operations research

S.L. COOK and M.F. SHUTLER

Introduction

Operations research (OR) has been described as a method, an approach, a set of techniques, a team activity; a combination of many disciplines, an extension of particular disciplines (mathematics, engineering, economics), a new discipline; a vocation, even a religion. It is perhaps some of all these things. The best way to put the components in perspective, and perhaps the only definitive way of describing it, is to recount how it has evolved historically.

The idea of using 'scientific' approaches to resolve problems of design and decision has been ascribed to many thinkers in history, from Archimedes through Leonardo da Vinci to Charles Babbage in the last century. But for our purpose it is perhaps enough to go back to the 1930s. In that decade, a number of the eminent scientists in Britain, most of them Fellows of the Royal Society, came to believe that science had taken a wrong turning. Pure science, the search for knowledge for its own sake, was esteemed above applied science and engineering — the application of scientific knowledge and scientific method to the problems of man and society.

The call to arms

New ideas do not automatically lead to action; but in the mid-1930s there was developing a sense of national and international emergency over the threat from Nazi Germany. Already, Robert Watson-Watt was leading a group of scientists and technologists in the development of radar, in great secrecy, for the defence of the United Kingdom against air attack. The approach of the Second World

1

War, and the war itself, provided the opportunity for the application of science on an unprecedented scale in the service of national objectives. In the course of this, OR under that name emerged as a specific scientific activity, first in the United Kingdom and then in the United States and Canada. We cannot go into the full story here, and a few key events must suffice.

Watson-Watt and his colleagues in 1937 were ready to demonstrate to the armed forces the application of their prototype radar equipment to the detection of approaching enemy aircraft and the deployment of anti-aircraft batteries and fighter planes to repel them. The first large-scale trials, however, had disappointing results, and the defence chiefs asked Watson-Watt to make a special study of the results of the trials and of the problems of using the equipment in real-life conditions. He selected from his group a small team of half a dozen, with a range of disciplines including physics, electronics, mathematics, statistics and psychology. The team came up with analyses of two particular man–machine interfaces: that of the service operators of the radar equipment, indicating how they might be trained to use it more effectively, and that of the service officers interpreting the information obtained from the equipment for the development of anti-aircraft guns and fighters, showing how this information could be converted to effective defensive tactics for a particular offensive situation.

Subsequent trials after implementation of the recommendations were much more effective, and the defence chiefs asked for the team to be kept in being to monitor the continuing development of radar. The team was given an office in Operational Headquarters, where it remained until radar was proving its value in the Battle of Britain in 1940. To identify the room and the non-uniformed scientists using it, the phrase 'operational research' was coined for the six-man team, and the door labelled to that effect. It meant 'research into operations' or perhaps 'research within operational headquarters'. It carried no broader connotations.

In 1939 Professor Patrick Blackett, the physicist, who was already famous for his work in the field of relativity, and who had been a naval officer during the First World War, offered his services as a scientific advisor to the Admiralty. He was involved in a number of crucial tactical and strategic issues to do with the Battle of the Atlantic, of which the best known are probably those concerned with the number of merchant ships and escort vessels in an Atlantic convoy, and the tactics of Coastal Command in seeking out and destroying U-boats around the coast. At the same time, Professor J.D. Bernal was advising the Home Office on the defence of the civil population against air raids, and other eminent scientsts were becoming similarly involved.

Up to this point, the various initiatives were separate attempts to offer scientific support to the defence services, but in 1940 Blackett and the others realized that this work involved a new kind of activity with a common thread running through it. They sought a name for it, which could be used in discussions with government to encourage its increased development and use in the war effort. Watson-Watt suggested that the label 'operational research' which had remained serviceable for three years for his team, might be adopted to describe the general activity, and it was agreed.

The United States, already deeply committed to supporting the United Kingdom with food and supplies, was moving towards full involvement in the war. Blackett wrote to his friend and fellow professor of physics at the Massachusetts Institute of Technology in Boston, Philip Morse, to tell him of the way science was aiding the war effort in Britain and to suggest that something similar might be done in the United States. Morse was able to arrange for a special conference in the United States of defence chiefs and scientists to which Blackett and some of his colleagues were flown by special plane. The Americans adopted the idea and the name, changing it only to 'operations research' because of their different usage of adjectival nouns. They quickly set up groups of OR scientists for the various branches of the armed forces, and throughout most of the war there were OR groups serving with the land, sea and air forces of the United Kingdom, Canada and the United States.

Swords to ploughshares

By the end of the war there were about one thousand scientists serving in the United States forces and a little over two hundred in the United Kingdom. They came from a wide range of disciplines but mainly the physical and the life sciences, with a very few psychologists. They had, of course, been entirely concerned with military problems, and it would have been understandable if the new activity had become recognized simply as a new branch of military science or logistics. However, some of the leading scientists concerned were convinced that OR could be at least as valuable in peace as it had been in war; the greatest impetus in this direction came, once again, in Britain, with the radical programme of reconstruction and reform following the war.

This created a sense of urgency for the peace-time application of science comparable to that felt ten years earlier with the approach of war. Several factors contributed to a rapid building up of OR in British industry in the late 1940s. First, the nationalization programme of the new Labour Government created large industrial corporations (coal, steel, gas, electricity, road, rail and air transport), some much larger than any previous industrial organizations and with unprecedented problems of reconstruction and development. Second, some of the leaders of these corporations came from government or defence positions where they had experienced OR help with strategy and tactics during the war. Third, some of the leading defence OR scientists chose to move to industry after the war rather than return to their original disciplines and careers.

The quick and effective establishment of OR groups in these and other industries was helped by two other factors. First, tens of thousands of scientists and technologists were being demobilized from the defence research establishments and looking for jobs where they could find the same kind of challenge that they had found in war time. Most of them had not known of OR during the war, since the secret was well kept, but now they began to hear of it and many were attracted to it. There was also a major campaign by leading scientists in the two or three years following the war — 'science and reconstruction' — to persuade scientists and politicians that science should never again become a purely backroom operation, but that it should be fully harnessed to the needs of the country and the development of a better society. This missionary zeal was particularly evident in the early groups in the nationalized industries, and remains an important factor: enthusiasm is an essential element of successful OR work.

In the years 1947–55, OR groups grew to play a major part in the development of most of the basic industries in the United Kingdom which had been nationalized. Operations research also began to spread in a smaller way to private industry, but the two largest groupings were in the coal and steel industries which had a major influence on the development of OR in the United Kingdom well into the 1960s.

Operations research in the United States

The initial post-war development of OR in the United States took place mainly in universities, in several important cases partially financed by the armed services, notably at Massachusetts Institute of Technology (US Navy), Johns Hopkins University (US Army) and University of California and RAND Corporation (US Airforce). From these three activities developed the impressive lead of the United States in the advanced mathematical techniques of operational research, particularly those based on mathematical probability and mathematical programming.

But it was a development from an altogether different direction which established the main basis for teaching the method of operational research and for developing the philosophy of the subject. In the late 1940s two young men who had obtained their doctorates in the philosophy of science in the University of Pennsylvania began to read of war-time OR and recognized it as, in principle, the combination of theory and action they had been seeking — the 'applied philosophy of science'. They visited a number of larger universities in the search for one that would sponsor an OR activity on these lines and eventually found it in the Case Institute of Technology in Cleveland, Ohio. The two men were

C. West Churchman and Russell Ackoff. They joined the university, and recruited a number of interdisciplinary like-minded people, forming a faculty OR group which quickly grew to a dozen members. At the same time, they obtained widespread support from industrial organizations to carry out OR studies on a consultancy basis. They launched a master's course in OR and offered part-time research assistant posts to students, who assisted with the consultancy assignments and were allowed to use the material from the assignments in their dissertations. In this way the teaching was geared very firmly to 'real-world' problem-solving.

At the same time they had to set up course work programmes for the students in methods and relevant techniques. They based the teaching of method on their earlier work in the philosophy of science which they related closely to the practical stages of problem-solving as they emerged from the work undertaken. For techniques, they took a range of those that had been used in one way or another in defence OR, and other techniques such as linear programming which had developed in business schools or in industrial engineering. With their wide range of consultancy opportunities they were able to select projects which would provide vehicles for the systematic development and application of particular techniques, and in this way, to develop material for teaching techniques and their areas of application at an increasingly advanced level. By 1957 they were able to publish the first textbook of OR, *Introduction to Operations Research* (Churchman *et al.*, 1957).

Of all those early teachers of OR at the universities, Churchman and Ackoff were probably the most insistent that OR is a basic method and approach rather than a set of techniques. Nevertheless, the appearance of their book, a large part of which was inevitably concerned with specific techniques and their applications, probably helped to develop the idea in the world at large that OR was mainly a set of techniques. The method and approach were not so easy to describe in a distinctive way; the techniques by contrast were completely tangible. Many who had up to then found it difficult to appreciate the nature of OR were happy to seize on the techniques as if they defined the subject, and this difficulty has remained until the present day.

The early divergence of emphasis in the development of OR between the problem-oriented industry-based groups of the United Kingdom and the more technique-oriented university-based groups of the United States was moderated considerably in the 1960s. Several leading UK universities set up OR departments and practising OR groups spread rapidly in US industry. These developments were helped by exchanges of people and ideas which began in 1954. Nevertheless, it remains true that UK 'operational research' is more practical and problem-based, while American 'operations research' tends to be seen by many as a form of applied mathematics. Whilst 'management science' is the term used in the United States to describe practical application, it is also the title of many university chairs in the United Kingdom. In the

United States too what British scientists would call 'operational research' is termed 'systems analysis'. In the United Kingdom this term usually applies to computing. The acronyms OR/SA and OR/MS are also in common use and in this book we use all terms indiscriminately.

Operations research in continental Europe

The growth of OR in continental Europe has owed much more to the United States than the United Kingdom. It remains therefore a subject more taught in universities than practised in firms and in this form it is firmly embedded in mathematics departments. Most practical OR is to be found in continental branches of international companies or carried out by academics in private consulting. However, almost every European country has an active OR Society, joined with the United Kingdom in EURO, the European Association of Operational Research Societies.

The interdisciplinary group

Very soon in the development of OR, the practice emerged of analysis by teams, rather than by individuals, however brilliant. At first, except for the Watson-Watt story, scientists were brought together regardless of their particular disciplines, but it was soon realized that a team containing a range of disciplines was more creative and more effective, with a wider range of potential approaches to a given problem, than one with its strength mainly in, say, physics or mathematics or biology. As the OR groups grew in size, the interactions between project teams as well as within teams were found to help creativity. The post-war industrial groups maintained this interdisciplinary approach. There were perhaps rather fewer biologists and psychologists (a loss, as we now well realize) but rather more engineers (research-minded electricals, mechanicals and civils), metallurgists and mining engineers, and (for the first time) a very few economists.

A particularly useful interaction between engineers and statisticians marked the early post-war years. Project teams were seldom more than three or four strong, but never less than two (almost always of different disciplines). Occasionally an individual would have special responsibility for a part of the project, geared to his own discipline, but generally 'interdisciplinarity' was taken to mean that all team members should be concerned with all major aspects of the problem.

In the mid-1950s it came to be realized that an OR group of this kind was more than just a problem-solving resource; it was also a 'learning system', a vehicle for developing very rapidly the problem-solving competence of its members, in fact 'a miniature university' within its host organization. Not surprisingly, perhaps, these groups did not always sit naturally in the organization structure, being usually more radical, more innovative, less observant of the rule book and, at least apparently, less disciplined than other parts of the organization. Thus the major groups during this period provided both the development laboratory for OR itself and the training ground for its practitioners.

As M.Sc. and B.Sc. courses in OR developed in universities and polytechnics, so a change came over the types of entrant to OR groups. In many groups, mathematics graduates now predominate. The groups continue to provide a training ground, but now very often for future managers. Among nationalized industries and in the private sector many OR scientists have reached the most senior levels of management and some are directors or even managing directors of the largest enterprises.

Limitations of operations research

There is not space to describe here how operations research relates to various other disciplines such as systems science or cybernetics, with all of which it has considerable overlap (Ashby, 1960; Forrester 1961; Weiner, 1961; Beer, 1966, 1975; Checkland, 1981; Jackson et al., 1989); nor how it relates to the various other professional activities assisting the management process, such as work study, organization and methods and systems analysis. There is not time to trace the growth of applications in government, notably in the health and social services, transport planning, local government, law enforcement and taxation, nor the growth in aspirations of operational researchers to move towards tackling some of the most taxing problems of present day society (such as the spread of diseases, aid to the Third World or the relation between economic growth and the quality of the environment).

At the time of the first edition of this book it was argued that some readers might feel that these aspirations of OR reflected a lack of modesty in the profession, claiming to be able (when it got around to it) to solve humanity's great problems. In the decade and a half since the first edition was conceived much has changed in OR, reflecting changes in its working environment. The number of industrial OR groups has declined, matching a decrease in numbers of industrial firms in particular sectors, caused either by mergers or by foreign competition. However, the number of OR workers, as measured by the number of members of the Operational Research Society, has remained constant.

The growth to compensate for industrial decline has come from three sources. First, many of those displaced from industry went into consultancy and all major consultancy firms have substantial numbers of employees with an OR background; in many they are partners. Secondly, there has been a growth in OR in the rest of the service sector — banks, building societies, supermarkets and transport — matching the growing economic activity in these areas — and in central government where measurement of efficiency and effectiveness is the order of the day.

Thirdly, the general availability and cheapness of microcomputers has given to OR a new ability to provide tools that are tailored to the decision-making problems of particular managers. Such computers can be installed in much less time than it took for a main frame computer to be programmed. Indeed so remarkable and distinct has this process been that a new acronym — DSS (decision support systems) — has been coined to describe the resulting applications. There is now no longer the traditional dichotomy between 'quick and dirty' and refined methods. A manager can have both, and the former may get 90 per cent of the right answers right now. The final 10 per cent can be achieved if the first stage can show how its attainment will be justified. Chapter 15 in particular gives examples of models in which the manager is one of the players and Chapter 16 describes one way of analyzing the manager's problem-structuring process.

This process may have not done much for the humility of the OR profession but it has done a great deal for the individual OR scientist. He is now able to interact with managers within a much shorter time-scale and hence contribute to some of their more pressing problems, as well as developing systems for the longer term. More managers, too, now have had some experience of business school training and hence have been more exposed to the methods of OR.

The major consequence of this is that all the techniques described in this book are to be found in standard application areas, many implemented through standard computer software. Linear programming is a staple planning tool in the oil industry. Queueing theory is used by British Telecom, the Post Office and the clearing banks. The construction and contracting industries use critical path methods without knowing that they were invented by OR scientists. Stock control, short-term forecasting methods and simulation are absolutely universal. It is the grounding in the application of these models that gives the OR scientist the confidence to support the manager in his short-term decisions, even though the vehicle through which the support is delivered may be nothing more sophisticated than a spreadsheet package.

As managers have become more used to models operating as part of the computer packages by which their businesses are run unseen, and as they have become more confident in the short-term advice they have been given, so they have allowed OR to work on more and more strategic problems, including the firm's strategy itself.

In a similar way, as OR scientists have gained confidence in their abilities to help particular managers, so they have aspired to a greater understanding of the decision-making processes and of the ways in which the senior managers in firms get together to achieve a common purpose despite their differing personal ambitions. In this interplay of ideas a new type of OR work has emerged: 'soft OR' to distinguish if from 'hard' mathematics. Nevertheless, it has theoretical foundations, but those are to be found in the social rather than the physical sciences (Kelly, 1955).

Examples of soft OR are given in the later chapters of this book. Whilst researchers in universities are still experimenting and developing new approaches, practitioners are successfully aiding managers to deeper insights into the way to achieve better decision-making within groups of particular individuals and better management of the aims of the enterprise. Operations research scientists and managers pursue common goals and much remains to be done to refine the understanding of how they may be attained. It is for this reason that any management showing enthusiasm for the development of creative and effective OR in its organization should have no difficulty in attracting competent and well-motivated OR scientists.

Operations research in management

So we come round to the theme of this book: OR in management. What do we mean exactly? We hope we have already established that OR is sufficiently interesting and perhaps sufficiently important for managers to want to know something about it as general background — especially since they will most often find themselves working with OR scientists. As we try to show in Chapter 17, for OR scientists and managers to work effectively in partnership, each needs to have a good understanding of the others' methods, beliefs and tasks.

But is there another possibility? The manager can become, if he wishes, something of an operations researcher himself. All that is needed is the inclination, the time to pull out of day-to-day preoccupations (not perhaps so easy unless on an MBA course) and some background in quantitative methods and scientific thinking. In Chapter 17 we discuss various ways in which this can be done without the full support of an OR group. There is in any case a wide range of OR applications. Most kinds, as we have said above, are no longer 'research', and this includes most semi-routine applications of the techniques in this book. With a little expert guidance, some of these can provide a straightforward task for the manager, who may even be able to do a better job than the professional because of his local knowledge and availability for follow-up. However, given the advent of software packages which claim to 'do it all', we believe that the knowledge gleaned from this book is going to be even more important in giving the student manager the critical powers to choose what he really needs.

References and further reading

Ashby, W.R. (1960) *Design for a Brain*, Chapman and Hall.
Beer, S. (1966) *Decision and Control*, John Wiley.
Beer, S. (1975) *Platform for Change*, John Wiley.
Checkland, P.B. (1981) *Systems Thinking, Systems Practice*, John Wiley.
Churchman, C.W., R. Ackoff and L.E. Arnoff (1957) *Introduction to Operations Research*, John Wiley.
Forrester, J. (1961) *Industrial Dynamics*, MIT Wiley.
Gray, G.W. (1943) *Science at War*, Books for Libraries.
Jackson, M.D., P. Keys and S.A. Cropper (1989) *Operational Research and the Social Sciences*, Plenum Press.
Kelly, G. (1955) *The Psychology of Personal Constraints: A theory of personality*, Norton.
Rivett, B.H.P. (1968) *Concepts of Operational Research*, English Universities Press.
Waddington, C.H. (1973) *OR in World War II: Operational research against the U-boat*, Paul Elek.
Weiner, N. (1961) *Cybernetics*, MIT Press.

– 2 –

Operations research/ management science method

M. PIDD

More than simply techniques

This chapter considers how operations research/management science (OR/MS) methods are put into practice, and is concerned with the *process* of OR/MS rather than the set of techniques that are often associated with the subject. Experience suggests that technical knowledge is not a sufficient condition for successful OR/MS practice because the issues which OR/MS analysts are asked to address do not come labelled as 'mathematical programming' or 'simulation' for example. One of the challenges faced by all practitioners is the need to find ways to put their technical expertise into action. After all, OR/MS is to be judged by its effect within an organization rather than merely by technical criteria.

OR/MS workers have always been conscious that problem-solving and analysis should come before the use of techniques. In the early days of OR/MS this was necessarily so because the techniques were rudimentary at best. But even now, when the analyst has a whole arsenal of mathematical methods and computers available, it still remains true that problem identification and the practical implementation of suitable solutions is at least as important as the technique which might be employed to find a solution. Therefore, there is considerable interest in the development of methodologies — that is, systematic procedures to be used in OR/MS practice.

Like many human activities, OR/MS involves both process and content, the latter being the concern of many chapters in this book. The *content* of OR/MS is made up of the issues and problems which its practitioners and researchers have to address and the technical methods and techniques which they bring to this task. The process of OR/MS is concerned with the best use of these technical skills and also with how the results of an OR/MS investigation are to be used within the organization. Of course, such a neat division into process and content is not so easy in reality. Different practitioners will, in varying circumstances, face diverse challenges and will bring their various technical skills to bear. Therefore, there must be some interaction between process and content and this must be kept in mind when reading this chapter.

The material covered here is descriptive; that is, it is based on observations of OR/MS practice, on personal experiences and reflections and discussions with others. It is also prescriptive because it attempts to suggest a general approach which seems to be fruitful and which can be adapted to fit particular circumstances. But there is no suggestion that the process model described here can be lifted straight from these pages and applied immediately. The idea is to encourage the reader to give at least as much careful thought and attention to process issues as to the technical detail.

Process models

Workers in OR/MS are apt to use the term 'model' in quite a cavalier way. It is used to denote the bundle of equations, concepts and computer programs which might be employed to explore the effects of policies and options. These models will, in this chapter, be called *technical models*. The term is also used, very confusingly, to cover the mathematical, statistical and computer-based methods and techniques which make up the tool-bag of OR/MS. Here these will be described simply as *techniques*.

What then is a process model? An alternative term might be 'methodology' as the word is used in the United Kingdom rather than the United States. A process model, or methodology, is an attempt to describe a general approach which, though it cannot guarantee success, will, if followed, at least ensure that a reasonable attempt has been made to act rationally. The process model to be described in this chapter is not novel, nor has it been defined solely by the author. It comes from a number of sources, notably the early texts on OR/MS (see for example, Churchman *et al.*, 1957), the hypothetico-deductive approach to scientific method of Karl Popper (1968, 1974) and recent theories of organizational and personal learning.

How to use a process model or methodology

No methodology should be followed slavishly or in a blinkered way. The idea of including one in this book is to make sure that anyone attempting OR/MS work is aware of the possibilities and pitfalls of analysis. As soon as one begins to formalize a methodology it becomes clear that no two people will go about the same problem in the exactly the same way. Thus no methodology should be regarded as a set of prescriptions which are to be followed like a robot moving on a wire-guided track. The prescriptions will need to be modified according to the following:

1. The personality of the researcher: for example, some people seem to be able to carry out several tasks at once, whereas others prefer to operate on one thing at a time.
2. The problems and issues under scrutiny: if the issues are clearly structured and well understood at the start of the OR/MS work, or if there have been similar applications before, then short cuts may be possible.
3. The resources available: it is generally possible to improve OR/MS work given more time, more cash, more people and more computer power (although the improvement may not be worth while). The availability of such resources will determine how time for the OR/MS project can be allocated between the stages.

It may be argued that there is nothing unique about the challenges facing an OR/MS worker compared to, say, a scientific worker in a laboratory or a computer systems analyst. However, there is something distinctive about the range of problems tackled by OR/MS workers and the responsibility taken by these workers for producing implementable recommendations. This means that the mathematical, statistical and computer techiques, though important, play a smaller part in successful OR/MS than might sometimes be implied in textbooks. Methodological aspects tend to loom large in practice.

It may be argued that a formal process model or methodology is of no great use. Perhaps some people are good at OR/MS and others will never be any use? There may be some truth in this point of view, but there are two reasons why a formal methodology needs to be taken seriously:

1. It helps in training. For example, it is crucial that medical students learn how to carry out a proper physical and, possibly, psychological examination of patients. Thus, at some point during their training they may well be given an explicit list of questions to ask and checklists to complete. Thus they learn a routine for a proper examination of patients which may later be modified according to their confidence, experience and personalities. They may even develop their own short cuts — but this can be dangerous. In a similar way, students of OR/MS may find it helpful to use a formal methodology whilst learning to deal with the sorts of problems which typify OR/MS practice. Later on, they may go on to develop a more individual approach.
2. It aids communication. Large-scale projects are often tackled by teams and some will require full-time project management. Obviously, the team will function better if its members have common goals and are in full agreement

about how to achieve them. This implies the need for the team to be built carefully and managed properly, and for its members to follow some common approach so that they can communicate effectively with one another. If the clients for the study are also aware of the methodology in use, then this may aid communication outside the team.

A process model or methodology

The broad outline of the methodology which will be discussed here is shown in Figure 2.1 and is based on the cyclic model of problem structuring described in Pidd and Woolley (1980). It is deliberately very simple and hides many complications. Nevertheless it serves as a useful vehicle for discussing how to go about performing OR/MS. Representing an approach in a simple figure is always deceptive, for the real complications are hard to show without obscuring the main logic of the diagram. Three phases are shown in Figure 2.1:

1. Problem structuring.
2. Modelling.
3. Implementation.

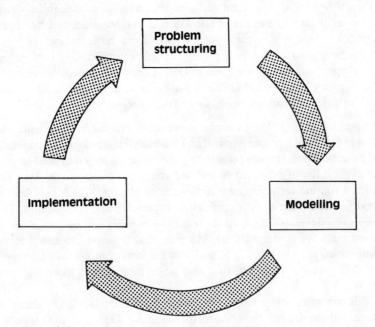

Figure 2.1   An outline process model of OR/MS

Each of them can be further divided into other activities. They are shown as a continuous cycle of activities in the figure, which implies that it may be vital to go round this loop several times during the course of OR/MS involvement with some work. They are also shown with other interconnections to indicate that backtracking may be necessary during the course of an OR/MS project.

An important assumption underlies Figure 2.1, which is that OR/MS analysts are only one part of decision-aiding or policy-making. Other groups and individuals have legitimate views and may possibly disagree with the approaches taken through OR/MS. Like any group in an organization, OR/MS will have to fight for the right to be heard and must also be humble enough to realize that its approaches have both plus and minus points.

Each of the three phases will be discussed in as much depth as possible given the space available in the remainder of this chapter. At this stage, only a simple definition will be given of the three phases:

1. *Problem structuring*: this is the attempt to take a 'mess' and to extract from it some agreeement about the particular problems which might be amenable to OR/MS. The hope is that this process of extraction will not remove all meaning from the 'mess' itself.
2. *Modelling*: this is usually taken as the technical heart of any OR/MS and involves the use of mathematical, statistical and computer methods to analyze the problems defined during problem structuring. The hope is that the modelling will not over-simplify the issues raised during problem structuring.
3. *Implementation*: this is the attempt to put into practice any recommendations that emerge from problem structuring and analysis. It is expected to be a continuing process from which the OR/MS staff will need to withdraw at some stage.

Problem structuring

Any process model for OR/MS needs to be built on a sensible foundation of a view of the nature of problems. Many texts imply that OR/MS is the use of mathematical and statistical methods to solve problems in business and not-for-profit organizations. This chapter takes the view that such a definition is far too simple and is, in many ways, very misleading. Following Ackoff (1979), the model proposed here is built on a distinction between messes, problems and puzzles. These three concepts are interlinked and can be viewed as a hierarchy (see Figure 2.2), as long as this is not taken too rigorously.

The easiest way to distinguish between the three concepts is to imagine them as a set of questions and answers:

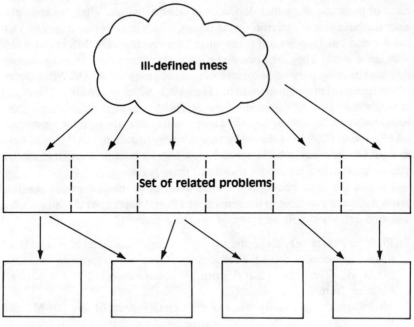

Figure 2.2   Puzzles, problems and messes

1. *A puzzle* exists when there is a single, well-defined question for which there is a single correct solution.
2. *A problem* exists when there is still only a single well-defined question but when there are several possible solutions which are defensible from different points of view.
3. *A mess* exists when there is no agreement about the questions to be asked and when there is, therefore, no common view about what constitutes an acceptable solution.

Puzzles are the sort of tasks which face a school student when learning mathematics. The student has to decide which method to use to attack a puzzle and can check whether the answer is correct. Somewhat confusingly, these puzzles are often called problems by mathematicians. As used here, problems are typified by Case-style teaching on MBA courses, in which students are presented with voluminous documents from which they must extract the relevant data, analyze it and make recommendations. Messes are more difficult to simulate in the classroom, but they are all too common in real-life and are typified by many viewpoints and, therefore, a lack of agreed structure.

It should be clear that a process model which is to be of any practical value must be able to cope with problems and messes, as well as with puzzles. Any process model or methodology which assumes that all is defined, agreed and understood is too far from reality to be of much value in OR/MS practice.

Problem structuring is an attempt to understand the issues which are being addressed in the project and an effort to decide what detailed OR/MS analysis will be appropriate. In one sense, therefore, it could be viewed as a mere preliminary to detailed modelling and computer work. However, to take such a view would be to miss the whole point made earlier about messes, problems and puzzles. Deciding which are the problems to be tackled and understanding their linkages is as challenging a task as the detailed formulation and execution of mathematical and statistical algorithms. The challenge in OR/MS is to be good at the full range of activities necessary for successful practice. And that includes problem structuring and implementation skills as well as quantitative analysis.

If the OR/MS analyst is breaking virgin ground in an organization, then problem structuring is the first phase of the work. How much time it will occupy will depend very much on the degree to which the work is already structured, on the skills and aptitudes of the OR/MS analyst and on the requirements of the client. In some cases, very little time may be spent in formal problem structuring; this is especially the case when the arena for the work is well mapped out and when there is considerable agreement about the nature of the work to be done. This is commonly the case in the tactical OR/MS work done in designing production planning algorithms. On the other hand, especially when working at a strategic level, considerable effort may need to be devoted to problem structuring — and it is possible that much of the benefit of the OR/MS may come from the problem structuring.

This chapter is not devoted to the topic of optimization, but consider one of the best definitions of sub-optimization that this author has come across. 'Sub-optimization is finding the best possible way to do something that should never be done at all!' This could be the best argument in favour of working hard at problem structuring in OR/MS. Above all else, trying to avoid wasting time on tackling the wrong issues is the reason for problem structuring. However, there are other reasons.

Some years ago, it was possible to buy a poster — the kind that students pin to their walls — which showed a large pig grovelling in the dirt. The caption across the top read, in large letters:

'FOR EVERY PROBLEM THERE IS A SIMPLE SOLUTION'

Now this is just the kind of motherhood statement that most people will agree with without thinking too hard. But at the bottom of the poster, in small letters, were the words:

'. . . and usually it's wrong!'

This captures the spirit in which many analysts are tempted to approach problem structuring, namely the desire to simplify the issues down to something manageable. Now, though this is to some extent one of the goals of problem structuring, over-simplification is certainly to be avoided. Most commonly it occurs when a too-blinkered view is taken, either of the range of possible analyses or of links with other problems and issues.

On the other hand, it is possible to overcomplicate things. Consider the following anonymous quote: 'I have yet to see any problem, no matter how complicated, which could not be made more complicated by looking at it in the right way!' So there are times when a simple approach will do. Knowing when this is so is one of the skills which comes with practice and experience. Over-complication is as much to be avoided as over-simplification. Finding the right balance is the goal of problem structuring.

It is not surprising therefore that there are many approaches to problem structuring in the OR/MS literature. A useful comparative description is given in Rosenhead (1989) and one of these approaches, cognitive mapping, is described in Chapter 16 by Eden, the person most strongly associated with its development and use. This chapter does not attempt to cover the same ground, but rather provides some general guidelines which may be of use whatever the detailed method followed. A general approach to problem structuring is shown in Figure 2.3, which identifies a four part cycle described

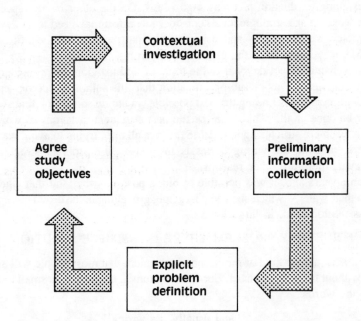

Figure 2.3 A general approach to problem structuring

below. As with the overall methodology, the cycle may be short circuited and may be repeated, depending on the circumstances.

Like beauty, problems are apt to exist in the eye of the beholder. That is, they are defined in particular ways by different people. The aim of problem structuring is to root out some manageable OR/MS work from the initial mess, or unsatisfactory state of affairs. It is as well to accept that there may be several stakeholders at this stage in the analysis, rather than a single client. The aim is to consider the views of these stakeholders and, if possible, to get them to reach some consensus about the detailed OR/MS work that should be carried out.

One very helpful way to do this is to use simple influence diagrams which map the links between the various factors and viewpoints that led to the OR/MS involvement. Three of the best known approaches to so-called soft OR/MS, namely cognitive mapping (Eden *et al.*, 1979; see Chapter 16), soft systems methodology (Checkland, 1981) and the strategic choice approach (Friend and Hickling, 1987) all make extensive use of such diagrams. They aim to show the influences at work in a particular situation and they have the advantage that they require nothing more than pen and paper. They also have the advantage that they may be drawn on-the-fly whilst in a meeting and form an independent record of what the participants are saying and of how they see the situation. That is, they allow people's views and opinions to become visible to others, albeit in a rough and ready way. Of course, this could be done in words, but relatively complex links are easier to show in a diagram.

As an example of an influence diagram, suppose that the manager of a biscuit factory calls in an OR/MS team because he is unhappy about the way that his high investment in stocks still seems to lead to shortages on the factory floor. During discussions with the various interested parties, the OR/MS analyst might construct the sequence of diagrams shown as Figures 2.4 and 2.5. Figure 2.4 is simply a map of the major, and obvious, systems involved in the stock policy. It shows three systems, of which the central one is manufacturing itself. This is linked to the external influence of the marketing policies for the finished goods and the purchasing policy for materials. Manufacturing policy is shown as linking material stocks, production facilities and finished stocks. As production is by continuous flowlines, there is little or no work-in-progress other than two hours or so of biscuits on each line.

Of course, things are much more complicated than this and further thought and discussion leads to the more detailed diagram in Figure 2.5. This makes it clear that the two sets of stocks imply the need for systems to control these and facilities to order, store and issue the materials and finished goods which they contain. It is clear too that there are links from the production facilities to the stocks via a production plan, which itself links to the marketing plan.

In practice, Figure 2.5 could be made more complex if the various systems and influences were mapped in more detail, but for present purposes the map

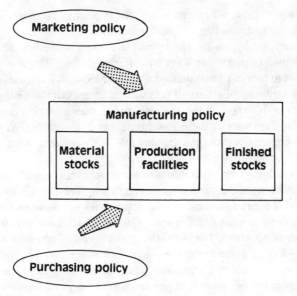

Figure 2.4   An outline influence diagram

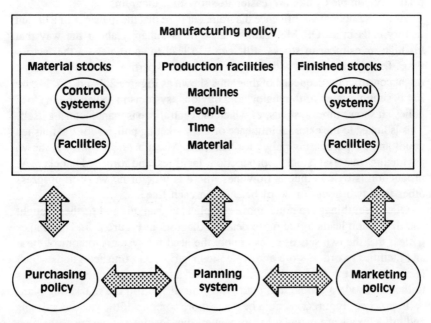

Figure 2.5   A more detailed influence diagram

can be left here. What should be clear is that such maps can act as very effective communication devices between analysts and their clients and between the analysts themselves. Eden (Chapter 16) makes clear how influence diagrams in the form of cognitive maps can serve as the basis of a debate if there are multiple stakeholders with conflicting viewpoints. Thus the process of understanding, which is so crucial to successful OR/MS, can begin at the start of a project.

Sooner or later, the process of drawing the influence diagrams leads to a need for more information. This does not imply the need for detailed data collection at this stage — that comes later if necessary. But it does mean that the analyst needs to ask common-sense questions of the 'who, what, where, how, why and when' type. These are the quesitons which any stakeholder can answer, but about which there can be surprising disagreement between stakeholders once the questions are taken seriously. The analyst must take little or nothing for granted at this stage of the work, but must check carefully how the various stakeholders see the issues connected with the processes being studied and the links between them.

It may also be sensible, in some cases, to collect *very limited* quantitative data at this point in order to get some view of the importance of the study. For example, in what eventually became a computer simulation study (Pidd, 1987), a rough and ready analysis of limited data revealed that each 1 per cent increase in the efficiency of a manufacturing plant would contribute an extra £10,000 of profit. This served as a spur to agreeing a more detailed analysis to try to achieve this payoff. Limited preliminary data will also show the scale of the work likely to be needed and this will be useful in agreeing the scale of the projects which might emerge from the problem structuring.

At some stage, therefore, the OR/MS analyst and the stakeholder(s) must agree about which areas and issues merit further work and investigation. The temptation is to cut corners by doing this without going through the two prior diagnosis phases. To do so is to risk not seeing the wood for the trees. In the example of the biscuit factory, it may emerge from the diagnosis that the following problems can be defined as important:

1. The computer or manual record system used to control stocks: is the current one adequate, or is a new one needed?
2. The information flow between the marketing department, purchasing department and the production planners: could this be formalized in some way so that sensible views are taken before, say, sales promotions are planned for the products?
3. Demand forecasts used for controlling material stocks: are these adequate for calculating requirements or could they be improved?
4. Could the various planning and stock replenishment systems be combined into a just-in-time approach by a radical review of the overall system and by talking to suppliers?

Now the analysts and stakeholders need to agree which, if any, of these issues will be the subject of some detailed OR/MS studies. Reaching such agreement may need to be a formal process which may result in a contract, formal or informal, between the OR/MS group and the stakeholders. Such a contract needs to state terms of reference for a detailed study and should include at least the following:

1. The detailed problems and issues to be addressed.
2. The time-scale, preferably indicating important milestones and agreed dates for review.
3. The expected costs and anticipated benefits from the study and an agreement to audit these following implementation.
4. An agreement about who will be responsible for implementing any recommendations which emerge from the study.

Such a contract, which may have legal force if the OR/MS group consists of external consultants, or may be an informal agreement if the group is internal, may seem over-bureaucratic. However, experience suggests that having to agree such a contract acts as a wonderful focus for the minds of all involved in the work.

The objections to entering into a contract are usually twofold. The first is that some OR/MS work is speculative and there is no guarantee of useful results from it. In such cases, there is an obvious answer. The contract needs to contain a number of phases and include reviews after each. At each review, the client and OR/MS group can agree whether the project should be allowed to continue. The second objection is that the world changes so fast that any contract will be out of date very quickly, especially if intermediate results are produced. The answer is, once again, very simple. Contracts can always be renegotiated if both parties are willing. A client is very unlikely to object to this if the work is going even better than expected when the original contract was drawn up.

Modelling

Most OR/MS studies use at least one formal model in the course of a study. Indeed some writers have argued that the use of what has been earlier termed a technical model is what distinguishes OR/MS from other attempts to aid management decision-making and control. In the context of OR/MS, a technical model is defined as a representation of a system of interest. It is used to study the effects of applying different policies to the system in preference to trying them out in practice. If the system of interest does not exist (for example because it is still being planned), then it is clear that a technical model will be the only way to understand and predict how it might perform.

As with problem structuring, modelling is best considered as a cycle of activities which can be short circuited. The modelling cycle is shown in Figure 2.6 and consists of four parts which, as ever, may merge into one another. Nowadays, the technical models used in OR/MS are predominantly computer-based and this discussion assumes that this will be the case.

A technical model is an abstraction of the important elements of the system under consideration in the study. For example, it may be focused on the cash flows anticipated in an investment decision or an expansion programme. It may be concerned with the flow of materials in a factory that is considering the use of a full just-in-time approach. Because the model is an abstraction, it will also be a simplification. Were this not so, the model would be as expensive or cumbersome or dangerous to use as the system being modelled. Indeed the reason that the technical model is being built is because it is expensive, inconvenient or dangerous to meddle directly with the system under scrutiny.

The simplest type of technical model might be what Ackoff and Sasieni (1966) term an *iconic* model. This is a model which retains the same properties as the system of interest but which scales them in some way or other. Models of the type used by engineers in wind tunnels or flotation tanks are obvious examples of scale models. In OR/MS they might be used to assess the feasibility of a suggested layout, say for a warehouse or factory. They can be constructed with pencil and paper or by using drawings or CAD packages on computers. Their main benefit is that they are simple to understand and to construct, but they are clearly very limited.

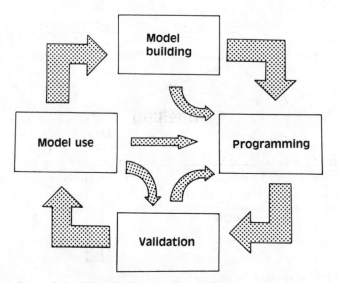

Figure 2.6 The modelling cycle in OR/MS

Ackoff and Sasieni mention a second type of model of use in OR/MS: an *analogue* model in which one property of the system is replaced by another in the model. A general example of this might be a map which uses contours to give a detailed representation of height. An equivalent scale model would be a three-dimensional relief map. These are more attractive but are difficult to carry around, inconvenient for navigation when lost on a mountain top and they do not fold well! The property of height is replaced by the contours as an anlogue simply for convenience.

An often mentioned but rarely used analogue model for distribution systems is that shown in Figure 2.7. This is of an imaginary country in which a company wishes to locate a single factory to serve its customers, which are conveniently located at a finite number of demand points around the nation. The analogue model consists of a map which is fixed to a table and on which the demand points are marked by holes drilled through the table top. A thread is passed through each hold, the threads being knotted together about the table. Below the table, at the demand point end of each thread, a weight is fastened which is proportional to the demand at that point. In the absence of friction, the threads will move so that the knot is located in the equilibrium position which will minimize the sum of the forces acting in the system. The position of the knot on the map will show where the factory should be built if transport costs are proportional to demands.

There are several reasons why this is not a very sensible analogue. The first is that it ignores the physical terrain that the map represents and assumes that all locations are equally desirable (in cost terms). The second is that having

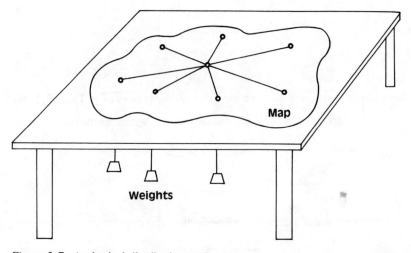

Figure 2.7 A physical distribution analogue

the weight proportional to demand is misleading as an analogue. Suppose that the knot settles in a position and then one of the demand points is shifted further from the equilibrium point but in the same compass direction. Clearly, the knot will not move since the vector of the demand point is unchanged. Despite these problems, it is obvious that such an analogue could be used to carry out simple experiments. For example, it could be used to show the effect of changing demands on the fixed demand points.

The most common type of technical model employed in OR/MS is the *symbolic* model and this is much the most convenient for analysis. Consider again the distribution system for which a simple symbolic model can be developed as follows.

Suppose that the cost of moving a quantity of goods q over a distance d is a function $f(Q, d)$. If a customer i is at a location which has the Cartesian co-ordinates (h_i, k_i) and if this customer takes Q_i goods, then the total cost of supply from a general location (H, K) of the depot is as follows:

$$c = \Sigma f(Q_i, d_i)$$

where $d_i^2 = (H-h_i)^2 + (K-k_i)^2$.

To minimize the costs, minimize c with respect to the two variables H and K. This requires that some form is assumed for the cost function. Suppose that

$$c = \Sigma(A + zQ_i d_i)$$

where A, d are constants, therefore

$$c = \Sigma[A + zQ_i \sqrt{((H-h_i)^2 + (K-k_i)^2)}]$$

Differentiating with respect to H and K and finding the minima gives:

$$\Sigma[Q_i(H-h_i)] = 0; \qquad \Sigma[Q_i(K-k_i)] = 0$$

That is

$$H = \frac{\Sigma h_i Q_i}{\Sigma Q_i}; \qquad K = \frac{\Sigma k_i Q_i}{\Sigma Q_i}$$

As an example suppose that there are just four customers as in Table 2.1. By

——— Table 2.1 ———

Customer	Location	Demand
1	(1, 1)	10
2	(8, 2)	7
3	(7, 8)	3
4	(2, 5)	6

using the above equations, it can be shown that the factory should be located at (3.8, 3.0).

Now the advantages of this model over the simple analogue are that it can cope with thousands of demand points and that it is easy to vary the demands at the points and so conduct 'what if' type experiments to see how sensitive the location might be to variations in demand. This latter point is crucial in OR/MS, where recommendations must be made which are robust towards anticipated changes in the environment. It is easily achieved when such analogue models are translated into computer programs.

The ways in which symbolic models may be used are many and varied. Some readily lend themselves to the use of optimization techniques. For example, if the costs and capacities of a manufacturing system can be formulated as a series of linear equations, then these equations may lend themselves to use the use of mathematical programming methods (see Chapter 4). Such methods guarantee finding the best solution from amongst those which exist in the model. On the other hand, symbolic models are also useful for extrapolation and calculation. As an example, the sales pattern of a product may be modelled using one of the time series methods described by Lewis in Chapter 6. By extrapolating with such a model beyond the actual data, an attempt may be made to forecast the coming sales of the product. A further possibility is the use of the model as a vehicle for experimentation, and the most common examples for this are financial models on spreadsheets such as Lotus 1-2-3™ and discrete simulation as described in Chapter 12.

All OR/MS models need data; indeed the problem-structuring approach described earlier included some preliminary data collection. However, this should not be of detailed data, for that should be part of the modelling process. However, it is important that the first stabs at model building should precede detailed data collection. That is, the model should drive the data and not the other way round. Why should this be?

To answer this question, consider the idea that OR/MS is a scientific activity of some form. If this is true then it is reasonable to expect OR/MS work to proceed in a way which is, in some sense, scientific. Karl Popper in his hypothetico-deductive approach (1968, 1974) argues that data and experiments should be used to test (and possibly, refute) theories rather than be used to generate them. In one sense, OR/MS symbolic models are like theories in that they embody relationships which are believed to hold in the system being modelled. Thus the data should be used to test and calibrate these relationships and may show that they need to be changed.

The model will therefore indicate what data are needed and should be collected. This is the opposite of the discredited notion that modelling consists of placing any half-reasonable data into a regression package and waiting to see what correlations emerge from the computer.

Modelling and computers

Figure 2.6 included the word 'programming'. This means considering here the ways in which models are turned into systems and programs which run on computers. In some cases, it may be necessary for the analyst to write a full computer program in some suitable language such as C, Pascal, APL or even Fortran. To help things along, the analyst may be able to use software tools from a library for common tasks and to provide a standard user interface. Increasingly, for numerical work at least, writing specific programs in this way is not necessary. Instead, the analyst may choose to use a numerical package such as spreadsheet or a database, or may choose to use specialist software such as that for mathematical programming, decision theory, simulation and statistical analysis. In many of these cases, the analyst has no need to undertake any programming but merely provides data to drive the computer package. In some cases, limited programming is needed, for example by using spreadsheet macros or an expert system shell.

The availability of cheap and powerful desktop and portable computers has revolutionized the practice of OR/MS since the late 1970s and it would be a very foolhardy person who imagined that this process is complete. In particular, many projects have as their goal the delivery of decision support software which will be used by the client and not by the OR/MS analyst. Needless to say, this means that the analyst must take a very professional view of the needs of his client and of the technology. As the technology changes, so the OR/MS analyst must make sensible use of the opportunities which it creates.

Model validation

Models are always simplifications of the systems they purport to mimic. This implies that no OR/MS model can possibly be valid for all purposes. It will always be possible to devise tests which show the model to be deficient in some way or other. This does not mean that such models are useless; rather it implies that they should be used with some care and should certainly not be pushed beyond the limits of their validity. The question then is, how can these limits be assessed?. Or, how can OR/MS models be validated?

A thorough discussion of this issue can be found in Pidd (1988) in relation to simulation models, and the same arguments apply to modelling in general. Two broad approaches to model validation are the black box approach and the white box approach. Under the black box approach the model's internal structure is assumed to be obscure but its performance can be observed. The idea is thus to compare the output of the model in response to certain stimuli with the performance of the system itself under the same stimuli. This means that two sets of observations need to be compared. One set stems from the model and the other from the system itself, and both sets are liable to errors of observation and interpretation. To compare the two sets of observations requires the standard armoury of the statistician. If two time series are being compared, then some of the more complex methods of statistical inference may be required.

Some care needs to be taken when attempting this form of validation, especially to ensure that the same data are not used both for building the model and for validating it. For example, if a time series model is to be used for forecasting (see Chapter 6) then the data series needs to be divided into at least two sets (see Figure 2.8). The first set should be used to establish the values of the parameters of the model, for example in the case of simple smoothing methods, the values of the smoothing constants. The second data set should then be used as the set of observations which is compared to the forecasts of the model. The assumption of black box validation is thus that the model is valid if its output adequately mimics the output of the system being modelled.

The term 'white box' validation is used in contrast with 'black', but it does not properly describe the process; 'transparent' might be better. The idea of this form of validation is that, since the structure of the model is fully known, it can be compared in detail with the structure of the real system. This comparison is especially important in computer simulation, for which the following questions need to be posed:

1. Is the static logic of the model valid? That is, do the logical rules of the model, which define how the entities of the simulation will behave, adequately reflect the operational rules of the system being modelled? Note the weasel word 'adequately', for it may be sufficient to use approximate

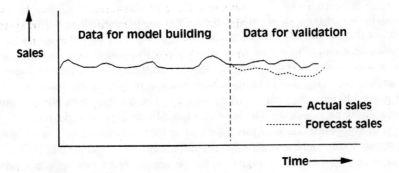

Figure 2.8 Using data to validate a time series model

logical rules if they are not thought to have a large effect on the output of the model.

2. Are the statistical assumptions of the model sound? For example, should discrete or continuous distributions be employed? Or do the set of values come from an infinite range or are they bounded (e.g. all are positive). If the values are bounded, then so should be the distribution within the model which is used to represent these values. Again, are the assumptions underlying the chosen distribution appropriate for the process being modelled? For example, one of the family of exponential distributions should only be employed if the assumptions of randomness hold good for the particular variables.

Thus white box validation goes beyond the simple comparison of two sets of observations which is at the heart of black box validation. It therefore requires the active co-operation of the analyst and the client, for the one has more knowledge of the model and the other of the system being modelled.

Implementation

The aim of most OR/MS work is to improve the performance of an organization in some way or other. Thus, one of the acid tests of the success of a project is the effect that the work has when its results or recommendations are implemented. This idea of implementation seems plain enough, but in fact things are not always simple, for OR/MS can be effective in a number of ways.

First, and most obvious, the OR/MS may be implemented when serious notice is taken of recommendations and they are put directly into practice. For example, the work may lead to a suggestion that a distribution depot should be located in a particular place and this may be accepted and a new depot built there. A second type of tangible implementation may occur when the OR/MS group delivers a tool, for example a piece of software, which can be used successfully by the client or his staff. An example might be an expert system for deciding how and when a plant is to be maintained. Other forms of implementation occur too, often as the project proceeds. For example, it is common to find that modelling provides insights into the way that a system is being run and could be improved, and this may occur before the model has been used. One instance of this happened in the simulation work described in Pidd (1987), when discussion of the data required to build a simulation model led the company to realize that such data should be collected routinely in any case to monitor the performance of manufacturing plant. This form of implementation could be thought of as organizational learning and is surprisingly common.

Organizational learning aside, the process of implementation needs to be managed and planned properly if the project is to result in something tangible. Various ways of ensuring that implementation proceeds smoothly can be identified.

OR/MS GROUP SOLELY RESPONSIBLE   This occurs when the client is either unwilling to see to the implementation or has insufficient resources or just prefers that someone else should do it. An example might be in a manufacturing company with the introduction of a computer-aided planning system in which the OR/MS group takes responsibility for running the system for a few weeks. This has the advantage that the analysts are around to sort out the inevitable teething troubles, but has the snag that the ways in which they use a system may not be the same as those in which the eventual planners will do so. If the OR/MS group accepts this responsibility, it must still plan and agree a strategy for handing over the system to its eventual users. The only escape from this is if one or more of the analysts opts to remain as the permanent user of the system — i.e. they leave the OR/MS group.

CLIENT SOLELY RESPONSIBLE   The OR/MS group and the client agree that the recommendations or new system are fully understood by the client, who then takes on the task of putting things into practice. This has the advantage that there is no doubt about the ownership of the results of the project and it frees the OR/MS group to get on with other work. In fact things are rarely as clear cut as this. More often than not the OR/MS analyst and client have actually been working together for a while and the client now feels confident enough to work alone, or, more negatively, the client wants the OR/MS groups to leave things alone!

JOINT RESPONSIBILITY   This is probably the most common, but may be the least satisfactory unless the implementation process is properly managed. This is because there can be a thorough confusion of roles. This means that the OR/MS analyst and the client need the equivalent of a hand-over contract which specifies who will be responsible for what and for how long. As with a contract for a project after problem structuring, this may sound bureaucratic, but it does make clear what needs to be done and may avoid misunderstandings later on.

CONTINUED INVOLVEMENT   This is often found when the client and the OR/MS group have, or are developing, a long-term relationship. In such cases, one project tends to spawn another and the OR/MS group keeps going round the methodology loop depicted in Figure 2.1. As with joint responsibility for implementation, it still can be useful to agree formally how each stage of the work is to be completed and how the next should continue. Such continued involvement is the aim of many OR/MS groups.

Summary

This chapter has attempted to show how OR/MS workers might go about their work in an effective way by regarding it as a cyclic learning process. Because the process is cyclic, it can be repeated. Thus, the implementation of one project may lead to structuring the next and so on. A repeated involvement benefits the OR/MS group, which gains knowledge of an area of work; and it also benefits the client, who gains confidence in the OR/MS group.

References

Ackoff, R.L. (1979) 'The future of operational research is past', *Journal of the Operational Research Society*, **30**, 93–104.
Ackoff, R.L. and M.W. Sasieni (1966) *Fundamentals of Operations Research*, John Wiley.
Checkland, P.B. (1981) *Systems Thinking, Systems Practice*, John Wiley.
Churchman, C.W., R.L. Ackoff and L.E. Arnoff (1957) *An Introduction to Operations Research*, John Wiley.
Eden, C.D., S. Jones and D. Simms (1979) *Thinking in Organisations*, Macmillan.
Friend, J.K. and A. Hickling (1987) *Planning Under Pressure: The strategic choice approach*, Pergamon.
Pidd, M. (1987) 'Simulating continuous food plants', *Journal of the Operational Research Society*, **38**, 683–92.
Pidd, M. (1988) *Computer Simulation in Management Science* (2nd edn), John Wiley.
Pidd, M. and R.N. Woolley (1980) 'A pilot study of problem structuring', *Journal of the Operational Research Society*, **31**, 1063–9.
Popper, K.R. (1968) *Conjectures and Refutations*, Routledge.
Popper, K.R. (1974) *The Logic of Scientific Discovery*, Hutchinson Educ.: Unwin Hyman.
Rosenhead, J.V. (1989) *Rational Analysis for a Problematic World*, John Wiley.

– 3 –

Transportation and network problems

S.C. LITTLECHILD

The nature of the transportation problem

Many companies produce goods in a relatively small number of factories and ship these to a number of warehouses throughout the country. The goods are then distributed from the warehouses to a large number of retailers. In the case of the major oil companies one is talking about refineries, depots and garages. Similar situations arise on the purchasing side — for example, the electricity generating companies purchase coal from a variety of collieries and transport it to their power stations.

The companies concerned have to answer the following kinds of question:

1. What is the best location for each factory/refinery/warehouse/depot/power station?
2. What is the best level of production/purchase at each factory/refinery/colliery?
3. Which factory/refinery/colliery should supply which warehouse/depot/power station?

Obviously, these questions are interrelated, and if a business is being started from scratch, they would need to be answered virtually simultaneously. However, an established business will already have factories located in certain places, which it would be a major operation to relocate. The location of the suppliers and customers is largely out of the hands of the business. Levels of production may be adjusted more easily, but there may be capacity limitations, existing commitments or specialization of staff or equipment, for example. Perhaps the most readily adjustable operations concern the distribution system.

It is therefore possible to pose the questions in the following manner:

1. Given the location of the factories/depots/suppliers/customers, and also given the volumes of production and requirements at these places, what is the best transportation or distribution pattern for the products in question?
2. In the light of the answer to question 1, what adjustments in levels of production are indicated?
3. In the light of the answers to questions 1 and 2, should the location of the company's premises be reconsidered?

This chapter will be almost entirely concerned with the first of these questions (i.e. the pattern of distribution) but it will be seen that the approach used throws a great deal of light on the second question (i.e. levels of production). At the end of the chapter we refer briefly to techniques for solving the plant location problem.

We shall not be concerned here with the mode of transportation (e.g. whether to ship by road or rail, whether to operate one's own fleet of lorries or buy outside) but rather with the pattern of distribution. More precisely, given a set of *origins* with specified product *availabilities* at each, given a set of *destinations* with specified *requirements* at each and given the *per unit cost* of transporting products from each origin to each destination, what is the cheapest feasible pattern of shipments from origins to destinations? This problem is known as the *standard transportation problem*. In the last section of the chapter we show how the transportation problem is one of a more general class of *network* problems, and in Chapter 4 we show that it is also a simple type of *linear program*. It will be seen that a wide variety of problems, which do not involve physical transportation, can nevertheless be formulated and solved as standard transportation problems.

The necessity for computer solution techniques

It may be thought that the standard transportation problem could be solved by hand, using a bit of common sense. It is indeed quite straightforward to enumerate and compare half a dozen possible distribution patterns. But bear in mind that if there are ten depots and twenty retailers, then a feasible pattern of distribution is going to involve at least twenty shipments (one for each retailer) and there are ten ways of choosing each shipment, so the number of possible combinations is of the order of 10^{20}. Suppose 99 per cent of these alternatives could be immediately discarded as inefficient. Even if each remaining pattern could be evaluated in one second, it would still take over 30,000,000,000 man-years to complete the job. This means that if the cheapest possible solution is to be found, not only will a computer have to be used but also some more efficient method than simply enumerating and comparing each alternative.

One may ask whether the best solution obtained by computer will be significantly better than that calculated by an experienced person. It may be only a few percentage points cheaper, but if the total distribution cost is of the order of millions of pounds per year, the savings are likely to be of the order of tens of thousands of pounds per year. For example, British Coal reported savings of 6 per cent on the cost of transporting coal from twenty-five sources to nine washeries, and incidental benefits of the same magnitude from meeting sulphur restrictions which had not been achieved before. The large oil companies, when they started using these techniques, obtained even larger savings, often up to 15 per cent of relevant distribution costs. That is why the use of these techniques is now standard practice in the vast majority of the large companies which face simular distribution patterns.

An example

Methods for solving the standard transportation problem can best be discussed in terms of a simple numerical example.

Suppose a company has factories at Manchester, Birmingham and London, and warehouses at Manchester, Coventry, Birmingham and Cardiff. For the coming planning period the factories and warehouses have the capacities and requirements set out in Table 3.1. (We shall show later that there is no difficulty in handling situations where total requirements are not equal to total capacity.) Per unit transportation costs, by the cheapest mode of transport currently available, are given in Table 3.2. What pattern of shipments will satisfy the requirements at minimum cost?

—— **Table 3.1** ——
Capacities and requirements

Factory	Capacity (units)	Warehouse	Requirement (units)
Manchester	20	Manchester	11
Birmingham	10	Coventry	13
London	25	Birmingham	17
		Cardiff	14
Total supply	55	Total demand	55

—— **Table 3.2** ——
Transportation costs (£ per unit)

	To: Manchester	Coventry	Birmingham	Cardiff
From:				
Manchester	1	6	3	6
Birmingham	7	3	1	6
London	9	4	5	4

Laying out the problem

It is convenient to set out the basic information in a simple table — called a *transportation tableau* — as shown in Figure 3.1. There is one row for each origin (factory) and one column for each destination (warehouse), consequently there is one *cell* for each possible shipment of goods. Capacities and requirements, as taken from Table 3.1, are noted on the border of the tableau. In each cell, the number in the top left-hand corner indicates the unit cost of

Destinations: Origins:	Manch.	Cov.	B'ham	Cardiff	Capa-cities	VAM diffs.
Manchester	1 (11)	6 (2)	3 (7)	6	20	2
Birmingham	7	3	1 (10)	6	10	2
London	9	4 (11)	5	4 (14)	25	0
Requirements	11	13	17	14	55	
VAM differences	6	1	2	1		

Figure 3.1 Transportation tableau with solution obtained by 'least-cost first' rule

that shipment, as taken from Table 3.2. (If for any reason it is impossible to ship along certain routes then, for the purpose of the present approach, a finite but very large cost is attributed to that cell; see, for example, exercise 2 at the end of this chapter.) The 'VAM differences' should be ignored until page 37.

Inside each cell we shall put the number of tonnes to be shipped along that route. A *feasible solution* is a set of entries which satisfies two conditions:

1. The entries must be non-negative, since (in this problem) negative shipments are not acceptable.
2. The entries must sum along each row to the capacity available at that factory, and down each column to the requirement of that warehouse.

The total transportation cost of any solution is obtained by multiplying each entry by the corresponding unit cost and summing overall entries. The object is to find the feasible solution(s) with the lowest total cost; this is called the *optimal solution* (strictly speaking, *an* optimal solution since it may not be unique).

'Least-cost first' rule

With a small problem like this it is possible to obtain a reasonable solution simply by inspecting the tableau. One could use the simple *least-cost first* rule of thumb: put as much as possible in the cell with lowest unit cost, then in the cell with second lowest cost, and so on. (In the case of a tie, arbitrarily pick one of the tied cells.) Thus, one would begin by shipping eleven units from factory to warehouse in Manchester, ten units from factory to warehouse in Birmingham, seven units from Manchester to Birmingham, and so on, to yield the solution already shown in Figure 3.1, which has a total cost of £154.

One difficulty with this rule is that it does not take into account the implications of each choice; it does not 'look ahead'. In the simple example shown in Figure 3.2 it would lead to shipments from A to C and from B to D, at a total cost of £1 + £10 = £11. However, a much cheaper solution is to avoid the least-cost cell AC altogether and to ship one unit from A to D and one from B to C, for a total cost of £2 + £2 = £4.

Vogel's approximation method

A procedure which to some extent gets round this difficulty is *Vogel's approximation method* (VAM) which 'looks ahead' one step by considering

Figure 3.2 Example of failure of the 'least-cost first' rule

the consequence of *not* choosing the best cell in each row and column. It therefore enables one to choose the cell which it is important not to miss. The method is quite simple.

1. Jot down the difference between the lowest and second lowest cost in each row.
2. Repeat for each column.
3. Identify the row or column with greatest difference (resolving ties arbitrarily).
4. Identify the cell in the chosen row or column which has the lowest cost.
5. Put as much as possible in the chosen cell.
6. Repeat the procedure, excluding the row or column which is now satisfied.
7. Continue until the entire amount is transported.

As with the least-cost first rule, one row or column is deleted at each step, so the maximum number of steps is the sum of the number of rows and columns.

VAM may be illustrated on our example. In Figure 3.1 the VAM differences have been calculated and noted alongside each row and column. Since the greatest difference is six, and the lowest cost in that column is one, ship as much as possible from the Manchester factory to the Manchester warehouse, namely eleven units. (The factory has capacity for twenty units but the warehouse requires only eleven units.)

The calculations are repeated in Figure 3.3, ignoring the Manchester warehouse (first column). The greatest difference is three and the lowest cost in that row is three, hence ship nine from Manchester to Birmingham, thereby exhausting capacity at the Manchester factory (first row). It may be verified that after four more steps the solution shown in Figure 3.4 is obtained. This has a total cost of £152.

Destinations:

	Manch.	Cov.	B'ham	Cardiff	Capacities	VAM diffs.
Origins: **Manchester**	1 [11]	6	3 [9]	6	20	3
Birmingham	7	3	1	6	10	2
London	9	4	5	4	25	0
Requirements	11	13	17	14	55	

VAM differences   —   1   2   1

Figure 3.3 VAM method in process

Destinations: Capacities

	Manch.	Cov.	B'ham	Cardiff	
Origins: **Manchester**	1 [11]	6	3 [9]	6	20
Birmingham	7	3 [2]	1 [8]	6	10
London	9	4 [11]	5	4 [14]	25
Requirements	11	13	17	14	55

Figure 3.4 VAM solution

Optimality and sensitivity analysis

The use of VAM will generally yield a good solution; in the present example it saves just over 1 per cent on the total cost of the previous solution. Is this the lowest cost solution available? If not, how can a better solution be found? As it happens, it is the optimal solution, but VAM itself cannot tell us this, nor can it locate any improvements if the solution it finds is not optimal.

Both VAM and the 'least-cost first' rule are examples of *algorithms* — that is, sets of rules for finding solutions to specified problems — but they cannot guarantee to find the optimal solution. Algorithms have been developed for completely solving the transportation problem, which are not difficult to understand but are somewhat lengthy to describe and, indeed, time-consuming to work through by hand. However, we can illustrate the method using the present example.

Instead of shipping from Manchester to Birmingham and also from Birmingham to Coventry, would it perhaps be cheaper to ship direct from Manchester to Coventry? If this is done, it can be seen from Figure 3.4 that in order to balance capacities and requirements it will also be necessary to increase the shipment from the Birmingham factory to the Birmingham warehouse. It can easily be verified that for every unit thus rearranged the net increase in total transport cost is £6 − £3 − £3 + £1 = £1, so the proposed modification is not worth while.

In the present example it is not too difficult to check all possible changes to see if the VAM solution can be improved. In a real problem of any size this would be quite impracticable. Fortunately, a procedure has been developed, known as the row−column sum or stepping-stone method, which systematically checks whether any new shipments can profitably be introduced, calculates what compensating changes need to be made to existing shipments, and repeats these checks and adjustments until the cheapest solution is obtained. These repeated adjustments are known as *iterations*. This is explained further in the solution methods for the exercises at the end of this chapter.

A second advantage of the stepping-stone method is that it makes use of *dual values* or *shadow prices*, which reflect the change in total transport cost induced by changes in capacities and requirements. We shall encounter shadow prices again when studying linear programming (Chapter 4), as in the solution methods at the end of this chapter, and the reader may well have met them when studying economics. Their immediate significance is that they allow us to carry out *sensitivity analysis*. We may wish to know how sensitive is the optimal solution to changes in costs, whether it is worth expanding factory capacities or adjusting warehouse requirements, etc. For example, answers can easily be provided to the following questions:

1. If unit transportation cost from London to Manchester were reduced from £9 to zero, would it be worth shipping along that route?

2. If the unit cost of shipping from Manchester to Cardiff fell by £1, would Manchester become a viable alternative to London as a source for the Cardiff warehouse?
3. At which factory should capacity be expanded for the greatest reduction in total transportation costs?
4. What adjustment of warehouse requirements will most reduce total transportation costs?
5. Is it ever possible to increase total units shipped and simultaneously *decrease* total transportation cost?

The reader may like to attempt to answer these questions himself.

Of course, in all this sensitivity analysis one would need to take into account the comparative investment and production costs of extending capacity at the different premises as well as a variety of other less easily quantified considerations. Moreover, these shadow prices have the drawback that they refer only to the first few units of extra capacity. For this reason, many companies do not utilize this information. However, many other users, particularly national planners, find that the shadow prices at least draw attention to crucial bottlenecks and suggest likely areas for further investigation.

Further applications of the standard transportation model

The model just described is as applicable to profit maximization as to cost minimization situations. It can handle situations where origin availabilities and destination requirements are in the form of upper and lower bounds, rather than exact requirements, and where total capacity does not equal total demand. This is done by simply introducing 'dummy' activities with zero cost corresponding to spare capacity or unsatisfied demand. Upper and lower bounds can also be imposed on individual shipments without too much difficulty. Unit costs which *increase* with the amount shipped, rather than stay constant, can easily be incorporated. Unit costs which *decrease* with volume (e.g. as a result of quantity discounts or internal economies of scale) present certain difficulties beyond the scope of the present book.

Various problems which appear to be quite different from the standard transportation problem (because they involve no notion of physical movement) in fact have an identical structure, and may therefore be solved by the same technique.

Suppose a company has a number of factories or production lines which are each capable of producing a number of different products. The total capacity of each factory, the total demand for each product and the unit cost of manufacturing each product at each factory are specified. The problem is formally identical to the standard transportation problem (with the different products in place of warehouses).

Or again, suppose a firm purchases raw materials at prices which vary month by month. Then it has to choose whether to produce to meet demand in each month or instead to produce in advance and hold inventory. This can be thought of as a transportation problem in which the origins and destinations correspond to different months of the year, and finished products or raw materials may be 'transported' from the month of production to the month of use at a specified inventory holding cost. An example is given in exercise 3 at the end of this chapter.

Now consider the problem of allocating salesmen to territories, where estimates can be made of the degree of success which each salesman is likely to have in each territory. Alternatively, consider the problem faced by British Coal in allocating different machines to different coal-faces in the light of data on machine efficiencies under different circumstances. If a different salesman/machine is best for each territory/coal-face, then there is no problem, but in general things will not be this simple. These problems may be thought of as transportation problems with salesmen/machines as 'origins' and territories/coal-faces as 'destinations'. There is a supply of one unit at each origin and a requirement of one unit at each destination. Unit costs are measured in terms of relative efficiencies. This special case of the transportation problem is known as the *assignment problem*, and even simpler techniques are available for solving such problems. The University of California is reported to use a student−professor−classroom assignment model, while Klingman and Phillips (1984) have developed a sophisticated model for the assignment of personnel in the US Marine Corps. This is described on page 47.

Network flow models

Instead of representing transportation problems in tableau form, we could, alternatively, represent them as *networks*, with nodes corresponding to origins and destinations, and arcs corresponding to potential shipments. The example problem is shown in Figure 3.5. Unit costs are shown in a small square on each arc (for a few arcs only). The problem is to choose flows on the arcs so as to minimize total costs subject to the condition that 'what goes in must come out' at each node.

Formulating the transportation problem in this way suggests that it is only one of a general class of network problems. Another type is a *trans-shipment*

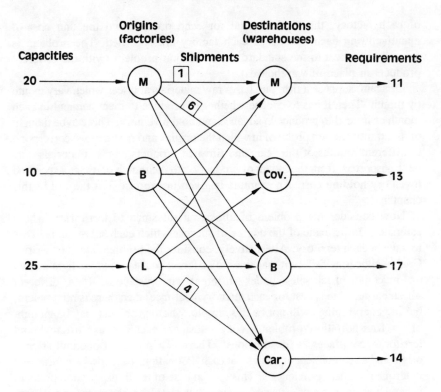

Figure 3.5 Network representation of transportation example

model in which commodities are shipped through one or more intermediate nodes. For example, the major oil companies have to plan the shipment of oil from various foreign sources through various refineries and regional depots to individual garages. This problem could be represented as in Figure 3.6. A similar model is used by Nabisco Inc. for scheduling production and distribution of their 'cookies' from factories to regional warehouses and then to local distribution facilities. The automobile example described in the next chapter is also presented in this way.

Inventory maintenance models are also of trans-shipment type. Here the 'origins' are purchases or production, at different dates, the ultimate 'destinations' are sales or usages, and the intermediate nodes represent inventory, as in Figure 3.7. An example is the Citgo problem referred to on pages 45−6. It is possible to extend these models to incorporate hierarchies of national, regional, area and plant stores. The problem of hiring and firing personnel in the presence of strong seasonal demand swings can be represented in a similar way.

The problem of finding the *shortest route* through a network of towns from,

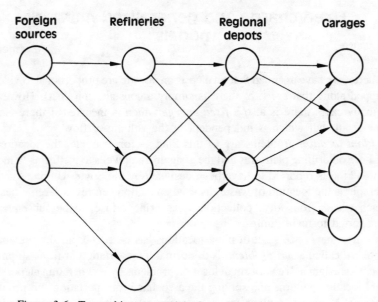

Figure 3.6 Trans-shipment model of an oil company

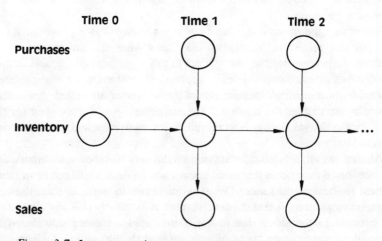

Figure 3.7 Inventory maintenance trans-shipment model

say, Birmingham to Edinburgh can be thought of as a trans-shipment problem with only one origin and one destination. (The 'cost' is measured in distance.) Similarly, the critical path method described in Chapter 9 involves the calculation of the *longest route* in a network (where the 'cost' is measured in time).

Fixed charge and generalized network models

Hitherto, we have assumed that total costs on any arc are proportional to volume shipped along that arc (i.e. there is simply a constant unit cost). However, in many cases there is also a *fixed charge* which is incurred if there is any flow at all, but which is independent of the volume of flow.

Plant location problems are of this kind — for example, the location of offshore oil drilling platforms and the assignment of wells to platforms; a model of this kind is reported to have been designed by the Soviet Union. Another example is the location of waste disposal collection centres in large cities, to which trucks from local collection areas bring refuse, to be subsequently transported to main dumps.

Notice that, once a set of plant locations has been chosen, the remaining problem, called a *sub-problem*, is of normal transportation or trans-shipment type. One might solve very small location problems by enumerating all possible plant location patterns and solving the associated transportation sub-problem for each. However, with as few as ten prospective sites this would entail the solution of more than a million transportation problems. More sophisticated techniques are required; this is an area where significant computational advances have now been made.

We have hitherto assumed that flow is not changed as it passes along an arc, but just as electric power suffers losses when transmitted over long distance, so inventories may be subject to pilferage or wastage, and money borrowed or invested depreciates or appreciates by the amount of the interest charge. Networks which include arcs of this character are called *generalized networks*. An example is a *generalized assignment model* developed for the US Office of Naval Research to minimize transportation and overhaul costs at naval shipyards.

Algorithms are available for solving all the various types of transportation and network flow models discussed above, but the details will not be of much interest to the general reader. What is important to note, as the following examples emphasize, is that the development of extremely efficient algorithms has brought to the aid of the manager the rapid computer solution of an increasing number and variety of very large-scale allocation problems.

Applications of network problems

In their recent paper (1989), Professors Glover, Klingman and Phillips have drawn attention to the exceedingly wide range of applications of pure network methods which are now to be found in government and industry. One example is direct network formulations of water resource management problems. In these, canals, river reaches and pipelines take the role of arcs, while reservoirs and pumping stations take the role of nodes.

The Texas Water Development Board and the government of Poland introduce 'what if' analyses into water resource management by using a succession of simulations having alternative supply and demand configurations, and solve the resulting network for each simulation run. The step of finding the optimum solution to each network problem is used to determine the best response to meet demands for water use, given a particular supply and demand configuration.

The problem of determining flows and heads in a general pipeline system (such as municipal water systems) with reservoirs, pumps, gate and check valves, given fixed inputs and withdrawals, has been shown to be equivalent to a particular type of trans-shipment problem.

Another important instance of the use of network models occurs in manpower promotion and assignment problems. AT&T in the United States has developed such models in order to guarantee acceptable hiring and promotion policies in accordance with government rules and regulations. A number of cash management problems can also be modelled as trans-shipment problems. These models include sources of funds in addition to cash (such as maturing accounts and notes receivable, sales of securities, borrowing, etc.) and uses of funds other than as a single 'investment'.

The three authors also give details in their paper of two particular practical applications. The first concerns Citgo Petroleum Corporation. To utilize forecasting data better and to provide economically rational operational decision-making, Klingman et al. (1986) developed an optimization-based support system for supply, distribution and marketing planning, called the SDM system. This system integrates Citgo's key economic and physical supply, distribution and marketing characteristics over a short-term (eleven week) planning horizon. This time horizon incorporates both manufacturing and distribution time-lags along with inventory planning. To represent this timing problem, the basic model is partitioned into time zones, and replications of the basic model are employed to accommodate the distinct time periods (weeks) as shown in Figure 3.8. Time zone 1 contains the product storage terminals that are within one week's travel time from the refinery. Time zone 2 contains those between one and two weeks away, etc. The vertical arcs between product storage terminal nodes (single circles) represent inventory held at storage terminals between time periods. The diagonal arcs between pipeline nodes (double circle) represent in-transit inventory, i.e. between time periods, product travels in the pipeline between adjacent time zones.

The system is used by top management to make many operational decisions such as where to sell products, what price to charge, where to buy or trade products, how much to buy or trade, how much product to hold in inventory

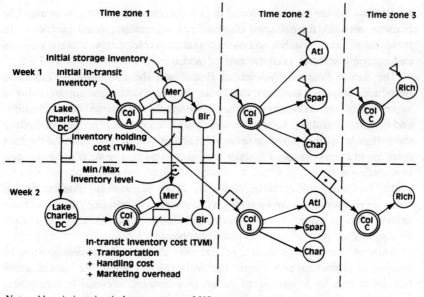

Note: abbreviations in circles are names of US towns (e.g. Atl = Atlanta)

Figure 3.8 Network representation of time zones and time periods

and how much product to ship by each mode of transportation. All information is provided by location, by line of business and by week. Thus, the critical timing considerations associated with all of these decisions are incorporated into the model.

The SDM system contains a separate minimum cost (or as an option, maximum profit) network flow model for each product (corresponding to the product managers who work with all supply, distribution and marketing personnel associated with each product). Each model is generated using input data from a corporate database, and the optimal solution is aggregated into output reports tailored for use by the individual operational managers. The objective function for the profit maximization model is calculated as total sales revenue less variable costs such as transportation costs, terminal handling costs and the interest cost associated with in-transit and terminal inventory. The constraints of the model include forecast price/demand functions, inventory capacities, exchange agreement options, spot volume limits, purchase/sale/ trade agreement options, retail demand etc.

The rapidity with which network models can be solved allows management to respond quickly to the dynamics of a commodity market industry by using the SDM system extensively in 'what if' sessions. For example, using a medium-sized computer, an IBM 4381 mod 2, each product model consisting of approximately 3,000 equations and 15,000 variables can be solved using an efficient network optimization code in approximately thirty seconds. The benefits of the SDM system include a US$116 million reduction (based on historical inventory-to-sales ratios) in product inventories resulting in a US$14 million per year reduction in working capital costs and an additional US$2.5 million per year estimated contribution to bottom line profits due to multiple supply, distribution and marketing insights provided by the system.

In another application of pure network trans-shipment modelling, Klingman and Phillips (1984) present a new modelling and solution approach for making enlisted personnel assignment decisions for the US Marine Corps. There are three primary types of goals that US military services seek to accommodate in assigning enlisted personnel to positions. Each goal type may have several subgoals, leading to a model which has numerous objective functions. These include the desire of the military to fill as many positions as possible in some priority fashion, the cost of assigning a person to a position, the utility of such an assignment to the military organization, and the desirability of the assignment to the person himself. In addition, the Marine Corps also specifies proportionate or disproportionate percentage fill policies for handling shortages within a job type. The criteria are pre-emptive and are handled in order of decreasing importance: maximum fill, maximum priority distribution fill and maximum fit.

To evaluate alternative modelling and solution approaches to the Marine Corps problem, a random parameter generator provided by the client was used to generate a single test problem. The generator produced a problem which had 10,000 persons, 240 job types and 3 job groups. Two of the groups had proportional fill criteria and the other a disproportional distribution fill criteria. The highest priority group required $5i$ persons to fill its ith job type and the other groups required a constant number of persons to fill their respective job types. The parameter generator randomly generated eligible person/job arcs and associated with each one four fit criteria co-efficients. Using this parameter generator yielded a large-scale multicriteria pure network trans-shipment problem with 10,245 nodes, 748,930 arcs and 11 criteria. The problem was solved using 6 different weighting strategies for aggregating the 11 criteria in the model. The best of these strategies required about 127 minutes of CPU time on a PRIME 550 minicomputer.

—— Exercises ——

Solution method

The row-column sum or stepping-stone method is not difficult to understand and teach, nor time-consuming to work through but, unfortunately, to explain it in this text would take more space than could be made available. An instructor with the time and inclination is encouraged to add this material, which is necessary to answer the questions fully. A brief outline would be as follows.

Select a basis, comprising $m + n - 1$ cells in independent positions (i.e. such that no 'rook's tour' is possible). When a new cell is added to the basis, compensating changes are required only on existing basis cells to preserve row and column totals. Identify profitable new cell and increase shipments until one existing cell leaves basis. Repeat until there are no profitable new entrants.

Shadow prices are a way of simplifying calculations. For example, take the least cost first solution of Figure 3.1. The net change in total cost from adding a cell (2.2) at unit level would be

$$\Delta_{22} + c_{22} - c_{12} - c_{23} + c_{13} = 3 - 6 - 1 + 3 = -1$$

i.e. a profitable decrease. Shadow prices have the property that row price (u_i) plus column price (v_j) equals unit cost (c_{ij}) for basis cells where any one shadow price may be chosen arbitrarily. Suppose we set $u_1 = 0$ then $u_2 = u_3 = -2$; $v_1 = 1$, $v_2 = 6$, $v_3 = 3$, $v_4 = 6$. Then

$$\Delta_{22} = c_{22} - (u_1 + v_2) - (u_2 + v_3) + (u_1 + v_3)$$
$$= c_{22} - (u_2 + v_2) = 3 - (-2 + 6) = -1, \text{ as before.}$$

In general, it is profitable to introduce a non-basis cell (ij) if $c_{ij} < u_i + v_j$. The optimal solution (= VAM solution) is obtained from the LCF solution in one step, with shadow prices (e.g.) $u_1 = 2$, $u_2 = 0$, $u_3 = 1$; $v_1 = -1$, $v_2 = 3$, $v_3 = 1$, $v_4 = 3$. These shadow prices may be used to answer the questions on pages 39–40, as follows.

It will be worth shipping along a non-optimal route if the unit cost c_{ij} falls to below $u_i + v_j$. Hence if the London–Manchester unit cost fell to zero, it would just be an equally profitable alternative (since $u_3 + v_1 = 1 - 1 = 0$). If the Manchester–Cardiff unit cost fell by £1 it would also just become viable since $u_1 + v_4 = 2 + 3 = £5$.

If factory i expands and factory j contracts then net change in cost is $u_i - u_j$ per unit, hence there would be most saving if the Birmingham factory expanded ($u_2 = 0$) and the Manchester factory contracted ($u_1 = 2$). Similarly, it is best to increase the warehouse requirement at Manchester ($v_1 = -1$) and reduce it at Coventry or Cardiff.

If an additional unit is available at Birmingham and required at Manchester, net change in cost is $u_2 + v_1 = 0 - 1 = -£1$, i.e. a net saving. This is an example of the 'more for less' paradox.

1. Draw up the transportation tableau of the problem depicted in Tables 3.3 and 3.4. *Hint*: introduce a 'dummy destination' with a requirement equal to spare capacity.

(a) Find a 'least-cost first' solution and a VAM solution.
(b) Find an optimal solution. Is it unique?
(c) By how much would total transportation costs be reduced if one more unit could be made available at origin 4 and one less at origin 2?

—— **Table 3.3** ——

Origin	Availability	Destination	Requirement
1	22	1	30
2	41	2	45
3	27	3	15
4	10		
	100		90

—— **Table 3.4** ——
Unit transportation
costs (£)

		Destination:		
		1	2	3
Origin:	1	3	1	4
	2	2	2	3
	3	1	6	2
	4	4	5	1

(d) At which of the three destinations would it be cheapest to meet increased requirements, and how much would it cost?

2. Before the advent of natural gas, British Gas West Midlands used to purchase coal from about fifty-seven pits in order to supply twenty-two gasworks. An important problem was to decide to which plant the coal from each pit should be shipped in order to minimize the total transportation costs. Operations research techniques were developed which eventually saved about £25,000 per year, or approximately 1 per cent of total transport costs. The following is a small-scale prototype problem. (Details of this example are taken from Bishop, 1965.)

Suppose British Gas has four works which require a total of 4,000 tonnes of coal per week, as set out in Table 3.5. It has contracted to buy supplies in that amount from four pits as set out also in Table 3.5.

In most cases, coal can be transported from any pit to any works by either road or rail and the transportation costs by each of these two methods is set out in Table 3.6. However, works 3 can receive coal only by road and works 4 can receive coal only by rail. In addition, pit 4 can ship only by rail. Assume that, apart from these restrictions, the cheapest method of transport may be used.

There is a second difficulty in that coal from certain pits is unsuitable for use in certain works, as indicated by the letter 'U' in Table 3.6.

—— **Table 3.5** ——
Present availabilities and requirements
(in 100 tonnes per week)

Pit	Contracted purchases	Gasworks	Requirements
1	8	1	6
2	14	2	15
3	15	3	12
4	3	4	7
Total	40	Total	40

—— **Table 3.6** ——
Pit to works transportation costs (in £ per 100
tonnes, including, where appropriate, extra
handling costs)

From pit	To works by road				To works by rail			
	1	2	3	4	1	2	3	4
1	121	U	100	—	96	U	—	98
2	U	99	U	—	U	81	—	85
3	U	100	100	—	U	78	—	81
4	—	—	—	—	80	80	—	84

(a) Under the present contract, what is the cheapest pattern of transporting the coal from the pits to the works while meeting the above restrictions?

(b) British Gas suspects that rather more coal could be made available at certain pits if it were to bargain with British Coal. At which pits should it press for the available limits to be raised? If necessary, what increased price per tonne on supplies above this limit should it be prepared to concede?

(c) At the same time, British Gas realizes there might be possibilities of rearranging production between its own works. What savings in coal transportation costs would be achieved by rearranging the first few units of production?

3. Ajax Ltd is a manufacturer of confectionery. Its production is seasonal with a peak just before Christmas. The company purchases packing cartons from a supplier at a price of £100 per thousand, paying cash on delivery. (Deliveries are made on the first day of each month.) There are no storage costs, but the cost of capital to Ajax is currently 24 per cent per annum. This means that Ajax saves approximately £2 per thousand cartons for every month by which purchases can be delayed, which is equivalent to a £2 per thousand per month discount after September. For this reason Ajax has traditionally purchased cartons in the amount required each month.

—— **Table 3.7** ——

Month	Ajax Ltd's production requirements	Supplier's price discount (%)
September	13,000	6
October	22,000	3
November	25,000	—
December	15,000	—
January	8,000	5
February	6,000	6

However, the supplier also has seasonal production problems, and offers discounts on cartons supplied in the supplier's own off-seasons. Column 2 of Table 3.7 sets out Ajax Ltd's schedule of monthly requirements of cartons for the next six months. Column 2 sets out the supplier's percentage discount policy. Ajax will have an initial stock of 15,000 cartons at the beginning of September, and wishes to have at least 10,000 cartons in stock at the end of February. The maximum quantity which the supplier can make available in any month is 25,000 cartons.

(a) Formulate this problem as a transportation problem and set out the tableau.
(b) Determine the six month purchasing schedule for Ajax Ltd which minimizes present value of cash outflows. Evaluate the benefits to Ajax of: (i) changing its own production schedule; (ii) pursuading the supplier to increase his maximum supply.

References and further reading

Bishop, P. (1965) *The Coal Transportation Problem*, Technical Report OR 5, British Gas West Midlands.

Charles, A. and W.W. Cooper (1961) *Management Models and Industrial Applications of Linear Programming* (2 vols.), John Wiley.

Glover, F., D. Klingman and N. Phillips (1989) 'Netform Modelling and Applications', University of Texas (unpublished).

Klingman, D. and N. Phillips (1984) 'Topological and computational aspects of pre-emptive multi-criteria military personnel assignment problems', *Management Science*, **30** (11), 1362−75.

Klingman, D., N. Phillips, R. Steiger, R. Wirth and W. Young (1986) 'The challenge and success factors in implementing an integrated petroleum products planning system for Citgo', *Management Science*, **16** (3), 9−19.

Smith, D.K. (1982) *Network Optimization Practice*, Ellis Horwood.

Wagner, H.M. (1975) *Principles of Operations Research*, Prentice Hall.

— 4 —

Linear programming

S.C. LITTLECHILD

Introduction

Linear programming (LP) is a mathematical technique which is particularly useful in a situation where there are decisions to be made about many variables (for example, the levels of production at each factory of a whole product line) and where there are numerous constraints relating to the availability of resources (for example, machine capacity, storage space, labour availability, etc.). The difficulty is that the decisions interact: if the production of item A is expanded this week, then the limited capacity might require production of item B to be cut back, but this in turn might free some skilled labour to work on product C, and so on. Linear programming is an attempt to aid the decision-maker in evaluating these multiple interdependencies.

Some of the practical situations in which linear programming has been found useful are as follows:

1. Production planning (performed quarterly for the next twelve months) in Hoogovens Steel Company, encompassing production levels at each plant, size of stocks on hand, transportation requirements, raw material inputs and supporting activities. Similar applications have been made in many large firms.
2. Agricultural planning by ICI Farm Advisory Service and many others for large arable and livestock farms to decide most profitable production patterns in the light of area available, crop rotation and animal food requirements, labour and machinery constraints, building capacities, capital limitations, etc.
3. The formulation of animal feed products at J. Bibby & Sons Ltd to ensure that the cheapest combination of raw materials is being used which meets the required nutritional specifications. This is a classic problem which stimulated one of the very first research papers on linear programming.
4. The blending of crude oils or molten metals to satisfy certain technical

requirements and capacity constraints while maximizing profits. It has been suggested, in fact, that almost all the electronic computers used in the oil industry were originally justified on the basis of such blending exercises and were only subsequently applied to other problems.

5. Manpower planning in the US Navy and many large corporations, in order to decide how many new personnel should be hired, at what levels and in what applications, bearing in mind retirement policy, natural wastage, anticipated growth of business, promotion policy, etc.

6. National planning in many countries to decide levels of production and investment in each industry. Similar applications have been made in particular sectors, particularly education and energy.

We shall illustrate the linear programming approach by means of a very simple example, involving only two variables and three constraints. This will enable us to represent and solve the model graphically before representing and solving it algebraically. (Modern computers using efficient solution codes are able to solve problems involving thousands of variables and constraints in a matter of minutes.) We shall then explore some aspects of sensitivity analysis, and introduce the 'dual' problem. Finally, we refer to some of the extensions known as non-linear, integer and stochastic programming which considerably increase the flexibility of this technique.

An example

A farmer has available 100 hectares of land which he can plant with either wheat or potatoes, or leave fallow. Taking into account expected yields, crop prices, planting and harvesting costs (including labour), etc., he calculates that his net profit will be £90 per hectare for wheat and £60 per hectare for potatoes. On average it takes 6 man-hours per hectare to harvest wheat and 3 man-hours per acre to harvest potatoes. During the critical autumn harvesting period he will have only 480 man-hours of help available. His maximum area quota for potatoes is 65 hectares. Assuming the farmer wants to maximize profits, what area should he plant of each crop?

This problem is sufficiently simple that we can represent it graphically as in Figure 4.1. Let the horizontal axis represent the area of wheat planted and let the vertical axis refer to potatoes. Any point on the graph then represents a particular planting pattern. Let us first delimit which areas on the graph correspond to *feasible* planting patterns, i.e. ones which do not violate any of the known restrictions. First, since it does not make sense to plant negative areas, the chosen pattern must be above the horizontal axis and to the right of the vertical axis. The maximum area constraint on potatoes is a horizontal

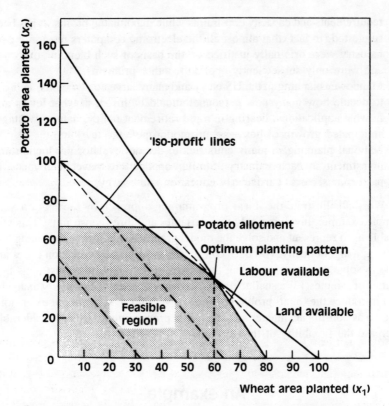

Figure 4.1 Graphical representation of farmer's crop-planting problem

straight line; the chosen production point must not lie above this line, as the arrow indicates. A simple constraint of this kind is known as an *upper bound*. A straight line drawn between the 100-hectare points on each axis represents all patterns of planting which take up exactly 100 hectares, so the chosen point must be on or below this line. Finally, if no potatoes were planted, it would be possible to harvest up to 480/6 = 80 hectares of wheat, and if no wheat were planted, it would be possible to harvest up to 480/3 = 160 hectares of potatoes. A straight line joining these two points comprises all the planting patterns which require exactly 480 hours of labour, so the chosen point must lie on or below this line.

The *feasible region* is the set of points which satisfies *all* constraints, and is shaded on the graph. Which of these points is the most profitable? Let us begin by plotting the set of planting patterns corresponding to some arbitrary level of total profit — say £3,000. This could be achieved with $33\frac{1}{3}$ hectares of wheat and no potatoes, or by 50 hectares of potatoes and no wheat, or in fact by any (linear) combination of these two points — for example $16\frac{2}{3}$

hectares of wheat and 25 hectares of potatoes. Draw in the straight line corresponding to £3,000 profit. This is sometimes called an 'iso-profit' (equal-profit) line. Note that some of the points in the feasible region lie on it, and so yield a profit of £3,000. Now repeat the procedure for £6,000. The second line is evidently parallel to the first and lies above and to the right of it. It, too, contains some points from the feasible region. This suggests that if we take a ruler, hold it parallel to the iso-profit curves and move it as far to the right as possible without going completely outside the feasible region, then we shall have found that feasible production pattern which yields the greatest total profit. In fact, this optimal point is to be found at a 'corner' of the feasible region where the areas may be read off the graph as 60 hectares wheat and 40 hectares potatoes, yielding a total rofit of £7,800.

Note that all the lines which we have drawn are straight. This explains the term 'linear' programming.

Algebraic formulation

It would not be difficult to represent additional constraints on this graph, but if an additional crop were considered then the graph would need three dimensions (and the constraint lines would become constraint planes). With four or more variables, graphical representation is impossible, and a mathematical approach is required. (Alternatively, by plotting resources along the axes, it is possible to represent graphically as rays from the origin any number of variables, but only two constraints can then be incorporated.) In fact, it is not difficult at all to represent the problem algebraically.

Let x_1 and x_2 be variables denoting the number of hectares planted of wheat and potatoes, respectively. Bearing in mind the expected profits per hectare for each crop, the total profit will be

$$90x_1 + 60x_2$$

This expression is known as the *objective function*. We wish to choose x_1 and x_2 to maximize the objective function subject to the following constraints:

land available $x_1 + x_2 \leq 100$
harvest labour available $6x_1 + 3x_2 \leq 480$
potato quota $x_2 \leq 65$
non-negative areas $x_1 \geq 0, x_2 \geq 0$

These various mathematical expressions constitute a simple linear programme.

In the present example, we know from the graphical solution that both land and labour are fully utilized, hence we may solve the two equations

$$x_1 + x_2 = 100$$

$$6x_1 + 3x_2 = 480$$

to give $x_1 = 60$, $x_2 = 40$, thereby confirming the solution read off the graph. Unfortunately, in general we do not know in advance which resources will be fully utilized at the optimum solution. A more systematic mathematical approach is therefore required, as outlined on page 58.

With obvious modifications it is possible to formulate linear programs which minimize cost instead of maximize profit, or indeed maximize any other objective, and to introduce 'greater than or equal to' or 'equality' constraints as well as 'less than or equal to' ones.

Sensitivity analysis

We might be interested not only in solving the problem but also in knowing how the solution would vary if the conditions of the problem were different. For example, perhaps more resources could be made available at a certain price, in which case it would be useful to know by how much profit could be increased by employing these additional resources. Alternatively, different activities might be considered.

Notice that the farmer's most profitable plan involves planting fewer potatoes than his maximum limit. This constraint is said to be *slack*. A small change in the level of this constraint would not affect the optimal solution. On the diagram, if the line corresponding to the slack constraint were shifted slightly, the optimum would not move. The farmer would attach no value (at present) to an increase in the potato quota.

By contrast, all the available land is planted and the harvest-period labour force is expected to be fully employed. These two constraints are said to be *tight* or *binding*. If more or less land or labour were made available, this would affect the optimum planting pattern. However, it would not necessarily alter it in an easily predictable pattern, and consequently the effect on profit may be difficult to calculate.

For example, how much could profit be increased if the farmer had 101 instead of 100 hectares? One's first reaction might be that extra land would not be any use without a simultaneous increase in labour. But a glance at Figure 4.1 suggests that if the land constraint were moved outwards slightly, the optimum point would move slightly up the labour constraint line. In other words, the area of potatoes would increase but the area of wheat would *decrease*. To measure the exact effect, solve the equations

$$x_1 + x_2 = 101$$

$$6x_1 + 3x_2 = 480$$

to yield $x_1 = 59$, $x_2 = 62$. The reduction of one hectare of wheat frees not only one hectare of land but also six hours of labour. Taken together with the new hectare of land this allows two extra hectares of potatoes to be planted and harvested. The effect on total profits is (2 hectares @ £60) − (1 @ £90) = £30. In other words, an extra hectare of land brings in an extra profit of £30 if the planting pattern is suitably reorganized. This value of £30 is often referred to as the dual value *shadow price* or *opportunity cost* of land. (Recall the discussion of shadow prices in Chapter 3.)

Two further points should be made. First, this value applies equally to a decrease in area available. There would be a drop in profits of £30 per hectare withdrawn. Second, this value applies only to small changes in area. Thus, as area is increased one could substitute two hectares of potatoes for one hectare of wheat only until the area allotment of sixty-five hectares of potatoes was reached, namely after five hectares have been added. Subsequent hectares cannot be utilized, so they bring no extra profit to the farm. Similarly, as hectares are withdrawn the farmer will switch to wheat, but only until potato area drops to zero after twenty hectares have been withdrawn. After that, the wheat area itself has to be reduced at a loss in profit of £90 per hectare. In general, the value of an extra unit of any resource decreases as the availability of that resource increases (so that the value of an extra unit increases as the total availability decreases). These changes in shadow prices occur in discrete steps as the corresponding resources are varied. (It is instructive to plot the shadow price of land against the amount of land available.)

Sensitivity analysis: new activities

We could go through a similar exercise to work out the value of extra labour, but a more general approach is preferable. Let u_1, u_2 and u_3 denote the value to the farmer of, respectively, an additional hectare of land, an additional hour of labour and an additional hectare of potato quota. These values are precisely the shadow prices just referred to. We wish to calculate u_1, u_2 and u_3. We already know that u_3 is zero, because the present potato quota is not fully utilized. Now one hectare of land plus six hours of labour must be worth *at least* £90, because those are the inputs necessary to generate a profit of £90 by planting a hectare of wheat. But we know that these resources cannot be worth *more* than £90 otherwise it would not be worth planting wheat, and we already know it is worth doing that. Hence we have

$$1u_1 + 6u_2 = £90$$

By an exactly similar argument with reference to potatoes we deduce that

$$1u_1 + 3u_2 = £60$$

These two simultaneous equations are easily solved to yield u_1 = £30 and u_2 = £10. The first value coincides, as expected, with our previous calculations of the value of land. The second value says that extra labour at harvest time is worth £10 per hour. This suggests that it would pay the farmer to hire extra labour for the harvest period, providing he could get it for less than £10 per hour above normal rates. This would enable him to substitute some wheat, which is a more profitable but also a more labour-intensive crop, for some potatoes.

Suppose a hectare of peas requires only two hours of labour at harvest time but generates a profit of only £40 per hectare. Would it be worth planting peas? Here the shadow prices come in handy again. In order to plant and harvest peas, the area of wheat and/or potatoes will have to be reduced, at a consequent reduction in profit. Will this outweigh the profit on peas? A hectare of peas requires one hectare of land and two hours of labour. We have already calculated that the value of land in growing present crops is £30 per hectare and the value of labour is £10 per hour. The resources necessary to grow peas therefore have a value of

$$(1 @ £30) + (2 @ £10) = £50$$

in growing present crops. This would not be compensated for by the profit on peas. However, if the profit on peas were to increase to over £50 per hectare, then it would be profitable to introduce peas and to reduce one of the other crops. Unfortunately, we cannot tell without further calculation exactly what the new pattern of activities would be.

Running a linear program

Solving even small linear programs is a tedious procedure best left to a computer. A most important solution algorithm, called the Simplex method, for many years formed the basis of most computer codes. The principle of this algorithm may be simply stated. As Figure 4.1 suggests, if all the constraints and the objective function are linear, then, whatever the numbers involved, the optimal solution will always lie at a 'corner' or *extreme point* of the feasible region. (If the objective function is parallel to a constraint, then all points along this constraint within the feasible region are optimal, including both corners.) The Simplex method starts at one extreme point of the feasible region and moves to an adjacent corner, then to another adjacent corner, and so on, always one step at a time, and always in a direction which improves profit, until the optimum is attained. Each move is called an *iteration*. The similarity between this Simplex method and the row—column sum method is not surprising. We shall see in the next section exactly how transportation problems are a special case of linear programming problems.

Nowadays linear programs often involve many hundreds or even thousands of constraints. Because the power of computers is increasing and more efficient codes are being developed, the problem of computing the optimal solution to a linear program is no longer the critical difficulty. It is, rather, the collection, inputting and revision of data and the interpretation of results. In the first instance, time is not well spent making sure that every coefficient is absolutely correct. Many resources or constraints will not be binding, and may variables or activities will not be utilized. Attention should be focused on those parts of the system that are critical. Sensitivity analysis will show what margin of error can be tolerated in the computation of each profit or resource availability. As regards data input and output, the usual procedure nowadays is to write (or hire) a separate computer program, called a *matrix generator*, which takes the data in a form convenient to the user and transforms it into a form convenient for the computer. Another program called a *report writer* transforms the linear programming results into a format specified by the manager — for example, involving tables or graphs.

Transportation problems as linear programs

The farm problem discussed earlier in the chapter can be set out in the following way. Single rows or columns of figures are called *vectors*; the rectangular block of coefficients is called a *matrix*.

	x_1	x_2		
	90	60	=	max

	x_1	x_2		
	1	1	≤	100
	6	3	≤	480
	0	1	≤	65

For the more mathematically-minded, this can be represented using matrix notation as:

$$\text{maximize } cx$$
$$\text{subject to } Ax \leq b, \; x \geq 0$$

or in summation notation as:

$$\text{maximize} \sum_i c_i x_i$$

$$\text{subject to} \sum_i a_{ij} x_i \leq b_j, j = 1, 2, \ldots, n$$

$$x_i \geq 0$$

The so-called '*dual problem*' can be written as:

$$\text{minimize } ub$$
$$\text{subject to } uA \geq c, u \geq 0$$

Here u is a vector of dual values (shadow prices) derived from the optimal solution of the primal problem. In words, the dual problem for the farm example can be expressed as 'given the availability of each input (b) and given a lower limit on the unit profits of wheat and of potatoes (c), what value (u) should be assigned to each input, so as to *minimize* the total 'value' of the input (ub)?'

A transportation problem may be represented as a linear program if we define the variable x_{ij} as the number of units shipped from origin i to destination j. The constraint on availability of capacity at origin 1 of the example in Chapter 3 would be written

$$x_{11} + x_{12} + x_{13} + x_{14} = 20$$

and the constraint on requirements at the first destination would be

$$x_{11} + x_{21} + x_{31} = 11$$

The whole problem can be represented in matrix form as follows (the blanks indicate zeros, which have been omitted for clarity):

x_{11}	x_{12}	x_{13}	x_{14}	x_{21}	x_{22}	x_{23}	x_{24}	x_{31}	x_{32}	x_{33}	x_{34}		
1	6	3	6	7	3	1	6	9	4	5	4	=	min.

x_{11}	x_{12}	x_{13}	x_{14}	x_{21}	x_{22}	x_{23}	x_{24}	x_{31}	x_{32}	x_{33}	x_{34}		
1	1	1	1									=	20
				1	1	1	1					=	10
								1	1	1	1	=	25
1				1				1				=	11
	1				1				1			=	13
		1				1				1		=	17
			1				1				1	=	14

Notice that the matrix of coefficients is very *dense* (i.e. has few zeros) for the first linear program (the farm problem) but is very *sparse* for the transportation problem. Moreover, the non-zero coefficients in the transportation matrix are all 1s arranged in a striking pattern. It is this special structure which makes transportation problems about a hundred times more easy to solve than arbitrary linear programs of the same size, as emphasized in the previous chapter. Typically, in a large linear program not more than 5 per cent of the coefficients are non-zero.

Extensions of linear programming

Linear programming is in fact a very flexible technique. There are a number of extensions and modifications, which collectively go by the name of mathematical programming, which may be used to model a great variety of situations. We shall briefly discuss a few of these.

Non-linear programming

For a single farmer, the price which he gets per tonne of crop is essentially independent of the volume of his sales. Because of this his production is small compared with the total market and therefore does not influence price. For other firms this might not be so — in order to sell more they would need to reduce price and per unit profit. The objective function becomes a non-linear expression instead of a linear one. Graphically, this would be represented by a family of iso-profit curves which were not straight lines. In the same way, situations of increasing or decreasing returns to scale give rise to non-linear constraints. It is possible to solve such models, but by no means as efficiently as one can solve linear programs. Accordingly, one often looks for linear approximation — for example, by dividing a sales variable into several new variables, each with upper bounds, corresponding to different sales volumes and having different prices.

Integer programming

Linear programs involve decisions about *continuous* variables, such as the level of production. In practice, one often has to make decisions about *discrete* variables, such as the number of aircraft to purchase, where the solution must be limited to *integer* values (whole numbers). In particular, many decisions are of the 'yes' or 'no' (or *logical*) variety, such as whether or not to build a factory in a particular location. The variables take only the values zero (no) or one (yes). Algorithms are available for solving such problems, but their efficiency seems to depend heavily upon the structure of the problem. National Westminster Bank used integer programming to decide which (if any) of a number of staff training centres should be kept open. The technique is regularly used for aircrew and machine scheduling, for minimizing waste in cutting up paper and timber, and for locating depots in distribution networks as described in the previous two chapters.

Programming under uncertainty

It may be that not all the elements in a linear program are sufficiently well known to be represented by a single number, particularly if the problem involves long-term planning. For example, it might be desired to provide sufficient capacity to meet demand next year, but the level of the latter is quite uncertain. The importance of this problem in oil companies led to the development of *chance-constraints*, which are required to hold only with a specified probability (say 97 per cent). After estimating the relevant probability distribution, the chance-constraint may generally be reduced to a normal linear constraint known as a *deterministic equivalent*. In the illustration just given, the oil company is effectively constrained to provide capacity to meet demand in a 3/100 winter (i.e. a winter so severe that it occurs on average only three times in every hundred years). More sophisticated versions involve *decision rules* for choosing future actions according to the outcome of events as yet unknown. Chance-constrained programming models have been used by American marketing firms to decide whether or not to go ahead with new products, where and how far to test-market, how to design the marketing strategy, etc. Other models, known by the names of *linear programming under uncertainty, programming with recourse, stochastic programming*, etc., have been used to determine efficient financial portfolios with specified risk levels and to design water resource systems of reservoirs and canals.

—— Exercises ——

1. Recalculate the optimal solution to the farm example in the text on the assumption that the potato allotment is only 35 hectares. What are the new shadow prices?

2. A smallholder owns six hectares of land and wishes to decide what proportion to plant with flowers and what proportion with strawberries. He calculates the average return (that is, proceeds of sale less costs of bulbs/plants and fertilizers, etc.) to be £80 per hectare for flowers and £100 per hectare for strawberries. However, the time he has available for cultivation and picking is somewhat limited, and the labour requirements by season are as given in Table 4.1 (in man-hours per hectare):

Table 4.1

Crop	Winter	Spring	Summer	Autumn
Flowers	10	40	0	10
Strawberries	10	20	50	10
Labour available (hours)	100	200	200	100

(a) What pattern of crops would you recommend the smallholder to grow?
(b) How much would you recommend he be willing to pay for extra labour during each season?
(c) Formulate and interpret the dual to this problem.

3. (Due to A.W. McCurdy) Rover Cars regularly used a linear program for scheduling car production. The following is a brief outline of the model. Attempt to formulate algebraically a small-scale version.

The objective of the LP is to select orders for production taking into account sales priorities and production control constraints. Orders are assigned priorities based on the type of order and the length of time they have been in the outstanding order bank. Production constraints such as overall mix of models to preserve line balancing are fed in, together with production control constraints on availability of major units, e.g. engines. Periodically a computer is used to select several shifts of orders so as to maximize the total 'priority score' while complying with the constraints. These orders are passed across to another computer which is used to schedule orders on an hourly basis on the assembly line. The LP matrix is quite large, containing thousands of columns, reflecting the large number of model variants. There are 200–300 rows.

Further reading

Charles, A. and W.W. Cooper (1961) *Management Models and Industrial Applications of Linear Programming* (2 vols.), John Wiley.

Sasieni, M., A. Yaspan and L. Friedman (1959) *Operations Research: Methods and problems*, John Wiley.

Wagner, H.M. (1975) *Principles of Operations Research*, Prentice Hall.

Williams, H.P. (1990) *Model Building in Mathematical Programming*, John Wiley.

Winston, W.L. (1987) *Operations Research Applications and Algorithms*, Duxbury Press.

– 5 –

Data envelopment analysis

A. LAND

Introduction

The economist's theory of the firm starts by assuming that there is a production function which relates the physical amounts of inputs (labour of various types, raw materials, capital, etc.) to the amounts of one or more types of output produced. Although it is obvious that an organization has usually many inputs, and often also many outputs, nevertheless some of the characteristics of the production function can be illustrated and discussed in terms of simplified cases with only two inputs and one output, or sometimes with two outputs and only one input.

For instance, if there are only two inputs and one output, and if one of the inputs is held constant while the other varies, then the amount of production will increase with the varying input, but at a decreasing rate, as illustrated in Figure 5.1. For example, a fixed amount of land to which increasing amount of labour might be applied. Economists call this *diminishing marginal productivity*. The function has the same general shape when there are many inputs and one is considering the effect of varying a single input.

The same production function, with two inputs and a single output, has another two-dimensional representation, the *isoquant* diagram, as in Figure 5.2. Each of the curves, or isoquants, in Figure 5.2 represents combinations of inputs 1 and 2 (say, land and labour) which can be combined to produce a certain amount of the product (say, wheat). Each isoquant can be thought of as a contour line of the third dimension, the level of production — the contour lines of a hill, rising towards the north east. In that way of thinking, Figure 5.1. represents a slice through the hill along the dotted line in Figure 5.2.

Economists customarily distinguish the case of increasing, constant or diminishing returns to scale. In terms of Figure 5.2, the isoquant for 1,000 units of output could be exactly twice as far from the origin as the 500 unit isoquant (constant returns to scale), or less than twice as far (increasing returns), or more than twice as far (decreasing returns). Figure 5.1 could represent the

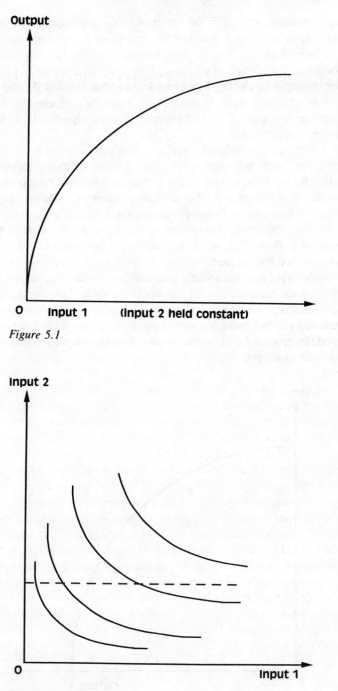

O   **Input 1**   **(input 2 held constant)**

Figure 5.1

Input 2

O   **Input 1**

Figure 5.2

case of decreasing returns if the horizontal axis represented not one input varying, but rather both inputs varying in a fixed proportion. However, in terms of computation, it is preferable to assume that if such a case is observed it is because there is some other input(s) *not* varying in the same proportion. In other words, we make the formal assumption that we always have the case of constant returns to scale. In practice, it is usually easy enough to identify some non-varying input if the real situation appears superficially to be a case of non-constant returns.

One other two-dimensional diagram which can serve as a useful mental picture is the Pareto substitution function. If there are two possible outputs competing for the same resource then we have a functional relationship of the general shape of Figure 5.3. We say that production is *Pareto-optimal*, or *efficient*, if it is not possible to have more of one output without having less of some other. The production of outputs 1 and 2 at a point such as A, inside the boundary in Figure 5.3, would not be efficient because it would be possible to have more of both outputs.

Similarly, if we pick out a single isoquant from Figure 5.2, say the isoquant representing the combinations of the inputs capable of producing 120 units of the product, then we should say that producing 120 units by the combination represented by P in Figure 5.4 would not be efficient. Either the same 120 units could be produced at Q, or the inputs at P could be used to produce OP/OQ × 120 units of output.

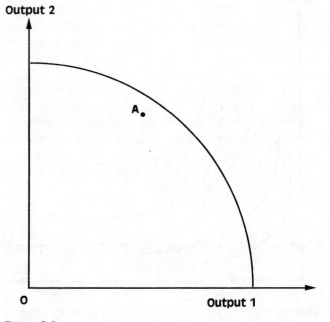

Output 2

A.

O   Output 1

Figure 5.3

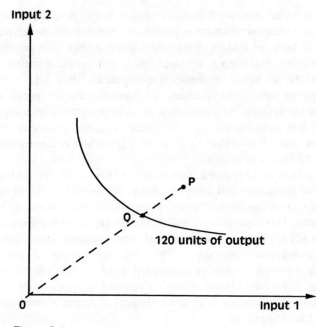

Figure 5.4

Traditionally in economics the theory of the firm does not concern itself with the entrepreneur's problem of achieving technically efficient production. It is assumed that the force of competition will eliminate the inefficient producer. Economic theory concentrates on the way in which the appropriate response to price relativities of inputs and outputs determines the particular point on the efficient frontier at which production will take place.

The operations researcher, on the other hand, is often concerned precisely to try to attain the efficiency frontier, rather than waiting to have his firm eliminated by its competitors. One difficulty about the notion of the production function is that it is not easy to determine its exact numerical parameters in a particular type of production. This is where linear programming and in particular Data Envelopment Analysis (DEA) has in recent years been found to be a useful tool.

A small example of data envelopment analysis

The following miniature data set is totally artificial, and is chosen simply for illustration and to relate to the 2-D diagrams of economic theory. Let us suppose that there are either seven small firms in the same line of production, or perhaps seven branch managers of a large organization. We shall use the term *decision management units*, or DMUs. Each DMU uses two inputs to produce some quantity of (the same) output, all measured over a standard period of time. We can list the seven sets of inputs and outputs in Table 5.1.

Although the DMUs are operating at different levels of output, we shall assume that the fundamental assumption of linear programming is appropriate — that any activity is capable of being operated at any non-negative level — and convert Table 5.1 to Table 5.2, where each DMU is represented by its inputs for 120 units of output.

We can represent these seven combinations of the two inputs, each of which is capable of producing 120 units of output, in Figure 5.5. By drawing the line (vector) from the origin through each point we are stressing that any combination of inputs on the line will produce a proportionate output — half the amount of each input can produce sixty units of output, and 1/120 of each input can produce one unit of output. The set of lines forming the *lower convex envelope* of the seven points, plus the vertical and horizontal extensions of those lines, is very like the economist's 120-unit isoquant, except that the isoquant is usually assumed to be smoothly varying, rather than consisting of piecewise linear segments.

We might consider using these points to estimate the coefficients of a smoothly continuous production function, but for the present purpose we shall simply make the assumption that the observed points and the lines joining them do represent the *efficient frontier*. For example, we are assuming that if the two inputs were combined in the proportions halfway between those of DMU$_3$ and DMU$_5$, say, 7.5 units of input 1 and 23.5 units of input 2, then that would

——— **Table 5.1** ———

DMU	1	2	3	4	5	6	7
Input 1	19	1	1	2	10	5	8
Input 2	10	1	6	15	17	1	1
Output	120	8	24	40	120	20	24

——— **Table 5.2** ———

DMU	1	2	3	4	5	6	7
Input 1	19	15	5	6	10	30	40
Input 2	10	15	30	45	17	6	5
Output	120	120	120	120	120	120	120

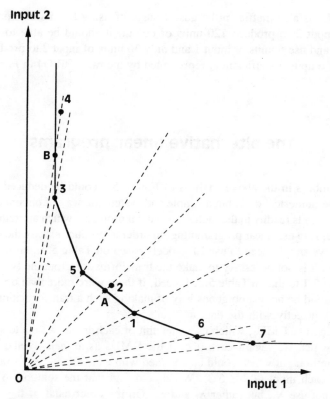

Figure 5.5

also yield an output of exactly 120 units. We are also implicitly assuming that our observed seven points represent all possible combinations of the inputs capable of producing 120 units of output, although we might have a suspicion that if we were able to observe several hundred DMUs rather than seven, the isoquant might be 'smoother' and that the five DMUs on the frontier in Figure 5.5 might turn out to be within the frontier with the larger number.

It is apparent that DMU_2 is not efficient, because we can imagine a 'composite' DMU, at point A, consisting of 0.438 times DMU_1 and 0.562 times DMU_5, on the isoquant between DMU_1 and DMU_5 which uses 13.937 of each input to produce 120 units of output, as compared to the 15 units of each input used by DMU_2. Alternatively, we could say that the composite DMU which could produce 120 units of output by combining the inputs at the point A, could produce 129.15 units if, like DMU_2, it used 15 of each input. Looking at it in either way, we can say that DMU_2 has an *efficiency* of 0.929 as compared to the composite DMU_A. The *efficiency number*, 0.929, is the ratio of the lengths OA/O2.

DMU$_4$ is also inefficient because instead of using 6 units of input 1 and 45 of input 2 to produce 120 units of output, it should be able to emulate DMU$_3$ and use 6 units of input 1 and only 36 units of input 2 to produce 144 units of output. Its efficiency, represented by the ratio OB/O4 in Figure 5.5, is 0.833.

The alternative linear programs

The numbers in the above analysis of Figure 5.5 could be deduced directly from the numerical data, but a simple and systematic way of obtaining them, which extends readily to the multidimensional problems which are rather more realistic, is to use linear programming. In order to produce exactly the numbers above, we should need to use LP models based on Table 5.2, but in the real situation it is not necessary to make the transformation from the type of data in Table 5.1 to that in Table 5.2. Indeed, if there were more than one output, there would be no unambiguous way of making such a transformation. So let us work directly with the data in Table 5.1.

To analyze DMU$_2$, which uses one unit of each input, we could set up an LP in which we regard each one of the DMUs as an *activity* and find the maximum output which could be obtained with an availability of exactly one unit of each input (Table 5.3). We should find that the solution to that LP would not use λ_2, but rather λ_1 and λ_5. On the other hand, if the LP were set up to analyze DMU$_1$ with right-hand side the 19 and 10 input units of DMU$_1$, the solution would use $\lambda 1$ only, at the level one.

However, we do not want to restrict ourselves to a single output, but rather set up the LP as in Table 5.4 to maximize a multiple of the *vector* of DMU$_2$'s outputs, with the limits set by its inputs, even though the vector in this case consists of a single element only (eight units of a single type of output). The solution to this LP is that $\lambda_1 = 0.031$, $\lambda_5 = 0.040$ and $w = 1.076$. This demonstrates that DMU$_2$ is *dominated* by a combination of DMU$_1$ and DMU$_5$, and that more output can be obtained by that composite DMU than

---
Table 5.3

Maximize $c\lambda$ subject to $A\lambda \leq b$, $\lambda \geq 0$

	λ_1	λ_2	λ_3	λ_4	λ_5	λ_6	λ_7	b
$A =$	19	1	1	2	10	5	8	≤ 1
	10	1	6	15	17	1	1	≤ 1
$c =$	120	8	24	40	120	20	24	

—— **Table 5.4** ——
Maximize w subject to $A(\lambda, w) \geq b$, $\lambda \geq 0$

	λ_1	λ_2	λ_3	λ_4	λ_5	λ_6	λ_7	w		
$A =$	19	1	1	2	10	5	8	0	$\leq$	1
	10	1	6	15	17	1	1	0	$\leq$	1
	120	8	24	40	120	20	24	-8	$\geq$	1
	0	0	0	0	0	0	0	1		

Note: the symbol $\leq$ denotes a mixture of $\leq$ and $\geq$ constraints.

by DMU$_2$ itself (1.076 as compared to 1.0). $1/1.076 = 0.929$, and we say that the *efficiency* of DMU$_2$ is 0.929, just as deduced above from Table 5.2 and Figure 5.5.

An alternative LP (Table 5.5) could have been set up which asks what is the *minimum* multiple of DMU$_2$'s input vector which could produce at least DMU$_2$'s output vector. The solution of this LP is $\lambda_1 = 0.029$, $\lambda_5 = 0.038$ and $z = 0.929$. The values of the λ variables are different, but if you divide them by 0.929, the value of z, the same solution as for Table 5.4 is apparent.

In general, given a set of n DMU$_j$, $(j = 1, 2, \ldots, n)$, each with a set of m inputs x_{ij}, $(i = 1, 2, \ldots, m)$ and a set of M outputs y_{kj}, $(k = 1, 2, \ldots, M)$, to determine for one particular DMU, say DMU$_p$, with inputs x_{ip} and outputs y_{kp} whether it is *efficient*, solve either LP1 or LP2.

LP1: find a combination of all DMUs which can be shown to use not more than p's inputs to maximize a scalar multiple of the vector of p's outputs.

LP2: find a combination of all DMUs which can be shown to yield at least p's outputs and to minimize a scalar multiple of the vector of p's inputs.

LP1   Max w

s.t. $\displaystyle\sum_{j=1}^{n} x_{ij}\,\lambda_j \leq x_{ip}$, $i = 1, \ldots, m$ (inputs)

—— **Table 5.5** ——
Minimize z subject to $A(\lambda, w) \geq b$, $\lambda \geq 0$

	λ_1	λ_2	λ_3	λ_4	λ_5	λ_6	λ_7	z		
$A =$	19	1	1	2	10	5	8	-0	$\leq$	0
	10	1	6	15	17	1	1	-1	$\leq$	0
	120	8	24	40	120	20	24	0	$\geq$	8
	0	0	0	0	0	0	0	1		

Note: the symbol $\leq$ denotes a mixture of $\leq$ and $\geq$ constraints.

$$\sum_{j=1}^{n} y_{kj} \lambda_j \;\geq\; y_{kp} w, \quad k = 1, \ldots, M \text{ (outputs)}$$

$$(w), \lambda_j \;\geq\; 0$$

LP2   Min z

s.t. $$\sum_{j=1}^{n} x_{ij} \lambda_j \;\leq\; x_{ip} z, \quad i = 1, \ldots, m \text{ (inputs)}$$

$$\sum_{j=1}^{n} y_{kj} \lambda_j \;\geq\; y_{kp}, \quad k = 1, \ldots, M \text{ (outputs)}$$

$$(z), \lambda_j \;\geq\; 0$$

Efficiency is defined as $z = 1/w$. The value of w in LP1 is at least 1, and the value of z in LP2 is at most 1, since in each case there is a feasible solution in which all $\lambda_j = 0$ except λ_p which equals 1.

The optimum solution of each of these LPs is determined by the cone of the activities (variables) which lie on the efficient frontier in the $(m + M)$-dimensional analogue of Figure 5.5. The cone is the same for both LPs, although the actual values of variables will be different for the two different optimizations (λ_j in LP2 = $z \times \lambda_j$ in LP1).

In terms of economics, the dual solutions of both LPs reflect the relative marginal productivities of the inputs (the slope of the isoquant in our 3-D model), and the marginal substitutabilities in production of the joint outputs. Like the primal variables, the dual variables in LP2 are the dual variables in LP1 multiplied by z.

Data envelopment analysis in practice

The first application of what has come to be called data envelopment analysis was by M.J. Farrell (1957) and was an attempt to measure productive efficiency using published statistical data for agriculture. But the technique has really only taken off in the 1980s, since A. Charnes, W.W. Cooper and E. Rhodes (Charnes *et al.*, 1978) started to apply it and to write about it. In Britain it has been applied to public sector data (education, local authorities, aspects of the health service, etc.) to try to assess the relative efficiency of various public bodies. It is also being used, rather less visibly, by some large institutions such as building societies and banks, which have a large number of branches in different parts of the country. In that context, DEA is explicitly being used not merely to rank the DMUs according to their measure of efficiency, but, much more importantly, to provide the detailed information necessary to raise the performance of the less efficient DMUs. In terms of our tiny example, it is less interesting to know that DMU_2 has efficiency of 0.929 than to know that DMUs 1 and 5 are in its reference set, and show what the manager of DMU_2 should be able to achieve with his similar set of resources.

The UK Monopolies and Mergers Commission (1988) examined the efficiency of the Crown Post Office branches in 1988. One of their recommendations was that Post Office Counters plc should give consideration to using DEA as a tool to improve the efficiency of those of their offices which appeared to be falling behind the required standard. The head office OR unit of the Post Office has subsequently conducted a large-scale DEA examination of some 1,400 individual branches, taking as inputs the different types of labour, and as outputs the various types of post office traffic (licences, stamps, giro payments, etc.). Obviously this was not simply a case of collecting a set of input and output data for each of 1,400 post offices and then solving 1,400 LPs. However, after considerable experimentation a form of useful information is now being presented to the area managers which shows for each less efficient branch those branches which can be reasonably said to be sufficiently similar, and which are clearly performing better. In so far as the area managers can say for some branches 'Yes, just as I expected' and for others 'That one is a surprise — let's see if it makes sense' it can be judged to be a useful tool and looks likely to become part of a standard efficiency audit with PO Counters.

Computing data envelopment analysis

The largest part of the work in making a DEA comparison of, say, 1,000 DMUs, each with perhaps a dozen inputs and outputs, is obviously the selection, collection and validation of the most useful input and output data. The actual computing of the 1,000 LPs with, say, twelve constraints and 1001 variables is comparatively straightforward, and could in principle be performed by any moderately large-scale mathematical programming package. However, these LPs are atypical in that their coefficient matrices are very dense, while the large-scale packages are all designed to be particularly efficient on sparse matrices. A PC-based special purpose DEA package is able to take advantage of the special characteristics of the DEA LP problems, for instance to modify the Simplex algorithm to make the appropriate choice when there are multiple LP solutions. It can take as its data set the list of inputs and outputs and the names of the DMUs, and produce outputs which are directly useful to the user (see exercise 2), as well as analyzing the 'efficiency' of the whole set of DMUs, or of a subset, in one computer run.

—— Exercises ——

1. Table 5.6 is derived from real data, suitably reduced and disguised to represent inputs and outputs during a three month period for thirty retail outlets in a national chain of clothing shops.

—— Table 5.6 ——

Branch No	Name	Sales area	Full-time hours	Part-time hours	Sales		
					Men's clothing	Women's clothing	Children's clothing
1	Aberdeen	7.300	5.744	0.00	13.2236	6.983	17.757
2	Birmingham	6.600	3.725	0.00	9.0976	5.246	13.734
3	Cardiff	2.630	3.684	0.00	10.3322	2.727	24.206
4	Dover	13.800	8.456	0.00	35.3468	37.149	85.580
5	Edinburgh	10.100	5.604	0.00	16.8504	12.671	20.812
6	Faversham	23.830	6.376	0.00	16.0910	9.349	41.808
7	Gateshead	6.200	4.190	0.00	14.6208	5.376	44.358
8	Hackney	8.100	2.729	8.29	11.0282	5.329	18.525
9	Ilford	5.041	3.528	0.00	9.2646	4.004	21.268
10	Jarrow	7.974	2.409	8.23	13.0067	5.265	24.366
11	King's Lynn	7.762	7.402	13.12	26.4499	13.106	39.128
12	Lambeth	5.100	3.253	2.33	9.7275	3.224	24.503
13	Marylebone	6.214	2.644	7.91	10.1996	0.335	22.240
14	Newquay	11.200	4.914	7.41	16.2573	11.045	28.254
15	Ongar	4.230	2.184	3.38	9.8548	2.655	27.876
16	Paisley	3.546	1.225	9.24	8.6668	0.238	25.209
17	Queensferry	5.400	3.689	6.11	14.1994	6.031	22.533
18	Rickmansworth	20.900	11.437	0.00	19.7720	10.514	25.072
19	Stourbridge	5.900	2.931	0.00	7.7236	3.769	10.764
20	Tonbridge	2.920	1.560	0.00	5.2306	1.953	11.874
21	Uttoxeter	10.000	6.860	10.23	17.3198	12.464	26.368
22	Ventnor	100.700	3.626	14.41	16.4283	7.024	28.305
23	Walthamstow	11.800	7.466	0.00	19.9379	6.142	39.470
24	Yeovil	2.100	0.667	5.95	5.7215	2.462	10.981
25	Zennor	2.900	1.606	4.64	7.7975	1.426	19.286
26	Aldborough	4.700	1.351	1.88	7.7036	1.626	20.678
27	Bristol	2.300	1.276	0.00	0.0000	1.967	0.000
28	Carlisle	19.000	12.354	0.00	33.3993	10.162	70.427
29	Dagenham	5.400	4.105	0.00	15.2188	3.459	28.738
30	Eastbourne	4.900	2.887	0.00	12.3599	2.475	26.599

Units: Each column has been scaled so that the numbers lie approximately in the range 1–100.
Sales area = square metres/10
Full-time hours = full-time staff hours worked/1,000
Part-time hours = part-time hours worked/100
Men's clothing = value of sales/10,000
Women's clothing = value of sales/10,000
Children's clothing = value of sales/1,000

Write down the format of the two alternative LP problems which you might submit to an LP package to determine the 'efficiency' of Branch Number 25 at Zennor.

2. Table 5.7 forms part of the output from the special-purpose DEA package applied to the above data. Explain these results to the managing director of the chain of shops.

3. (An artificial, mini-problem.) Use the same kind of analysis as that following Table 5.1 in the text to determine which of the DMUs in Table 5.8 can be considered to be efficient. Pay particular attention to DMU 3.

4. (Another mini-problem.) Use a diagram analogous to Figure 5.3 to determine which of the DMUs in Table 5.9 are 'efficient'.

------ **Table 5.7** ------

The analysis of DMU No. 25 Zennor

Efficiency = 0.983,755,47 computed by *minimizing* the *input* vector.

Sum of DMUs . . .				Yields	As
3	4	16	24	'composite'	compared to
multiplied by . . .				DMU	DMU No. 25
0.146	0.056	0.314	0.279		

Inputs . . .					'Slack'	
2.630	13.800	3.546	2.100	2.853	.	2.900
3.684	8.456	1.225	0.667	1.580	.	1.606
0.000	0.000	9.240	5.950	4.565	.	4.640
Outputs . . .						
10.332	35.347	8.667	5.721	7.798	.	7.798
2.727	37.149	0.238	2.462	3.229	(1.803)	1.426
24.206	85.580	25.209	10.981	19.286	.	19.286

DMU names:
  3 Cardiff
  4 Dover
 16 Paisley
 24 Yeovil

------ **Table 5.8** ------

DMU	1	2	3	4	5	6	7
Input 1	2.1	3.3	0.25	2.6	1	0.45	3
Input 2	2.8	0.3	2.75	9.1	0.6	3.6	1
Output	70	30	25	130	20	45	50

—— **Table 5.9** ——

DMU	1	2	3	4	5
Input	10	10	10	10	10
Output 1	10	11	4	6	12
Output 2	8	3	12	10	2

References and further reading

Banker, R.D. and R.C. Morey (1986) 'The use of categorical variables in data envelopment analysis', *Management Science*, **32**, 1613−27.

Charnes, A., W.W. Cooper and E. Rhodes (1978) 'Measuring the efficiency of decision making units', *European Journal of Operational Research*, **2**, 429−44.

Dyson, R.G. and E. Thanassoulis (1988) 'Reducing weight flexibility in data. envelopment analysis', *Journal of the Operational Research Society*, **39**, 563−76.

Farrell, M.J. (1957) 'The measurement of productive efficiency', *Journal of the Royal Statistical Society, Series A*, 255−83.

Levitt, M.S. and M.A.S. Joyce (1987) *The Growth and Efficiency of Public Spending*, National Institute of Economic and Social Research.

Monopolies and Mergers Commission (1988) *Post Office Counters Services*, Chapter 9, HMSO.

Seiford, L.M. (1978−86) *A Bibliography of Data Envelopment Analysis (1978−1986)* Department of Industrial Engineering and Operations Research, University of Massachusetts, Amherst, MA 01002, United States.

Thanassoulis, E., R.G. Dyson and M.J. Foster (1987) 'Relative efficiency assessments using data envelopment analysis: an application to data on rates departments', *Journal of the Operational Research Society*, **38**, 397−411.

– 6 –

Demand analysis and short-term forecasting

C.D. LEWIS

Introduction

In many planning situations in industry and commerce it is necessary to produce an estimate of the likely future demand for products, services, etc. Both *predictions* and *forecasts* attempt to estimate the future but use different concepts to achieve results.

Forecasting can be defined as 'a process of estimating a future event by casting forward past data where such past data are systematically combined in a predetermined way to obtain an estimate of the future', whereas predicting can be defined as 'a process of estimating a future event based on subjective considerations other than just past data'.

In summary, therefore, forecasting as a procedure is a scientific process which attempts to arrive at an unbiased estimate of the future and is based on the assumption that identifiable patterns in past data will be continued into the future, i.e. no discontinuities will occur. For a range of products or services this assumption will often be valid but there may be occasions when the prediction of a future event will be more meaningful and should be used to modify a scientifically produced forecast. For instance, if a pattern of demand has been in existence for some time, a forecast will simply assume that that pattern will be continued. However, were it confidently predicted that a strike was to occur which would affect that pattern of demand, it would be sensible to modify that unbiased forecast.

Being subjective, however, predictions always involve human intervention and could, therefore, be considered relatively expensive. They should only be resorted to when the subjective evidence on which they are based is strong.

Independence of demand and forecasting methods

Most forecasting systems assume that the demand for one product or service is independent of other products or services. Such independence is exhibited, for example, in the demand for tins of baked beans within a supermarket which can reasonably be assumed to be independent of, say, demand for tins of caviare. Such independence does not prevail in many manufacturing situations where the demand for parts and assemblies at lower levels depends totally on the demand at higher levels. Hence, the demand for wheels for cars is totally dependent on the demand for complete cars; it being assumed currently that one car requires five wheels — four for the road and one as a spare. For such *dependent* demand situations, forecasting as defined above is often not appropriate, and future demand is estimated by an explosion of predicted sales or demand figures at the top level in the manufacturing system with subsequent aggregation at lower levels using material requirements planning procedures (see Krajewski and Ritzman, 1987).

It is convenient to categorize forecasting methods on the time unit on which the data being forecast are based (see Table 6.1).

Short-term forecasting of demand typically involves forecasting a few days ahead at the level of the retailer, often weeks ahead at the level of the wholesaler and a few months ahead at the level of the manufacturer. For such purposes it is generally sufficient to limit attention to previous demand data, using such forecasting methods as exponential smoothing.

For purposes of medium-term forecasting, relating to the next few months or years, it is generally necessary to relate the demand for the product to various technical, economic and social factors, called explanatory variables, and to

——— Table 6.1 ———

Category	Time unit	Examples	Techniques
Immediate term	Hour-day	Demand for electricity	Various
Short term	Week-month	Sales forecasting	Exponential smoothing
		Demand forecasting	Moving averages
Medium term	Month-year	Profit forecasting	Regression/ curve fitting
		Forecasting market	Box-Jenkins Bayesian

make independent forecasts of the latter. Examples of this procedure include national income, consumer purchasing powers, levels of prices and employment, population change, etc. Multiple regression techniques are found useful here.

Long-term forecasting, ranging from one year to even a decade ahead, is typically concerned with technological change. The scope for statistical techniques here is more limited, and long-term forecasting itself is still in its infancy.

Although operational researchers are frequently involved in all kinds of forecasting situations, limitations of space preclude a comprehensive treatment here. This chapter will concentrate on short-term forecasting for purposes of inventory control, with emphasis on exponential smoothing methods, the predominant forecasting technique used in this widespread field of application.

Basic trends in demand

In a so-called *stationary* situation, successive values of demand exhibit a random variation about a reasonably steady average. Superimposed on this stationary demand element one might find a *linear growth* element. To expect demand to increase by a fixed amount per month would, of course, be extremely naive; in general, as well as their being random variation in the stationary element of a demand situation, there would also be random variation in the growth element. Over and above the stationary element with superimposed random growth there might also be a *seasonal* element, i.e. for particular months of the year more or less demand compared with an average month's demand would be expected. It is evident that the situation could be yet further complicated by having random variations in the seasonal factors, and in practice other changes not associated with either the linear or seasonal trend can make the real-life situation even more complicated.

This discussion indicates how a complicated demand situation can be composed but, in forecasting, the problem is that data already exist. What one wishes to establish is which underlying models might best explain those particular data. Hence, the process of forecasting is essentially one of decomposing existing data values into certain model types (such as those linear or seasonal characteristics) whose parameters can be estimated. These models are then used to make forecasts of likely future values.

In the next four sections we shall examine ways of forecasting the average demand and the variability of demand in a stationary situation. The section on p. 87 discusses the problem of dealing with trends in a non-stationary situation. A method of monitoring forecasts is then outlined, in order to identify when a forecasting system breaks down because the underlying demand situation has changed. The final two sections discuss under what circumstances it is worth forecasting and what type of method is most appropriate.

Forecasting average demand in a stationary situation

If demand remains fairly steady over a reasonably long period of time, an obvious approach to estimating average demand is to take an arithmetic average of the last n periods of demand data; this is called a *moving average*. If d_t denotes the observed value of demand in period t, then the moving average in period t is defined as

$$m_t = \frac{1}{n} \{d_t + d_{t-1} + \ldots + d_{t-n+1}\}$$

$$= \frac{1}{n} \sum_{i=t}^{t-n+1} d_i$$

This value of m_t is used as a forecast of demand in period $t+1$.

Such a moving average, although simple in concept, has several major disadvantages when used for forecasting purposes:

1. When starting a moving average, at least n items of demand data are required.

2. The most recent $n-1$ values of demand data must always be stored for further forecasts to be made. As any average based on less than about a dozen values tends to be too sensitive for forecasting purposes, when forecasts based on twelve or more data periods are made for many items (as is generally the case in manufacturing organizations) the amount of accumulated data storage becomes prohibitive.

3. The sensitivity of a moving average is inversely proportional to the number of data values included in the average. It is relatively simple to increase the sensitivity by reducing the number of periods incorporated and thus discarding demand data. However, in order to decrease the sensitivity, the number of periods must be increased and very seldom will the demand data be available for long-past time periods.

4. With a moving average, all data included within the average are equally weighted by $1/n$. In most forecasting situations, with some specific exceptions, demand data can be assumed to become less relevant as they grow older. For forecasting purposes, therefore, one generally requires an average which gives greater weight to more recent observations.

Exponential smoothing methods

Holt (1957), the originator of exponential smoothing, indicated that most of the disadvantages of the moving average can be overcome by using weights which decrease with time. Because, for a mathematically true average, the sum of weights must be unity, what is ideally required is an infinite series of weights with decreasing values which converge at infinity to produce a total sum of one. Such a series is the exponential series with successive weights

$$\alpha, \; \alpha(1-\alpha), \; \alpha(1-\alpha)^2, \; \alpha(1-\alpha)^3, \; \ldots$$

which sum to one at infinity if α lies between zero and one. Choosing a value of 0.2, the first seven values of such a series would be

$$0.200, \; 0.160, \; 0.128, \; 0.102, \; 0.082, \; 0.066, \; 0.052$$

which sum to 0.79; it is apparent that if sufficient values are taken, the sum will be near enough one.

Incorporating the exponential series as the weighting series yields an exponentially weighted average (u_t) defined by

$$u_t = \alpha d_t + \alpha(1-\alpha)d_{t-1} + \alpha(1-\alpha)^2 d_{t-2} + \alpha(1-\alpha)^3 d_{t-3} + \ldots$$

or

$$u_t = \alpha d_t + (1-\alpha) \, [\alpha d_{t-1} + \alpha(1-\alpha)d_{t-2} + \alpha(1-\alpha)^2 d_{t-3} + \ldots]$$

Since the term in square brackets is precisely u_{t-1}, the exponentially weighted average can be rewritten very simply as

$$u_t = \alpha d_t + (1-\alpha)u_{t-1}$$

As before, u_t is used as a forecast for period $t+1$. A numerical illustration is given in the first five rows of Table 6.2.

It is apparent that the exponentially weighted average overcomes the problem of storage (since all previous data are neatly compacted into a single figure represented by u_{t-1}) and the problem of starting up with no previous data (since, once an initial guess for u_{t-1} is made, when fresh data, d_t, arrive the next forecast can be directly evaluated). The sensitivity of the forecast can be changed at any time, simply by changing the value of α, which is known as the *exponential smoothing* constant. This is typically chosen from a range of values between 0.05 and 0.3; the values of 0.1 and 0.2 are the most used.

In the stationary demand situations, because no growth or seasonality is assumed, the forecast for any month in the future is the same as for one month ahead. It is accepted, of course, that the further ahead that forecast is made the wider will be the possible range of demand values that could be expected to fall either side of that average value.

—— **Table 6.2** ——
Fully expanded forecasting schedule for smoothing constant $\alpha = 0.2$

Row	Description	Formula	Jan.	Feb.	Mar.	April
1	This month's demand	d_t	60	70	55	80
2	Last month's forecast for this month	u_{t-1}	70.00*	68.0	68.4	65.7
3	$\alpha \times$ this month's demand	αd_t	12	14	11	16
4	$(1-\alpha) \times$ last month's forecast for this month	$(1-\alpha)u_{t-1}$	56.0	54.4	54.7	52.6
5	This month's forecast for next month	$u_t = \alpha d_t + (1-\alpha)u_{t-1}$	68.0	68.4	65.7	68.6
6	This month's forecasting error	$e_t = d_t - u_{t-1}$	−10.0	2.0	−13.4	14.3
7	0.2 × absolute value of this month's forecasting error	$\alpha|e_t|$	2.0	0.40	2.6	2.85
8	0.8 × last month's mean absolute deviation	$(1-\alpha)MAD_{t-1}$	10.00*	9.60	8.0	8.54
9	This month's mean absolute deviation	$MAD_t = \alpha|e_t| + (1-\alpha)MAD_{t-1}$	12.00	10.00	10.08	11.4
10	This month's estimate of standard deviation	$\sigma_t = 1.25\ MAD_t$	15.0	12.5	13.4	14.1
11	0.2 × this month's forecasting error	αe_t	−2.0	0.4	−2.08	2.85
12	0.8 × last month's smoothed error	$(1-\alpha)\bar{e}_{t-1}$	0*	−1.6	−0.96	−2.91
13	This month's smoothed error	$\bar{e}_t = \alpha e_t + (1-\alpha)\bar{e}_{t-1}$	−2	−1.2	−3.64	−0.06
14	Trigg's tracking signal	$T_t = \bar{e}_t/MAD_t$	−0.17	−0.12	−0.34	0

* Assumed to be obtained from estimated values in December of the previous year:
$u_{t-1} = 70$, $e_{t-1} = 0$, $MAD_{t-1} = 12.5$.

Table 6.2 shows a fully expanded schedule using simple exponential smoothing with $\alpha = 0.2$. The forecast calculations take place in rows 3, 4 and 5.

The forecasts from the schedule shown as Table 6.1 (i.e. for $\alpha = 0.2$) together with forecasts produced for a value of $\alpha = 0.5$ are shown in Figure 6.1, from which the reader should note the following:

May	June	July	Aug.	Sept.	Oct.	Nov.	Dec.	Jan.	Feb.	Mar.	Apr.
90	65	70	75	60	80	90	100	95			
68.6	72.9	71.3	71.0	71.8	69.4	71.6	75.2	80.2	83.2	83.2	83.2
18	13	14	15	12	16	18	20	19			
54.9	58.3	57.0	56.8	57.4	56.6	57.2	60.2	64.2			
72.9	71.3	71.0	71.8	69.4	71.6	75.2	80.2	83.2			
21.4	−7.9	−1.3	4.0	−11.8	10.6	18.4	24.8	83.2			
	4.28	1.57	0.25	0.79	2.36	2.11	3.69	4.95	2.96		
	9.11	10.71	9.82	8.05	7.07	7.54	7.72	9.12	11.25		
	13.4	12.3	10.09	8.87	9.46	9.68	11.43	14.09	14.23		
	16.7	15.3	12.6	11.0	11.8	12.1	14.3	17.6	17.7		
	4.28	−1.57	−0.25	−0.79	−2.36	2.11	3.69	4.95	2.96		
	−0.04	3.39	1.46	0.96	1.40	−0.77	1.07	3.81	7.00		
	4.24	1.82	1.20	1.75	−0.96	1.34	4.76	8.75	9.96		
	0.32	0.15	0.12	0.20	−0.10	0.14	0.42	0.62	0.70		

1. The higher the value of α, the more sensitive the forecast.
2. When growth is present in the data, forecasts based on the simple exponentially weighted average lag behind the data.
3. As the simple exponentially weighted average assumes no growth, the true forecasts ahead of the data are fixed in value, i.e. the forecast (when α = 0.2) for February of 83.2 (as calculated in January, row 5) would also be the forecast for March, April, etc.

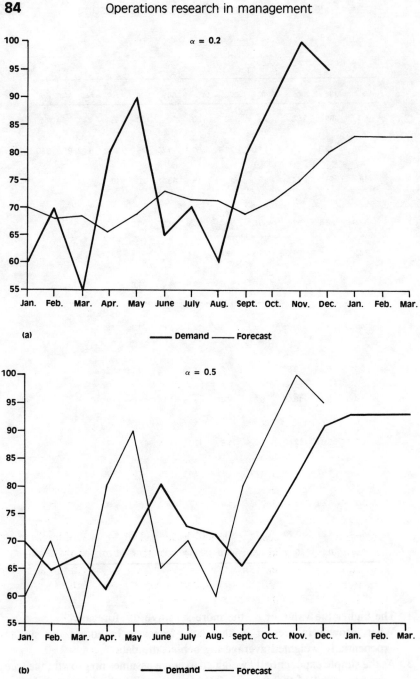

Figure 6.1   Forecast response for differing α

Measures of forecasting accuracy

It is necessary to maintain a measure of forecasting accuracy in order to achieve the following:

1. To determine which forecasting model is most appropriate for a particular set of data.
2. To establish, even with the most appropriate forecasting model, whether the forecasts being produced are in retrospect reasonably accurate.

Mean squared error

The mean squared error (MSE) is defined as the mean (or average) of the squared forecasting errors and is evaluated as:

$$\text{MSE} = \frac{1}{n} \Sigma e_t^2$$

where e_t is the forecasting error at time t.

Selection of forecasting models is often based on a criterion of minimizing the MSE, as is the selection of parameters controlling forecasting models. Thus in most forecasting packages where a variety of exponentially weighted forecasting models are available, the model to be used (and for simple exponentially weighted average models, the value of α to be used) will normally be selected on the basis of achieving a minimum MSE.

Mean absolute percentage error

The most useful *relative* measure of forecasting accuracy is the mean absolute percentage error (MAPE) defined as:

$$\text{MAPE} = \frac{1}{n} \Sigma \frac{|e_t|}{d_t} \times 100 \text{ for } d_t <> 0$$

For typical industrial and commercial data the following can be assumed:

1. MAPE < 10 per cent forecasts are potentially very good.
2. MAPE < 20 per cent forecasts are good.
3. MAPE < 30 per cent forecasts are reasonable.
4. MAPE > 30 per cent forecasts cannot necessarily be relied upon.

Calculation of the standard deviation of demand

Examination of Figure 6.2 reveals that, although the average demand has remained at approximately a hundred units over the whole year, after June a distinct change in the pattern of demand has occurred. It is apparent that it is the spread of demand values about the average which has changed significantly rather than the average level of demand itself. Such a change would not be detected in a change in the forecast and could, therefore, only be detected by a separate measure of 'spread'.

The statistic most used in short-term forecasting to measure spread is known as the *mean absolute deviation* (MAD). As its name indicates, the MAD is simply the mean or average of the absolute values of errors or deviation from the long-term average level of demand. With the present forecasting model, the MAD for period t can be calculated as the exponentially weighted average of the absolute value of forecasting errors

$$\text{MAD}_t = \alpha |e_t| + \alpha(1-\alpha) |e_{t-1}| + \alpha(1-\alpha)^2 |e_{t-2}| + \dots$$

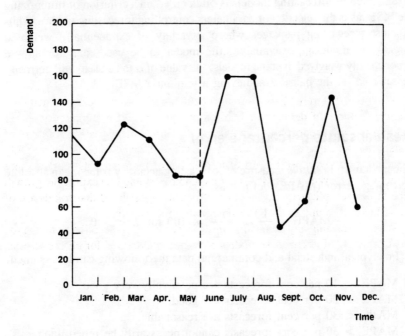

Figure 6.2   Change in the spread of demand abut a steady average value

which simplifies as before to:

$$MAD_t = \alpha|e_t| + (1-\alpha)MAD_{t-1}$$

where $|e_t|$ denotes the absolute value of e_t (see rows 7–9 of Table 6.2). A measure of variability of demand which is particularly useful in analyzing the inventory control situation (as in the next two chapters) is the standard deviation σ. It may be shown that, for all practical purposes, the estimated standard deviation for period t is given by $\sigma_t = 1.25\,MAD_t$ (see row 10 of Table 6.2).

Non-stationary demand situation

Where the average demand value does not remain relatively constant over a period of time, the assumption of a stationary demand process can no longer be substantiated and forecasts based on the simple exponentially weighted average are no longer appropriate.

The variation of an average with time is known as a *trend* and such trends in a demand situation can vary in character and type. As mentioned earlier, the character of a trend may be *linear* (either increasing or decreasing over time) or *seasonal* (varying in some cyclical fashion, often yearly). The chief types of trends are additive and multiplicative. An *additive* type of trend is one in which a regular amount is added to or subtracted from each consecutive average demand value. A *multiplicative* (or ratio or exponential) type of trend is subject to a regular *percentage* increase or decrease. Of course, one may have trends exhibiting combinations of these basic characters and types.

Why such different types of trends occur can sometimes be associated with distinct features of demand or marketing situations. If a company is either holding its own proportion of an expanding market or increasing its share of a static market, one would expect its growth in demand to be additive. Only if the company were in the fortunate position of increasing its market share of an overall market which was itself expanding, would one expect the growth type to be multiplicative. In practice, it is usually assumed that trends are of an additive type unless they are obviously multiplicative.

When describing any demand trend, it is necessary to describe both its type and character. Mathematical models have been developed for all the various combinations of character and types of trends described here. However, because of the mathematical complexity of these models, the detailed description of methods for handling non-stationary demand situations lies beyond the scope of this book. The methods are fully described in Lewis (1989), including such techniques as Brown's double smoothing method and the Holt-Winters de-seasonalizing method.

Monitoring forecasting systems: Trigg's smoothed error method

Once any routine system for making forecasts has been set up, it is necessary to have some form of monitoring method to indicate when demand becomes so different from the level expected that the forecasting system breaks down. All forecasts are delayed in their response to sudden changes, and the resultant lags brought about by such delays naturally produce larger than usual forecasting errors.

Once a monitoring method has indicated a lack of control in forecasting, questions can be asked as to what is responsible for this sudden change, whether the change is likely to be sustained or not, and if not when is it likely to end. Such information obviously cannot be derived from the forecasting system itself; it is in this type of situation that the market intelligence of the company's sales force may give useful clues.

The monitoring method proposed by Trigg (1964) is based on the definition of a *tracking signal* whose value indicates, with specified degrees of statistical confidence, the failure of a forecasting system because of a change in the demand pattern.

Define the *smoothed error*, $\bar{e}_t$, in period t as the exponentially weighted average of forecasting errors in previous periods:

$$\bar{e}_t = \alpha e_t + \alpha(1-\alpha)e_{t-1} + \ldots$$
$$= \alpha e_t + (1-\alpha)\bar{e}_{t-1}$$

Trigg's tracking signal for period t (denoted T_t) is defined as the ratio of the exponentially smoothed error to the mean absolute deviation:

$$T_t = \bar{e}_t/\text{MAD}_t$$

This tracking signal ranges between $+1$ and -1; the higher its absolute value, the more likely it is that the forecasting model is out of control because of a sudden jump in demand. Table 6.3 gives statistical confidence levels for various values of the tracking signal, on the assumption that the value of the smoothing constant α is 0.2. Thus, if the calculated value of Trigg's tracking signal becomes larger than 0.74, this would indicate with 95 per cent confidence that the forecasting system was out of control.

Now refer back to rows 11−14 of Table 6.2, which present calculations of smoothed errors and tracking signals for the twelve month period. The low of the tracking signal in March, April and May (-0.34, 0, 0.32) does not suggest that the jumps in demand from 55 in March to 80 in April to 90 in May (top line) represent a fundamental change in demand. However, because the tracking signal rises to 0.70 in the final period, this confirms with about 94 per cent confidence that the four successive high values of demand of 80,

—— **Table 6.3** ——
Tracking signal confidence levels (α = 0.2)

Level of confidence (i.e. cumulative probability)	Absolute value of Trigg's tracking signal $\lvert T_t \rvert$ (α = 0.2)
80%	0.54
90%	0.66
95%	0.74
98%	0.81
100%	1.00

90, 100 and 95 from October onwards do represent a genuine or significant change in underlying conditions of demand.

When starting the calculations for the tracking signal, it is essential to provide reasonable numbers for the immediate past values of the mean absolute deviation (MAD_{t-1}) and, to a lesser extent, the smoothed error ($\bar{e}_{t-1}$). Without such *initialization* the first tracking signal will be either $+1$ or -1, indicating to all eagerly awaiting the first computer printout that everything is totally out of control! A reasonable working assumption for initializing these variables is to set MAD_{t-1} equal to one-tenth of the initial forecast estimate u_{t-1} and $\bar{e}_{t-1}$ equal to zero.

A fairly obvious method of using the tracking signal concept in monitoring the stability of forecasts for many products would be simply to highlight those items whose tracking signal exceeded a value of, say, 0.70. This rather naive approach is unfortunately embodied in much of the computer software in this area. It may highlight as out of control a wildly varying number of items each time an analysis is made. This is not usually very helpful for the investigating team which is trying to find the reasons why certain forecasts have gone out of control and which is attempting to get the forecasts back in control. (The reasons might be a competitor's strike temporarily reducing market competition and thus creating a sudden surge in sales, or alternatively a sales promotion having the same effect.) What such a team requires is a system which highlights a fixed number of items.

Finally, mention should be made of *adaptive forecasting*, the term used for forecasting methods which adapt themselves to the nature of the demand information with which they are dealing. The basic requirement of any such adaptive forecasting method is that as the demand data become relatively more changeable, so the forecast itself responds and becomes more sensitive. Conversely, as the demand becomes relatively more stable, so the forecast becomes less sensitive in order to filter out extraneous 'noise'. In technical terms, this requires that the value of the exponential smoothing constant should increase as demand data become more changeable and should decrease as demand becomes more stable.

One solution to this problem has been suggested by Trigg and Leach (1967) and sets α, the value of the exponential smoothing constant, equal to the *absolute* value of the original tracking signal proposed by Trigg (1964). Figure 6.3 illustrates the improved forecast response of such a proposal.

Grouping methods: Pareto or ABC analysis

The methods so far described can be invaluable where it is important to obtain regular and up-to-date forecasts of demand, but it would be foolish to spend time and energy applying them to unimportant or slow-moving products. It is, therefore, worthwhile classifying a firm's products into several different groups and examining what kind of forecasting system (if any) is most appropriate for the products of each group.

In most industrial organizations a few items represent a large proportion

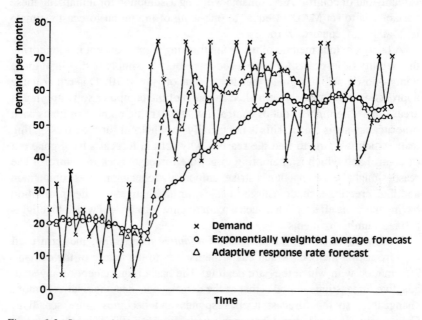

Figure 6.3 Improved response of adaptive response rate forecast to step change in demand

of annual usage value: turnover, profit, invested capital or some other indicator of 'importance'; in fact, the distribution of items follows a Pareto distribution, as illustrated in Figure 6.4.

The particular shape of a company's Pareto curve can vary in detail depending on the type of organization being studied, but as a general rule the following can be said, approximately:

1. The first 10 per cent of the stocked items represent 60 per cent of the usage value: these items are termed A items.
2. The next 30 per cent of the stocked items represent 30 per cent of the usage value: these are termed B items.
3. The remaining 60 per cent of stocked items represent only 10 per cent of the usage value: these are termed C items.

The division of an organization's stockholding into three such groups is known as Pareto or ABC analysis. We now discuss the most appropriate forecasting method for each group.

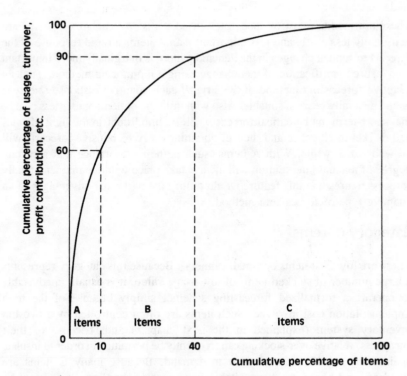

Figure 6.4 Pareto distribution for stocked items

Choice of forecasting methods

Category A items

These are expensive or much used items, usually excluding engineering spares for which separate treatment is more appropriate.

With this category of item it will generally be advisable to monitor forecasts so as to identify rapidly changes in the demand pattern. Instigating a monitoring scheme for A items is also reasonably practical because relatively few items are involved. The use of a monitoring scheme will generally preclude the use of adaptive forecasting methods of the Trigg/Leach adaptive response rate type and thus a non-adaptive forecasting system will normally be adopted. The choice between non-adaptive methods will generally be centred around the fact that the more comprehensive the forecast, the more accurate the results, but the higher the cost of implementation.

Category B items

These are medium cost or moderately used items. As category B items are marginally less costly and less important than A items a rapid response of the forecast to sudden changes in the demand pattern is marginally more important than a sure identification of that change using a monitoring method. Thus an adaptive forecasting method of the Trigg/Leach adaptive response rate type would generally be most suitable. Also with this type of item there is less chance that short-term mathematical forecasts will be 'modified' in the light of sales and market intelligence and, hence, obtaining more responsive forecasts will be well worth while. With A items, such is their importance that a certain degree of manual intervention will always take place with the mathematically forecast figures and this feature would nullify the particular advantages of an adaptive type of forecasting method.

Category C items

These are low-cost items or 'small runners'. Because this category represents a large number of stocked items of low usage value, it is usually inadvisable to operate a formalized forecasting scheme, simply because of the high implementation cost involved. Such items are often controlled by a two-bin inventory system (explained in the next chapter) and, because of their cheapness, relative over-stocking can frequently be permitted in order to insulate against any significant variations in demand. Because many C items are standard, and hence rapidly available from several suppliers, it may not be necessary even to take this precaution. It is, therefore, not usual to have a formalized system of forecasting for C items. Rough annual assessment of demand is usually sufficient.

Conclusion

Short-term forecasting really became of age as a set of powerful techniques in the early 1960s subsequent to the proposal by Holt (1957) for use of a moving average with exponentially decaying weights, i.e. the exponentially weighted average.

Within the United States, Brown (1959, 1962) was a powerful advocate for the use of the rapidly expanding family of forecasting models based on the exponentially weighted average concept which, although it could never be claimed actually produced better forecasts than, say, simple moving averages, was a far more practical approach for everyday operations since it involved storing much less data in the computer and it was a flexible concept which could be improved on for more difficult forecasting situations. Hence, both Brown and Holt suggested models which could cope with the lag problem engendered by growth in the data series, and Winters (1960) suggested a method of analyzing seasonal data.

In the United Kingdom, ICI was the first company to accept the practical usefulness of exponentially weighted average forecasts, and that company's internal reports supporting the implementation of such forecasting schemes were eventually published for a wider audience (ICI, 1964). Again within the United Kingdom, the proposal by Trigg (1964) of Kodak Ltd for a tracking signal based on the 'smoothed error', improved on an earlier proposal by Brown (1962) and was to be adopted as the standard method of monitoring forecasts.

Subsequently, Trigg in conjunction with Leach (Trigg and Leach, 1967) suggested substituting the absolute value of the original tracking signal as the exponential smoothing constant to provide a forecasting model which automatically adapted its sensitivity in sympathy with the data being analyzed.

The family of exponentially weighted average based forecasting models developed during the 1960s have over time proved to be so robust that many of the original proposals still underpin much of the forecasting software in use today and are fully documented in Lewis (1989).

However, for more complex forecasting situations the proposal by Box and Jenkins (1970) for a family of ARIMA models based on autoregressive integrated moving averages, offers a process of the following:

1. Identifying one of a whole range of forecasting models which is likely to be the best model for the time series under consideration.

2. Estimating the parameters of that model using a non-linear estimation procedure.

3. Verifying the identified and estimated model by subjecting the model to diagnostic checks of its adequacy.

Where a purely time series approach to forecasting cannot be justified, it is often necessary to form a forecast judgementally, particularly before any data become available. In such situations Harrison and Stevens (1971) have suggested a Bayesian approach which attempts to encode judgemental forecasts as probability distributions which can then be used as a forecasting mechanism when combined with data values as they become available.

——— Exercises ———

Although it is possible to answer all the following questions using manual calculations, use of a spreadsheet package such as Lotus 1-2-3™ or VPPlanner™ simplifies the exercises significantly and also permits values of α to be altered and the resulting forecasting performance to be noted.

All three questions are based on the worksheet given in Appendix 2. Assume that the value of α for evaluating the smoothed error and MAD is 0.2 throughout.

1. Using a simple exponentially weighted average forecasting model based on a value of α of 0.5, does the value of the tracking signal indicate at any time that the forecasting system is out of control?

2. Using a simple exponentially weighted average forecasting model based on values of α of 0.2, 0.3, 0.4, 0.5 and 0.6, choose which value is best.

3. Does the delayed adaptive response rate forecast produce better forecasts than the best simple exponentially weighted average forecast?

References and further reading

Box, G.E.P. and G.M. Jenkins (1970) *Time Series Analysis Forecasting and Control*, Holden-Day.

Brown, R.G. (1959) *Statistical Forecasting for Inventory Control*, McGraw-Hill.

Brown, R.G. (1962) *Smoothing, Forecasting and Prediction of Discrete Time Series*, Prentice Hall.

Harrison, P.J. and C.F. Stevens (1971) 'A Bayesian approach to short-term forecasting', *Operational Research Quarterly*, **24**, 2.

Holt, C.C. (1957) 'Forecasting seasonal and trends by exponentially weighted moving averages', *Naval Research Memorandum No 52*.

ICI (1964) *Short-term Forecasting*, ICI Monograph No 2, Oliver and Boyd.

Krajewski, L.J. and L.P. Ritzman (1987) *Operations Management: Strategy and analysis*, Addison-Wesley.

Lewis, C.D. (1989) *Business Forecasting in a Lotus 1-2-3 Environment*, John Wiley.

Trigg, D.W. (1964) 'Monitoring a forecasting system', *Operational Research Quarterly*, **15**, 3, pp. 271–4.

Trigg, D.W. and A.G. Leach (1967) 'Exponential smoothing with adaptive response rate', *Operatonal Research Quarterly*. **18**, 1, 53–4.

Winters, P.R. (1960) 'Forecasting sales by exponentially weighted moving averages', *Management Science*, **6**, 324–42.

— 7 —

Inventory control

C.D. LEWIS

Introduction

Inventory control is the science-based art of ensuring that just enough inventory (or stock) is held by an organization to meet economically both its internal and external demand commitments. There can be disadvantages in holding either too much or too little inventory; inventory control is primarily concerned with obtaining the correct balance or compromise between these two extremes.

As with short-term forecasting, inventory control theory applies primarily to items subject to independent demand; for items where demand is not independent, material requirements planning (MRP) (Krajewski and Ritzman, 1987) is the appropriate technique.

The different types of stock held by business and industry and the purposes for which they are held are as follows.

Raw material stocks

By holding stocks of raw material, an organization decouples its primary production sections or processes (e.g. machine shops and press shops) from its raw material manufacturers or stockists. This allows primary production to be initiated in a shorter period of time than the raw material supplier's delivery time.

Work-in-progress or stocks-in-process

The holding of both raw material stocks and stocks of finished goods is generally a planned activity, whereas in-process stocks are likely to exist in any manufacturing organization whether or not they are planned for. The decoupling function provided by this category of inventory is to buffer the demand of a later stage in the production process (e.g. sub-assemblies and final assemblies) from the supply of an earlier stage (e.g. machine shops and press shops); this facility is essential for any production process. Without such decoupling all manufacturing stages would need to be perfectly synchronized — a practical impossiblility.

Finished goods

The stocking of finished goods provides a buffer between the customer demand and the manufacturer's supply. In many cases, because the size of orders required by customers are much less than those supplied by the manufacturer, a wholesaler or stockist can act as intermediary.

We shall begin by describing the two basic inventory control policies, then discuss the costs and usage patterns which determine the design of an appropriate control system.

Inventory policies

An organization's stockholding policy is implemented by a series of rules which determine how and when certain decisions concerning the holding of stocks should be made. This series of rules is known as an inventory policy.

There are two basic types of inventory policies. Those in which decisions concerning replenishment are based on the level of inventory held are known as *re-order level policies* and those in which such decisions are made on a regular time basis are known as *re-order cycle* or *periodic review* policies.

Re-order level policy

An order for replenishment is placed when the stock on hand equals or falls below a fixed value M known as the *re-order level*. Stock on hand includes the stock actually held in stores plus any outstanding replenishment orders less any demand orders which have already been committed to the production programme. In this policy, therefore, the amount of inventory held must be reviewed continuously.

When a replenishment order is placed within a re-order level policy, it is generally for a fixed quantity. A typical example of inventory balances for a re-order level policy is shown in Figure 7.1. The solid line in this diagram represents the inventory actually held, the broken line is the stock on hand (actual stock plus outstanding replenishments less committed stock). When the re-order level M is broken, a replenishment order of size q is placed but there is a delay before the order actually arrives; this delay is known as the lead time (L). In each case, the stock on hand immediately rises by q (since the moment the order is placed it is technically outstanding) but the actual stock continues to be depleted by successive demand withdrawals until the lead time expires and the replenishment order is received at time t_1'. The process is repeated as soon as stock on hand again falls to re-order level M at time t_2.

The excess of the re-order level over the expected demand during the lead time is called the *safety stock* or *buffer stock* (B). If the buffer stock is exhausted, then back-ordering may be permitted, whereby demand orders are accepted even when no actual stock remains, thus in effect allowing negative stock to build up.

The most common practical implementation of the re-order level policy is known as the two-bin system. Two bins of the stocked item are kept and a replenishment order is placed when the first bin becomes empty. Further stock is then withdrawn from the second bin until the replenishment order is recieved to refill the second bin, the remainder being placed in the first bin. The amount of stock held in the second bin, therefore, represents the size of the re-order level. In practice, of course, it is not always necessary to have two separate bins to operate this system; for instance a single bin with a dividing layer or

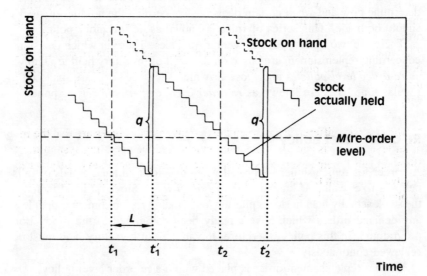

Figure 7.1   The re-order level policy

partition serves exactly the same purpose. Some retailers operate by placing a 're-order now' card at an appropriate place in the stock of each item on the counter. However, this single- or two-bin adaptation of the method cannot be used for items that deteriorate or for items which for some reason must be controlled with a first-in, first-out policy.

The single- or two-bin system operates most successfully with physically small items such as nuts, bolts, washers, etc., where committed demand orders are not generally allowed and usually only one outstanding replenishment exists at any time. The system obviously becomes impracticable when large items such as castings and sub-assemblies are involved, where space occupied does not necessarily represent number stored. To be really cheap and effective as a means of controlling stocks, the two-bin system is operated without any formal stock recording, and even auditors are now taking sample estimates of overall stock levels as evidence for audit assessment.

The re-order cycle or periodic review policy

The stock on hand is reviewed at fixed periods of time (R), and a replenishment order placed at every review. However, unlike the policy previously described, the size of a replenishment order is variable. This variable replenishment quantity is calculated as that amount of stock which, if there were no lead time, would bring the stock on hand up to some fixed maximum stock level, S. Thus, the size of the replenishment order is equal to S less the stock on hand, and can be different at every review. This replenishment policy ensures that when the level of stock on hand is high at review, a smaller-sized replenishment order is placed than when it is low. This can be quite clearly seen in Figure 7.2 which shows a typical stock situation when operating a re-order cycle policy. Orders are placed at time t_1, t_2, t_3, which are a fixed time R apart; the first order arrives at time t_1'. In the example shown the lead times also vary.

The essential differences between the two inventory policies are that the re-order level policy is one of continuous review, and the operating system must allow replenishment orders to be placed at any time, rather than to be planned in advance as with the re-order cycle policy. One of the principal advantages of planned replenishment is that a single order can be raised to cover many replenishments being placed with a common supplier, thus considerably reducing the cost per replenishment. This advantage is offset by the fact that cyclical policies in general require higher average levels of stock in order to offer similar levels of service (one possible definition of the level of service being the probability of meeting demand 'off the shelf').

A domestic comparison can be drawn between the situations of working

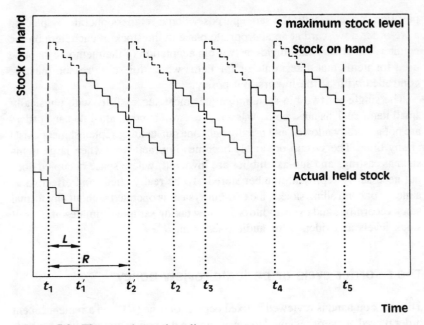

Figure 7.2 The re-order cycle policy

and non-working wives. The non-working wife, who has the opportunity to shop on any day and knows that her family consumes a maximum of 250 g of butter per day, might operate a re-order level policy with a re-order level of 250 g. Her stockholding costs based on an average 250 g of butter would be very low, but against this she would incur high replenishment costs plus the lost opportunity cost of not working. By contrast, in this same situation, a working wife shopping only once a week would be forced to operate a cyclical policy such that when shopping she would replenish up to $7 \times 250 = 1.75$ kg of butter to ensure supplies for the following week. Her storage cost would be relatively high (based on an average stockholding of 875 g of butter) but her replenishment costs very low (based on a single replenishment per week).

The relative advantages and disadvantages of the two principal inventory policies are shown in Table 7.1.

Inventory operating costs

There are three main costs involved in operating an inventory system, namely the cost of ordering stock (C_o), the cost of holding stock (C_h) generally given

——— **Table 7.1** ———
Advantages and disadvantages of re-order level and
re-order cycle stock control policies

Policy	Advantages	Disadvantages
Re-order level	Relatively low stock levels Can be implemented as a two-bin system Short 'period of risk' equal to the lead time	Continuous review of stock levels required Without movement reports, can lead to retention of obsolescent stock
Re-order cycle	Regular reviews allow for the placing of multiple replenishment orders Lower purchasing overheads because of regular reviews	Relatively high stock levels Long 'period of risk' equal to the review time plus the lead time

as a percentage (i) of the stock's value C_m, and the cost of running out of stock (C_s). We shall discuss these in turn.

Ordering costs (C_o)

1. All purchase department costs (which usually includes a healthy proportion of an organization's telephone bill) could be included as part of the ordering cost if replenishment orders are obtained from outside. Such costs are usually apportioned across all stock items ordered through the department, so that the cost of ordering is generally assumed to be the same for all items irrespective of their value. Where replenishment orders are obtained within the organization the cost of ordering should include the cost of implementing the work's order and also any set-up cost that might be involved.
2. For purchased-out items, the cost of receiving goods (which should include any transport costs) might be included in the ordering costs. Again, these are usually allocated on an apportionment basis.
3. Those quality control costs incurred as a result of checking received replenishment orders might be included in the cost of ordering, but rarely are, as these costs are absorbed as general overheads.
4. Where replenishment orders for purchased-out items are overdue or where internally manufactured items are behind schedule, the cost of 'chasing' or 'expediting' such overdue orders should be included in the cost of ordering.

At current UK prices in 1990 a manufacturer's order cost of less than £30 is unrealistic, which highlights the advantages of multiple replenishment orders. High order costs also explain why manufacturing organizations stipulate minimum quantities below which they are not prepared to trade and why cheaper prices are quoted for cash transactions which can bypass much of the invoicing procedures and their associated costs.

Holding or storage costs (iC_m)

C_m is the works prime cost of the stocked item (materials + labour + overheads or, perhaps more simply, materials + value added, but not including profit). Holding cost is expressed as a percentage, i, of prime cost, where i is normally of the order of 25 per cent and is made up as follows:

1. The opportunity cost of capital invested in stock. This is usually taken to be the existing rate of interest encountered in obtaining capital from the company's normal sources or the rate of return the company estimates it could obtain by investing capital elsewhere, and has traditionally been of the order of 10−15 per cent (but see following note).
2. All costs directly associated with storing goods, i.e. storemen's wages, rates, heating and lighting, store's transport, racking and palletization, protective clothing, weighing equipment, etc. (2−6 per cent).
3. Deterioration costs, including the costs incurred in preventing deterioration (1−4 per cent).
4. Obsolescence costs, including possible rework or scrapping (4−7 per cent).
5. Fire and general insurance ($1\frac{1}{2}$ per cent).

The above figures give a range for i between $17\frac{1}{2}$ and $34\frac{1}{2}$ per cent; the median of 26 per cent represents $\frac{1}{2}$p in the £ per week.

Note: until recently the effect of inflation on the prices of goods has not been regarded, except by economists, as an important enough feature to be included in the holding interest rate. However, with price inflation rates having reached 12% in recent years, it is very debatable whether this ignoring of the effects of inflation should continue. In principle, the expected rate of increase in stock prices should be deducted from the cost of holding stock, thereby promoting a tendency to build up stocks by 'buying now rather than later'. However, such a policy requires a further cash investment and such 'spare' cash is not generally available in times of inflation, especially since interest rates will tend to increase to reflect inflation (though not completely).

Stockout or runout costs (C_s)

These costs are most difficult to assess and to incorporate in mathematical inventory models, since they depend upon such imponderables as loss of customer goodwill, reduction in future orders, change in market share, etc. For this reason, stockout costs are frequently not computed in practice, and are generally only incorporated in the more sophisticated mathematical inventory models which are beyond the scope of this book. Instead, attention is focused on the level of service provided, without trying directly to evaluate that service. Of course, the cost of providing any service level indirectly implies a valuation of that service.

Service levels

The efficiency of any stock control policy is indicated by the level of service it offers to potential or existing customers in terms of providing stock 'off the shelf' or 'ex-stock'. Opinions as to which definition of service is best have varied widely, but the two most commonly used definitions are 'the probability of not running out of stock' and the 'proportion of annual demand met ex-stock'.

The probability of not running out of stock, as a measure of the effectiveness of a stock control system, has the advantage of being calculated fairly easily but suffers from the disadvantage that it can also be misinterpreted very easily. A 95 per cent probability of not running out of stock strictly interpreted means that, on average, for every hundred replenishment orders placed by the stockholder for his own replenishment, on ninety-five occasions customer demand will be met ex-stock before the replenishment order is received. On five occasions per hundred, therefore, stockouts do occur before the replenishment order is received.

From the customer's point of view, the probability of not running out of stock does not indicate how frequently the holder of stock will be out of stock (unless the stockholder's frequency of replenishment is known, which is most unlikely, except where the stock is raw material or work in progress, and the 'customer' is in fact another department of the same firm). Moreover, it does not indicate how badly or how long the supplier will be out of stock when a stockout does occur and it certainly does not indicate what proportion of the customer's demand will be met ex-stock. From an even more practical point of view, it also does not cover the situation of part-deliveries, where a customer would be more than satisfied to receive a part-delivery on time and the remainder of the order at a later date.

Because the probability of not running out of stock is easy to calculate, it has been used up to now more than any other definition of service in spite of its many disadvantages, and is still the method used by some computer packages. Because (in this author's opinion) the probability of not running out of stock is more an indication of good housekeeping on the part of the supplier or vendor than a meaningful measure of service to the customer, this measure of service will be termed the *vendor service level*.

From the customer's point of view a more useful measure of the service offered by a stock control system is the proportion of demand met ex-stock per annum. Such a measure permits the customer to allow for an expected amount short over a year and to protect himself against it, either by arranging to absorb such a shortfall or by holding a limited amount of stock on his own. As this measure is more useful to the customer, it will be referred to here as the *customer service level*. Because the proportion of annual demand met ex-stock (the customer service level) can now, as we shall see later, with advances in statistical theory be calculated relatively easily, and indeed linked with the probability of not running out of stock (the *vendor service level*), it has now been adopted as the measure of service offered by most inventory control software packages.

Demand: the link with forecasting

The design of any stock control system requires estimated values of the following three parameters:

D, the average demand per unit time,

σ, the standard deviation of demand per unit time, and

L, the lead time.

(If the lead time is variable, one needs also to estimate the mean and standard deviation of the lead time; we shall ignore such complications in this chapter.) The values of D and σ may be obtained from a forecasting model as discussed in the last chapter. It would appear sensible to suppose that these values should be updated every time an analysis of the demand situation produced a new forecast. With computerized inventory control systems this is indeed the general practice but, where a manual system of stock recording is in operation using stock record or bin cards, such substitutions are not easily effected, particularly over a large number of items. It must be accepted that the manual system itself limits the degree of control that can be exercised over stocks, and in such situations it might be expedient to update control parameters in line with forecasts at annual intervals and whenever a significant change in demand occurs (see pages 88–9).

Traditional approach to the evaluation of stock control parameters: re-order level policy

The traditional method is to determine, quite separately, the replenishment order size (q) and the re-order level (M). The former is calculated as that size which minimizes the total cost of ordering and storing. The latter is obtained by management specifying an appropriate vendor service level (i.e. probability of not running out of stock). It is possible to take into account interactions between q and M, but because of its relative simplicity, the traditional method of separate evaluation will be considered here.

Economic order quantity

The replenishment quantity is most usually evaluated on the criterion of minimizing total annual inventory operating costs, comprising inventory storage costs plus replenishment ordering costs.

Annual inventory storage costs are given by the percentage i multiplied by the average stock valued at unit cost C_m. The average stock will be the buffer stock (B) plus *half* the order quantity $(q/2)$. Annual storage costs thus total

$$\left(B + \frac{q}{2} \right) iC_m$$

Note that they increase with order size q.

The annual cost of ordering is the cost of placing a single replenishment order (C_o) multiplied by the number of replenishments (or cycles) per annum (A/q), where A is the annual demand. Annual order costs thus total $C_o A/q$. Note that they decrease with order size q.

Combining these two costs, the total cost C of ordering q units each time is:

$$C(q) = \left(B + \frac{q}{2} \right) iC_m + C_o \frac{A}{q}$$

Setting the derivative with respect to q equal to zero to obtain a minimum yields

$$\frac{dC}{dq} = \frac{iC_m}{2} - \frac{AC_o}{q^2} = 0$$

hence an optimal value

$$q^* = \sqrt{\frac{2AC_o}{iC_m}}$$

This is the so-called *economic order quantity* (EOQ) which minimizes the cost of operating the present simple inventory system. A diagrammatic representation is provided in Figure 7.3. Note that, at the optimum quantity, annual storage costs equal annual ordering costs.†

---

† Geometrically, the derivative represents the slope of the curve, hence the point where slope is zero is the flat point where total cost is at a minimum. With storage and replenishment cost functions of the form assumed, minimum total cost will always be at the quantity where the two component curves intersect. This is not generally the case for the sum of two curves drawn arbitrarily.

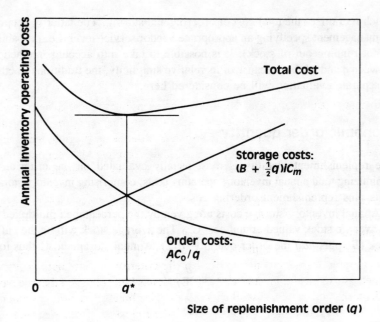

Figure 7.3 Evaluation of the traditional economic order quantity

To illustrate this, suppose demand (D) averages 100 per week, totalling 5,000 (A) in a 50-week year. Suppose the order cost C_o is £30, the value of the product C_m is £3 per item and annual holding costs are 25 per cent of this value. Then economic order quantity is

$$q^* = \sqrt{\frac{2 \times 5,000 \times £30}{0.25 \times £3}} = 632 \text{ items}$$

The above derivation of the economic order quantity assumed that replenishment occurred instantaneously rather than over a period of time. Although this assumption is usually valid for most 'purchased out' items and for some items manufactured internally, it may be necessary to consider what the minimum cost quantity should be in situations where replenishment does occur over a period of time. The relevant replenishment quantity in this situation is the *economic batch quantity* (EBQ) which, using a similar approach to that for developing the economic order quantity, is given by

$$q_b^* = \sqrt{\frac{2AC_o}{iC_m(1-D/p)}} = q^* \sqrt{\frac{1}{(1-D/p)}}$$

where p denotes production rate (measured in the same units as demand D).

To continue the previous example, if $D = 100$ per week and $p = 300$ per week, then $(1 - D/p) = 2/3$, hence

$$q_b^* = q^* \sqrt{\frac{3}{2}} = 1.225 \times 632 = 774 \text{ items}$$

In many manufacturing situations it is more sensible to express the economic batch quantity in terms of number of weeks of production q_b^*/p. Such values of weeks of production are always rounded to the nearest whole week or to the nearest production planning time unit. In the example, the economic batch quantity involves ordering $774/300 = 2.58$ or 3 weeks' production each time.

The concept of the economic order (or batch) quantity was originally developed as long ago as the 1920s, and the simple square-root formulae shown here have become the parents of a whole family of formulae of ever-increasing complexity. Such formulae have been developed to take into account either (a) that some of the assumptions made in the original model may not be valid in many practical situations, or (b) that the criterion of minimum cost may not necessarily be the most relevant. Thus, it has been objected that the basic model takes no account of stockout costs or price breaks (quantity discounts), that cost of replenishment may not be independent of order size and that deviations from the optimum order quantity are not important because the total cost curve is relatively flat. Alternative criteria which have been proposed in certain circumstances include maximum profit per batch, maximum rate of return and minimum cost subject to restrictions on capital, storage space or set-up costs.

However, from all these theoretical considerations, one common factor which appears to be generally agreed is that although the values of individual economic order quantities may not always be relevant, the *ratio* of the value of the economic order quantity for one stocked item to that of another *is always relevant*. This concept can be shown to be valid by several different approaches and is also a very useful one as it relates the size of order quantities between items rather than in isolation. This feature of relative size means that if EOQs for two different items come out at 300 units and 100 units, what is of most importance is that replenishment orders for the first item should be three times larger than for the second.

Re-order level

The re-order level (M) is set equal to the expected (or average) demand during the lead time (the re-order level policy's 'period of risk' — that time when the policy is at risk and no remedial action can be taken) plus the buffer stock (B). The latter is an allowance for occasions when demand exceeds the average level. It is conveniently expressed as a specified number (k) of standard deviations of lead time demand. Assume that demand is normally distributed† with a mean of D per week (or per month, etc.) and a standard deviation of σ per week. Assume also that demand in any week is essentially independent of demand in any other week. Then average demand over L weeks' lead time is DL and standard deviation of lead time demand is $\sigma\sqrt{L}$. The re-order level is given by

$$M = DL + k\sigma\sqrt{L}$$

The parameter k is called a *standard normal deviate*; evidently, k will be greater the better the vendor service level required. From standard normal distribution tables (see Table 7.2) we can extract information of particular reference to the inventory problem which shows the following relation between k and stockout probability per cycle.

To illustrate this, let demand average $D = 100$ per week, with a standard deviation of $\sigma = 30$ per week, and lead time $L = 4$ weeks. Suppose a vendor service level of 97.7 per cent is required, hence $k = 2$. Then re-order level is

$$M = (100 \times 4) + (2 \times 30 \sqrt{4}) = 520 \text{ units}$$

Of this amount, 400 units are active stock required to meet average demand during the lead time, and 120 units represent buffer stock (B) to meet above-average demand. The situation is illustrated in Figure 7.4.

In many companies, re-order levels are expressed in terms of weeks (or months, etc.) of average demand rather than in units of stock. Thus a re-order level may be expressed as 'four weeks' supply' rather than as 400 units. To do this, simply divide the re-order level by the rate of demand, hence

$$\text{re-order level (in time units)} = \frac{M}{D} = L + \frac{k\sigma\sqrt{L}}{D}$$

In the present example, a re-order level of 520 units represents 520/100 = 5.2 weeks' supply. Too often, however, when this type of definition is used the practice is to make the re-order level simply equal to the average lead time demand. Such a rule of thumb does not take into account more than average demand and, hence, results in a very low level of vendor service (theoretically only 50 per cent).

It is quite straightforward to relate probability of stockout to expected number of stockouts per year. If A denotes annual demand and q the replenishment order quantity, then there will, on average, be A/q replenishment cycles per year. If P denotes the probability of *not* running out of stock, then the expected

---

† In practice, the normal distribution may not give as accurate a representation of demand as the lognormal, Poisson, negative exponential or gamma distributions. Similar formulae and tables are available for these distributions also, but discussion of these is beyond the scope of this book.

----- **Table 7.2** -----
Vendor service levels, stockout
probability and partial expectation:
normal distribution

Standard deviate k	Vendor service level (%)P	Probability of stockout	Partial expectation E(k)
0.60	72.6	27.4	0.169
0.70	75.8	24.2	0.143
0.80	78.8	21.2	0.120
0.90	81.6	18.4	0.100
1.00	84.1	15.9	0.083
1.05	85.3	14.7	0.076
1.10	86.4	13.6	0.069
1.15	87.5	12.5	0.062
1.20	88.5	11.5	0.056
1.25	89.4	10.6	0.051
1.30	90.0	10.0	0.046
1.35	91.2	8.8	0.041
1.40	91.9	8.1	0.037
1.45	92.7	7.3	0.033
1.50	93.3	6.7	0.029
1.55	94.0	6.0	0.026
1.60	94.5	5.5	0.023
1.65	95.1	4.9	0.021
1.70	95.5	4.5	0.018
1.75	96.0	4.0	0.016
1.80	96.4	3.6	0.014
1.85	96.8	3.2	0.013
1.90	97.1	2.9	0.011
1.95	97.4	2.6	0.010
2.00	97.7	2.3	0.008
2.25	98.8	1.2	0.004
2.50	99.4	0.6	0.002
2.75	99.7	0.3	0.001
3.00	99.9	0.1	0.000

number of stockouts per year is $(1-P)A/q$. For the numerical example just given, where the economic order quantity is $q^* = 632$ and annual demand is $A = 5,000$, there would be $5,000/632$ or approximately 8 replenishments per year. If the vendor service level is 97.7 per cent, then the average frequency of stockout would be:

$$(1-0.977) \ \frac{5,000}{632} = 0.182 \text{ times per year}$$

or approximately once every $5\frac{1}{2}$ years.

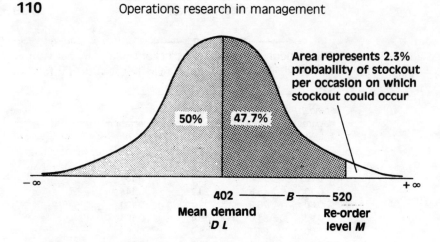

Area represents 2.3% probability of stockout per occasion on which stockout could occur

50%

47.7%

$-\infty$

$+\infty$

402 ——— B ——— 520

Mean demand   Re-order

$D L$ level M

Figure 7.4   Probability distribution of normal demand during the lead time

Traditional approach to the evaluation of parameters: re-order cycle policy

Within the re-order cycle policy (see Figure 7.2) the two parameters which control the policy's operation and which have to be determined are the *period of review R* and the *maximum stock level S*. For obvious practical reasons, the period of review is not normally evaluated but specified as a convenient time unit, i.e. week, fortnight, month, etc. Given that the period of review has been specified, it then follows that S is the only other parameter controlling the operation of the policy that then needs to be evaluated.

Based on the traditional concept of operating the re-order cycle policy by offering a specified level of *vendor service level* (i.e. probability of not running out of stock per demand occasion), the re-order cycle policy can be viewed as being analogous to a re-order level policy where stock levels are always below the maximum stock level S which can be considered as a re-order level. Such a policy will be continuously at risk and would, therefore, operate at a maximum 'period of risk' which can be shown to be the review period plus the lead time, i.e. $(R + L)$. This can be visualized more clearly by examining in detail the stock balances shown in Figure 7.2. In this figure it should be clear to the reader that the placing of a relatively large replenishment order at time t_1 has very little influence on whether a stockout occurs at time t_1' — a lead time later. However, the placing of that relatively large order at time t_1 does influence the level of stock which is reached when the order placed at that time is received at time t_1' and it is this which then influences the probability of a stockout occurring at time t_2' — a review period plus lead time later.

If one accepts the concept that the re-order cycle policy is analogous to a re-order level policy operating with a re-order level of S — rather than M — and a 'period of risk' of $(R + L)$ — rather than just L — then it follows from the previous discussion on pages 108−9 that:

$$S = D(R + L) + k\sigma \sqrt{(R + L)}$$

For the numerical data considered previously for the re-order level situation (i.e. demand average $D = 100$ per week, standard deviation of demand — 30 per week and the lead time $= 4$ weeks) assuming a review period of $R = 8$ weeks; to offer again a vendor service level of 97.7 per cent (for which the standard normal deviate $k = 2$) it follows:

$$S = 100 \times (8+4) + 2 \times 30 \sqrt{(8+4)}$$
$$S = 1,408 \text{ units}$$

Thus to offer the same level of vendor service with the two principal stock control policies, for the re-order level policy it is required that the re-order level be set at 520 units whereas for a re-order cycle policy operating with a review period of 8 weeks the maximum stock level requires to be set at 1,408 units.

A more up-to-date approach to the evaluation of stock control parameters: re-order level policy

As we noted earlier, although in the early 1970s, when scientific inventory control was in its infancy, the most mathematically convenient measure of the level of service offered by stock control systems was 'the probability of not running out of stock per occasion', it was later recognized that such a measure of service was virtually meaningless to most customers of such systems. Subsequently it has been largely replaced by a more appropriate definition; namely 'the proportion of annual demand met ex-stock'.

In Figure 7.5 we have magnified the tail end of the normal distribution of demand during the lead time shown as Figure 7.4. It was stated earlier that the *area* of this section of the normal curve (namely that above the re-order level) represented a 2.3 per cent probability of a stockout occurring on those occasions stockouts could occur, i.e. following the placing of a replenishment order. The area which represents this probability is in fact the *first* integral of the normal probability density function between the limits of the value of the re-order level of 520 and $+\infty$. (Appendix 1 gives values of the integral between $-\infty$ and x, i.e. one minus the probability in which we are interested here.)

Now, since the *first* integral of the normal probability density function between these two limits represents the *probability* of demand during the lead time not being satisfied per occasion, it should not be too hard to imagine that the *second* integral of the normal probability density function between those same limits represents the *average value* of units of demand not satisfied per occasion. Clearly there must be an average number of units of demand between these two limits. If this value could be established, it would represent the units of demand during the lead time that exceeded the value of the re-order level, i.e. the average shortage per occasion.

Knowing the average shortage per occasion and the number of occasions (replenishments) per year when this shortage can occur, it is then a simple matter to calculate the annual demand shortage and hence 'the proportion of annual demand met ex-stock', henceforth referred to as the *customer service level*.

The second integral of the normal probability density function is known as the partial expectation $E(k)$, and its values are given in Table 7.2. For the situation depicted in Figure 7.5, in which a *vendor service level* of 97.7 per cent was offered, with $k = 2$ it follows from Table 7.2 that $E(k) = 0.008$. Since the demand during the lead time is distributed with a standard deviation of $\sigma \sqrt{L}$, it follows that the average shortage per occasion in this situation is given by $E(k) \times \sigma \sqrt{L}$.

If replenishment orders are made equal to the economic order quantity $q*$ of 632 units, with an annual demand of 5,000 (A), it follows that with $A/q*$ orders placed per annum, the annual shortage will be given by:

$$E(k) \times \sigma \sqrt{L} \times A/q* = 0.008 \times 30 \sqrt{4} \times 5,000/632 = 3.8 \text{ units}$$

Hence, with an annual demand of 5,000 and a mere 3.8 units of demand not met ex-stock, it follows that the *customer service level* P' is given by:

$$P' = (5,000 - 3.8)/5,000 = 99.9\%$$

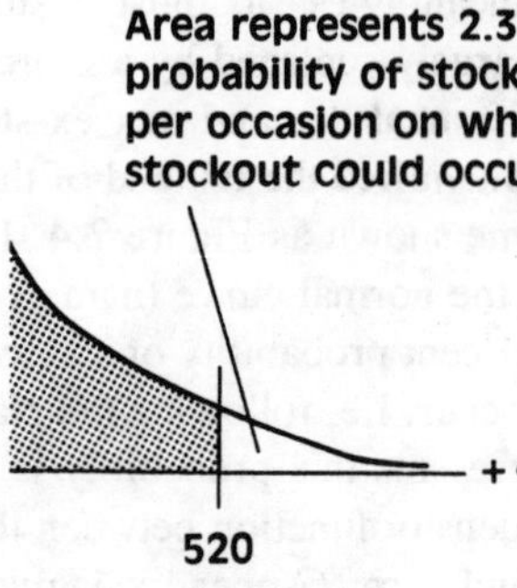

Area represents 2.3%
probability of stockout
per occasion on which
stockout could occur

520

Figure 7.5   Tail end of probability distribution of normal demand during the lead time

Hence with a traditional *vendor service level* of 97.7 per cent customers actually experience a 99.9 per cent *customer service level* and in general terms it can be safely assumed that the CSL is always above the VSL.

It is possible that the reason that the concept of a *vendor service level* which is statistically convenient but generally misinterpreted in practice has remained so long in both the literature and the software is due to this relationship, namely that in terms that customers understand, i.e. the *customer service level*, they always receive a better level of service than that originally offered, i.e. the *vendor service level*.

More generally, given that the *customer service level* P' is defined as the proportion of annual demand met ex-stock, it follows that the shortage or annual demand not met ex-stock per annum is given by:

$$(1 - P') \times A$$

With A/q orders placed per annum for each of which it is assumed there is an average shortage of $E(k) \times \sigma \sqrt{L}$, it follows that the expected shortage per annum is given by:

$$\frac{A \times E(k) \times \sigma \sqrt{L}}{q}$$

Equating the defined annual shortage and the expected annual shortage, it follows that:

$$P' = 1 - \frac{E(k) \times \sigma \sqrt{L}}{q}$$

A more up-to-date approach to the evaluation of stock control parameters: re-order cycle policy

Applying the same basic approach of equating the annual shortage as defined by the *customer service level* with the expected annual shortage for the re-order cycle policy based on a review period R expressed in weeks and, hence, offering $50/R$ reviews per annum we have:

$$(1 - P') \times A = (50/R) \times E(k) \times \sigma \sqrt{(R+L)}$$

and

$$P' = 1 - \frac{50 \times E(k) \times \sigma \sqrt{(R+L)}}{R \times A}$$

For the re-order cycle situation discussed earlier (see pages 110–11) with

$k = 2$ offering a *vendor service level* of 97.7 per cent and a corresponding value of $E(k) = 0.008$, with $R = 8$ it follows that:

$$P' = 1 - \frac{50 \times 0.008 \times 30 \sqrt{(8+4)}}{8 \times 5,000}$$

$$P' = 99.9\%$$

again confirming that the CSL is generally above the VSL.

In the last two sections we have reviewed the characteristics of two popular inventory policies: the re-order level and the re-order cycle. Each may be appropriate for different types of stock items. When deciding which to use, a necessary first step is to group items using some measure or criterion of importance. Having grouped stocked items on a basis of relative importance, it is then possible to use the properties of the method of grouping itself to arrive at an overall comprehensive stocking policy. The situation is exactly analogous to that of forecasting and, in fact, the Pareto approach may be used as described in the last two sections of the previous chapter.

Category A items

It is usual with valuable items such as these (typically three times the average individual value) to try to obtain a high degree of control of stocks. There is a tendency therefore to use inventory control policies of the periodic review type for this category of item. Such policies ensure that the stock position is reviewed regularly, irrespective of demand, whereas in a re-order level type of policy it is the demand situation which determines when reviews take place. In the latter type of policy, if demand is particularly low for a period of time, the frequency at which reviews of the stock situation take place drops significantly compared with the average, and this can be a prime cause of dead stocks being created as items gradually become obsolete.

The pure re-order cycle policy ensures that replenishments are placed regularly at each and every review although the size of the individual replenishment order varies. Such a method of replenishment might fit in well with contract buying.

Category B items

For these medium-cost items a re-order level policy is generally most suitable. Where replenishments for several items are obtained from a single source, however, again it may be practical to operate a regular review type of inventory policy to enable several orders to be placed simultaneously, thus reducing ordering and transport costs.

Category C items

The re-order level of two-bin (or single-bin) policy is usually most appropriate for C items. This method offers a reasonable degree of control with a minimum of record-keeping. If space allows, a degree of overstocking can generally be allowed, simply because of the cheapness of the items involved, in order to reduce the probability of stockouts. Readers are reminded that the two-bin type of policy is not suitable for items that deteriorate as it is essentially a last-in first-out (LIFO) policy rather than a first-in first-out (FIFO) policy. For C items it is not usual to update stock control parameters in line with forecasts, as forecasts will not generally be made for this type of item — annual updating is, therefore, more usual. Often, in fact, this policy is operated with no paper records at all and auditors accept limited sampling as a method of assessing value for audit purposes.

Conclusion

Inventory control is an area where operations researchers have found a fruitful field in which to hypothesize models and produce theoretical solutions to those models. However, the practical application of these theoretical considerations — usually embodied in the form of algorithms within computerized stock control packages — remains very limited as a proportion of what has been published. Perhaps one of the best examples of this surfeit of impractical imaginative thinking on the part of the researchers has been the *economic order quantity* which has become the progenitor of thousands of equations resulting from the imposition of different restrictions or criteria for best performance. At the end of the day, though, the fact that the theoretical economic order quantity can be shown — using several different approaches — to establish replenishment order values which between products are at least in the correct ratio, has meant that the use of the EOQ with a 'fudge factor' (set at less than one if capital investment or physical space restrictions are imposed, or greater than one if machine utilization is a priority) is more than sufficient for most practical purposes.

Most stock control situations are a mixture of dependent and independent demand and it is important that for those elements where demand is definitely dependent that MRP procedures are adopted and that where demand is definitely independent that policies of the type described in this chapter should prevail.

Perhaps the most obvious example of an independent demand environment is that seen in large supermarkets. It is clearly apparent that the demand for *bacon* is not tied to the demand for *tinned plums* in such situations, and for the larger supermarket chains within the United Kingdom the ability to capture information using point-of-sale technology and to communicate that information to a central computer system daily allows such organizations to operate very effective stock control policies which offer high customer service levels with a minimum of stock.

——— Exercises ———

1. What probability of not running out of stock per occasion is afforded within a re-order level stock control policy when the re-order level is set at 170 units, demand per week is normally distributed with a mean value of 40 and a standard deviation of 20 and the lead time is fixed at 3 weeks?

2. Calculate the value of the economic order quantity for the situation in which the annual sales turnover is 3,000 items, the cost of placing a replenishment order is £30, the value of the items is £5 and the annual storage interest rate is 25 per cent (i.e. the annual storage cost is £1.25 per item). What would the storage and ordering costs be per annum were the economic order quantity used for replenishment?

3. If the situations described in exercises 1 and 2 were to be combined, what would the proportion of annual demand met ex-stock be?

4. For the same demand situation described in exercise 1, what maximum stock level needs to be operated when operating a re-order cycle policy with a review period of 12 weeks and a lead time of 3 weeks if a vendor service level of 94 per cent is to be offered? In this case what customer service level would be offered?

References and further reading

Bennett, D., C. Lewis and M. Oakley (1988) *Operations Management*, Philip Allan.

King, J. (1985) *Management of Engineering Production*, Frances Pinter.

Krajewski, L.J. and L.P. Ritzman (1987) *Operations Management: Strategy and analysis*, Addison-Wesley.

Lewis, C.D. (1981) *Scientific Inventory Control*, Butterworths.

Reinfield, N.V. (1987) *Handbook of Production and Inventory Control*, Prentice Hall.

Silver, E.A. and R. Peterson (1984) *Decision Systems for Inventory Management and Production Planning*, John Wiley.

Stair, R.M. and B. Render (1984) *Production and Operations Management*, Allyn & Bacon.

Tersine, R.J. (1982) *Principles of Inventory and Materials Management*, North-Holland.

Thomas, A.B. (1980) *Stock Control in Manufacturing Industries*, Gower Press.

− 8 −

Inventory control:
Theory into practice

A.H. LINES

Introduction

Without the modern computer the classical inventory theory described in the preceding chapter would remain just that — interesting but impractical. Experience gained during the late 1950s and early 1960s established that the theory worked, but the cost of performing the necessary calculations exceeded the savings which could usually be realized except in very large businesses. It was not until the middle 1970s that sufficiently cheap and reliable computers were available to make the application of inventory theory to a business an economic proposition for smaller firms as well. Today, even the smallest of business computers — PCs and laptops — can handle the calculations necessary to control stocks of literally thousands of items and at a relatively small cost.

Unfortunately, realizing the benefits of inventory theory involves a great deal more than translating equations into coding. This chapter sets out the steps in creating a working system, and concludes with two case studies.

Steps in building a system

Translating theory into practice means developing a set of rules and procedures which incorporate the theory and by which the user can realize the benefits. To construct a modern computer-based inventory control system involves going through the following steps:

1. Establishing inventory policy: a qualitative statement of what is the job of the inventory, and a quantitative one of how well that job has to be done.

117

2. Preparing a 'specification' of the system which includes:
   (a) the data required to run the system;
   (b) the source(s) of the data;
   (c) the person responsible for making sure the information is available;
   (d) whether and how the data are to be validated to ensure accuracy;
   (e) the types of calculation to be carried out;
   (f) the timing of the calculations;
   (g) the form in which the results are to be presented;
   (h) how the results are to be used.
3. Concurrently with the preparation of the specification it is often necessary to teach prospective users the principles of inventory theory so that they can understand the potential of the system and respond to enquiries about their particular requirements (for incorporation into the specification).
4. A company installing a modern inventory system usually has a computer already programmed with the standard commercial procedures concerned with entering orders, invoicing and recording stock movements. The designer of the new system has to establish how the information available on stock movements, levels, etc., can be extracted from the computer files or database and then processed to determine the stocks needed. The systems analyst will have available the technical specification prepared by the operations research analyst describing the inventory calculations needed and how they are to be carried out.
5. The system specification is translated into computer code.
6. Extensive testing of the system, both in modular and completed form, is necessary to make sure that the requisite calculations are carried out correctly under all the possible conditions which may be encountered.
7. During the system development stage, training of the users and computer operators should be commenced so that by the time the system is fully tested the users are reasonably familiar with the way it is to be used.
8. The successful completion of the first production run does not mark the end of the work of building the system, however. Experience shows it takes six to twelve months for the users to become accustomed to working with the system and for all the various bugs and inconsistencies to be ironed out.
9. Proper documentation of the system is essential as a training aid and as a document for future reference in case anything goes wrong or a modification has to be made.

Specifying the policy

Money spent on building up stocks, whether to enable production to proceed smoothly or to give customers a better service is just as much an investment of company funds as is money spent on new machinery. Although in most companies the finance department is concerned to keep stocks as low as possible, on the majority of balance sheets the amount of working capital represented by stocks and work in progress is a prominent item and, in some cases, the largest.

Stocks are essential for most selling and production activities. Quick and reliable delivery is as important a factor as price in getting business, so most sales managers insist on large stocks of finished goods being held. Where goods are made to order the emphasis is on availability of parts and sub-assemblies so that manufacture can be completed quickly.

As we noted in the previous chapter production managers are responsible for ensuring that stocks of finished goods are maintained at agreed levels and special orders met by the date promised. At the same time they have to keep factories occupied by arranging for a smooth and even flow of work. To achieve these ends, adequate stocks of materials and components must be held.

All departmental managers will argue that they are working in the interests of the company but it is apparent that if any one manager's aims prevail too much there will be a dislocation of production, dissatisfied customers or a shortage of cash. The aim is to arrive at the best compromise for the company, but how can this be done?

Where the finance department's view predominates, it is often the practice to set inventory levels in terms of targets which may not be exceeded — usually expressed as 'day's stock' or 'stock turn'. Such targets, however, provide no real guide to the inventory controller and can, in fact, make it impossible for him to meet the legitimate needs of the operating departments.

What is needed is a clear policy from the general management but this cannot be established unless the amount invested in stock can be related to performance in terms of customer service or production efficiency expressed in quantitative terms. Scientific inventory theory as set out in the previous chapter enables these relationships to be determined and the most suitable policy for any set of circumstances to be identified.

To establish scientifically an optimum inventory policy, an analysis has to be made of the factors which dictate or influence the amount of inventory required to meet the needs of a particular situation. The following are the factors usually considered:

1. The purpose for which the stocks are held (see discussion in previous chapter).
2. The relationships with associated activities, e.g. production, distribution, maintenance, selling.
3. The type of demand/usage/sales pattern, lead (supply) time characteristics.
4. Stock availability and service level.
5. The costs of ordering and holding stocks.
6. The costs and other consequences of not having stock.

The different roles of stock in a business

The different roles of stock have been described in detail in the previous chapter. Note that whatever the purpose for which an item is stocked, the absence of stocks when they are wanted will lead to problems of one sort or another. If raw materials are not available then manufacture cannot proceed; if components are not in stock or only some are in stock, then assembly cannot be completed. Absence of some finished goods will prevent an order being shipped or permit only part shipment. In either event, the customer will be dissatisfied, possibly two sets of transport costs will be incurred and next time the customer may go elsewhere.

Non-availability of stocks within the distribution system may result in trucks being delayed or being sent out half full. In all cases, shortage of stock will increase costs.

Quantitative inventory policy: service level

It follows that from the user's point of view, there is a strong incentive to aim for a 100 per cent reliable service in terms of stock availability. However, in theory at least, perfect service can only be achieved by carrying an infinitely large quantity of stock. Whatever the size of stock carried, there is always a chance, however small, that someone will want a larger quantity than is in stock. Customer service level was defined in the previous chapter in respect of individual stock items. Most stocks hold thousands of items and customers place demands for more than one item at a time. It is therefore necessary to expand our previous definition to cope with this. There are a number of ways, of which the most usual are the following:

1. The proportion of a customer's requirement for units of product which on average can be met immediately from stock (termed 'piece fill'). If requirements over, say, a year total 1,000 units of which 950 are met immediately from stock then the service level is 95 per cent. This is the same as the 'customer service level' defined in the previous chapter.
2. The proportion of a customer's order lines filled completely and immediately from stock (termed 'line fill'). Note that an order line may be for any number of units of one particular product.
3. The proportion of complete customer orders (any number of order lines) filled completely and immediately from stock.

Line fill is a popular method of judging stock management performance; unfortunately it is an arbitrary measurement and provides no firm basis on which to determine stock levels. The point is best understood by considering an example.

Suppose there is a stock of 1,000 units of a particular product and the orders to be filled are one order for 500 units and eight orders each for 100 units. Suppose the large order is filled first; the line fill will then be 1 × 500 + 5 × 100 or six orders out of nine (66.7 per cent). However, if the small orders are filled first, the fill will be eight out of nine or 88.9 per cent. Stock managers judged on line fill have been known to resort to selective picking!

The piece fill performance on that particular occasion is 1,000 units filled out of 1,300 units demanded, or 76.8 per cent. If a demand had been made up of thirteen orders of 100 units, the two measures would have given the same figure of 76.9 per cent. The conclusion is that there exists no definite relationship between piece fill and line fill. The latter depends on the mix of small and large orders and the sequence in which they are filled. In practice, with many products and orders, line fill does settle down to an average figure, but the piece fill service level needed to achieve a desired average line fill can only be determined by trial and error. For stock control calculations piece fill is the figure which should be specified. The task is made more complex if part of a firm's product range is set to achieve a different service level from the rest; selective targeting of key products is a popular marketing tactic.

The third measure of service is important to the supermarket and also to the manager of an assembly shop. If there are three different items on the shopping list or bill of materials, what is the chance that all three will be met from stock simultaneously? Suppose the piece fill service level is set at 95 per cent for each item, then the chance will be 95 × 95 ×95, or 85.7 per cent. The more items there are on the list, the smaller the chance they can all be supplied from stock together. If the target is 90 per cent of all customer orders, each averaging N lines to be filled completely, the piece fill service level of each individual line needs to be $N\sqrt{0.9}$.

Supermarkets have therefore to maintain very high piece fill service levels if their customers are not to be disappointed in more than, say, two out of forty items on an average shopping list. In engineering companies, assembling complex machines from hundreds or thousands of parts, it is plainly uneconomic to carry sufficient stocks to ensure an uninterrupted assembly programme. Instead the assembly programme is first laid down and then the necessary components purchased or manufactured. This means that the time needed to build the assembly is longer than would have been the case had the components been in stock. If components' stocks are to be kept small, either relatively large stocks of the complete product have to be carried or the customer has to wait while the parts are procured and then assembled.

To help the manager to determine the appropriate level of customer service to set for his business, the inventory scientist needs to demonstrate how the amount, and hence the cost, of the stock is affected by the customer service level chosen. Using similar calculations to those required to produce Table

7.2, a modern inventory control computer program can be used to generate curves of the type shown in Figure 8.1 which relates the average stockholding to the service level provided in terms of 'line fill'. Such a graph can be constructed for the whole of a company's inventory or a sample can be analyzed to give the basis for fixing the target service level for the whole. From the figure we can see that as the level of service approaches 100 per cent the stock required increases rapidly: if we knew the cost of running out of stock, we could determine a service level which minimized all expected costs in the system, but it is only rarely that this cost can be estimated. However, there is always a point at which marginal improvements in customer service do not justify the cost of the additional stocks which would be necessary.

Then comes the more difficult task of deciding exactly what an improvement in customer service is worth in terms of more business, smoother production

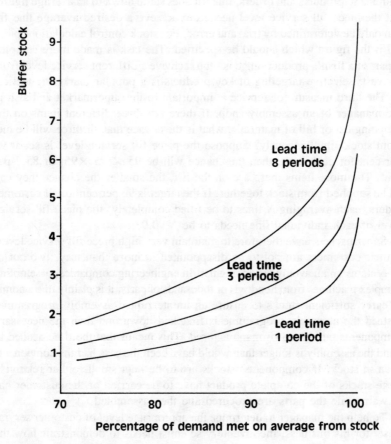

Figure 8.1 Buffer stocks, service levels and lead times

or a quicker turn-round of maintenance and repair work. Usually the only way is to set the service level to a certain figure, experience the benefits or otherwise of that level, then modify the level to see what effect the change has.

Realizing a service level policy

Inventory control, by its nature, is a time-dependent process. As stock levels fall so they must be replaced. The main characteristics of the alternative forms of stock control system, namely the order level and the order cycle systems, have been described in the preceding chapter. To recapitulate, the re-order level system is defined by two parameters, namely, the re-order quantity (Q) and the re-order level (M). The latter is calculated from the formula $M = DL + K\sigma \sqrt{L}$, where D is the average demand, L the lead time and $\sigma\sqrt{L}$ is the standard deviation of lead time demand.

In the case of the re-order cycle or periodic review policy system, the maximum stock (order up to) level (S) is given by the formula $S = D(L+R) + K\sigma \sqrt{(L+R)}$, where R is the time interval between successive reviews.

Note that in both formulae the values of D, the demand, and L, the lead time, are unlikely to remain constant for very long in most businesses. Unless these values are reviewed at reasonably frequent intervals, therefore, it is likely that the re-order level or maximum stock figure will become incorrect so that either too little or too much stock will be kept, with a consequent effect on the service.

It should be emphasized that stock is held in anticipation of future customer requirements which may not necessarily be the same as past ones. The demand D is a forecast of customer requirements and L a forecast of how long the next order will take to be received. Both quantities therefore will usually be in error. The buffer stock is calculated using the standard deviation (variability) of demand over lead time. The assumption made is that the forecast of demand will be subject to an error which will be of the same magnitude as the amount by which past demands have fluctuated about the past average demand. The formula also tacitly assumes that the lead time will not vary. In a typical large company carrying anything up to 100,000 items of inventory a significant number of the items will have demands and lead times undergoing change at any one time. Maintaining a steady and reliable level of service entails updating demand and lead time forecasts at frequent (e.g. monthly) intervals and at the same time recalculating the re-order level or maximum stock figures to take account of the updated forecasts and forecast errors. In the case of supermarkets this update process is often carried out weekly. Note that the updating and recalculation of the control values need not necessarily coincide with the actual triggering of orders in the case of the re-order level system or the review and re-ordering of stock in the case of the order cycle system.

A typical sequence of events in the case of an order cycle system might be as follows:

1. At month end for each item of stock at each location customer demand during the month just ended is determined. This is not as easy as it appears since most often users have no means of determining true demand and only sales figures are available. This means that the forecast demand will be based on numbers which are probably too small, a fact which has to be compensated for by setting the service levels slightly higher than those desired.

2. The demand data are then used to update the forecast for the month just ended, using (usually) a form of exponential smoothing (Chapter 6).

3. The lead time estimate is updated using data on the actual lead times from the latest replenishment orders received.

4. The maximum stock is recalculated using the new forecasts.

5. The current stockholding plus orders placed but not received is then compared with the new maximum stock and if necessary a further replenishment order placed. Stock reviews and re-ordering may take place at, say, weekly intervals even though the maximum stock figure is only updated monthly or four-weekly.

6. If a minimum order quantity or economic order quantity is specified, the calculated figure is rounded up to this quantity or to a multiple thereof.

7. The stock replenishment order may activate a purchase or manufacturing procedure. The information may be communicated either by printing out an order, writing the information back to another computer procedure or sending it to a distant (supplier's) computer by EDI (electronic data interchange) network.

Starting up a system

One of the most difficult and least discussed aspects of inventory control is introducing a new system into a business (or even adding a new product to an existing inventory). Suppose one is aiming to install a modern system along the lines discussed in the preceding pages — how does one begin? The system described previously is self-adapting, that is to say, given time it will correct itself so that stocks held are in line with customer demand and the desired service levels will be achieved. However, this process can take from six months upwards depending on the accuracy of the starting values used. Meanwhile users of the system and customers may lose confidence in its ability to produce the anticipated service and stock levels. It is, therefore, important that the day a new system starts to operate, the calculated stock levels are appropriate for the service levels specified.

Provided that (a) at least six and preferably twelve months' past demand (sales) is available (two years for seasonal products), (b) actual, measured, lead times are known, (c) a system for recording stock levels and purchase orders placed but not received is in use, and (d) ordering and stockholding costs are known, start-up values for a new system can be determined.

The start-up process comprises the following steps.

If seasonality is suspected, at least two complete years' past data must be analyzed to determine whether there is some form of repetition in the demand pattern from year to year which would suggest seasonality. If a statistical significance test (Moroney, 1958) confirms this, a seasonal index is calculated using, for example the Holt Winters method (Winters, 1960). The results of this analysis should be discussed with the marketing department to confirm that there are good reasons why demand for a particular product should be seasonal.

The second stage is to analyze for all products the last twelve months' demand (or sales) data in the following manner:

1. For seasonal products de-seasonalize the data using the index determined by the above procedure.
2. Classify each individual item according to whether it is:
   (i) a normal, fast-moving product, i.e. with frequent demands reasonably stable and 'normally' distributed from period to period;
   (ii) fast moving but with a trend, either upwards or downwards (determined by regression analysis; Moroney, 1958).
   (iii) a lumpy or spasmodic demand pattern — for example during half the months there is no demand but in the others it ranges from 1 to 100 or 1,000 units;
   (iv) some other form of semi-fast-moving pattern which does not approximate to a normal distribution (e.g. it follows a gamma distribution);
   (v) slow moving, that is to say demands are infrequent and small;
   (vi) a new or obsolete product.
3. Future lead times are estimated either by reference to past actual lead times or through discussions with suppliers and purchasing staff.
4. The minimum order quantity (or frequency of re-ordering) appropriate to the costs involved is determined by using coverage analysis (Lines, 1983; or possibly the standard economic order quantity (Chapter 7)) or by consideration of transportation or manufacturing cycles.
5. If there is no trend in past demand then the starting forecast is simply the (de-seasonalized) average. Regression analysis is used to determine with

a statistical degree of probability whether a trend exists. If there is a trend, it must be removed from the data *before* calculating the standard deviation. Otherwise too high a figure would be used and the starting buffer stock would be too large.

6. One further task is to edit past demand to remove 'flyers' (misleadingly large or small figures) which may be due to stockouts, price changes, advertising campaigns or other unusual events. If such figures are not excluded, starting forecasts will not reflect the underlying demand level and buffer stocks will be too large.

7. The stocks needed to ensure that the desired level of customer service is achieved can then be calculated. Different calculations will be needed according to which statistical distribution best fits the historical demand pattern. Those for the normal distribution have been given in the previous chapter. Slow-moving stocks can usually be handled by reference to cumulative Poisson tables but lumpy demand patterns present considerable problems. There is no 'good' method but an article by Croston (1972) contains some helpful ideas. Another approach is to attempt to fit an E_K (or gamma) distribution, allowing K to take fractional values. Developing methods to take account of the quite wide variety of demand distributions encountered in practice is one of the 'skills' the OR scientist acquires with experience.

New products

Increasingly fast rates of technological change and competitive forces compel most businesses continuously to update their product range, introducing new lines and discontinuing others. This not only affects what finished goods have to be stocked but also the range of spare parts and accessories needed to support them.

New products can be divided into a number of classes, namely:

- the new product takes the place of an existing one;
- the product is new, but the market is fairly well known;
- it is a completely new product whose market performance is difficult to predict.

The first class is easy to handle. The usual assumption made is that the demand characteristics of the product being replaced can be used for the new one, at least at the outset. 'Supersession', as it is termed, involves designing a computer procedure to write the demand history of the old product over to the code number of the new one.

Where the market of the new product is fairly well known it is usually possible for marketing management to specify an opening demand forecast together with some idea of expected growth. Groups of products often have very similar characteristics in terms of the ratio of their standard deviation to their average demand. Given an expected opening demand, therefore, it is possible to make a reasonable estimate of an opening standard deviation and hence calculate the buffer stock needed to provide a target service level. As regards the start-up of the system, there are two possible approaches:

1. Marketing management put in their own forecasts and stock level figures for the first six months. Thereafter the system procedures are used to calculate and update the correct control values.
2. Starting estimates are put in by management and the system then used to update these in the normal way. Here again, after six months there is sufficient data for starting values to be reviewed and correct ones to be calculated.

For the third class of product it is preferable for stock levels to be set by management for the first few months. It may be necessary to review trends and results at very frequent intervals, possibly weekly. Here again, once there is sufficient evidence of the underlying demand rate, the standard stock management procedures can be employed.

One thing which has to be watched very carefully in new product start-ups is to allow for what is known as 'pipeline fill'. Particularly where a product is being sold through a distribution chain, it takes a considerable volume of product to stock up retailers and wholesalers. This results in a substantial demand for the product at the outset. Once the pipeline is filled, the ongoing demand for the product more closely reflects true demand. Consequently the first two or three months' figures may be totally misleading.

Multi-level systems

The majority of stock control theory and practice is concerned with the management of a single level of stock, e.g. a wholesaler or a spare parts department. Today many companies operate multi-stage distribution systems, the simplest form of which is a factory-finished goods warehouse used to supply field depots, which in turn ship to the ultimate customer. Traditionally, the field depot and branch managers determined their own stock requirements and notified these to the factory or central warehouse. In effect the local managers were acting as independent customers, placing orders on the centre irrespective or policy or stock availability. Numerous studies have shown that this is no longer the most satisfactory way of operating, given the availability of data-links and computer networks.

Central warehouse stocks exist mainly to ensure that what the branches require is available when they want it and to make direct shipments to larger customers. The correct basis for determining central warehouse stocks is therefore a forecast of customer demand for the company as a whole.

In traditional systems the only information the centre had about customer demand was what branch managers ordered. Such managers tend to place orders for larger quantities at less frequent intervals than the demands they themselves experience from their own customers. If a central warehouse forecast is prepared on the basis of the branch managers' orders recieved, this will entail analyzing a pattern with a higher degree of variability than there should be. Hence short-term forecast errors will be relatively large and higher buffer stocks than necessary will be carried. If central warehouse forecasts are based on the actual orders received at the branches, generally forecast errors are smaller and so central warehouse buffer stocks can be reduced proportionate to demand without affecting service (see Figure 8.2).

In a modern computer-based two-level system the raw demand at the branch level is used first to determine forecasts and stocks for the branch in question and is then passed up in *raw form* to the centre. Demand data for each product for all branches is then summed and the forecasting and stock control procedures repeated to determine central warehouse stocks necessary to meet the total demand over the supply lead time either from the factory or from external suppliers. If branch lead times are to be maintained then the level of service at the central warehouse must be set fairly high.

The purpose of a two-level system is to minimize the total of the stock held both at the central warehouse and at the branch warehouses, consistent with providing the ultimate customer with the specified service. The lowest cost answer is usually to set branch service levels somewhat higher than the specified level of customer service and to set the central warehouse service level a little lower than the, say, 99.9 per cent needed to ensure that branch supply lead times are reliable. Models to determine this economic balance have been developed, by the author, but are beyond the scope of this book; for further reading see Rosenbaum (1981) and Silver and Peterson (1985).

Training

A modern inventory control system is a man—machine system. Much of the tedious and routine calculation can now be handled by the computer, but the policy objectives must still be determined by management. Furthermore, not

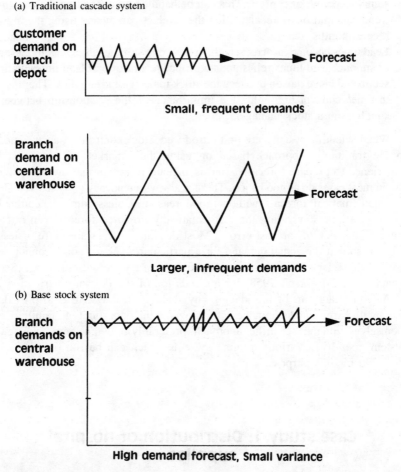

(a) Traditional cascade system

Customer demand on branch depot — Forecast

Small, frequent demands

Branch demand on central warehouse — Forecast

Larger, infrequent demands

(b) Base stock system

Branch demands on central warehouse — Forecast

High demand forecast, Small variance

Small but frequent demands = small forecast errors
Hence small safety stocks!

Figure 8.2 Forecasting and forecast error in two-level inventory systems

all situations which arise can be foreseen and incorporated in a model and the manager has to intervene. Examples where this arises are as follows:

1. Forecast demand for a product may be distorted by a planned sales promotion, a price change, unusual export orders or a change of technology. Since the forecast is based on an analysis of past demand these events cannot be forecast mathematically and must be allowed for by overriding the computer forecast.

2. A rapid trend in demand either upwards or downwards causes the tracking

signal to go out of control. This can be handled by overriding the current trend rate and/or by recalculating the product parameters using the most recent months' data.

3. Lead times become incorrect resulting in wrong stock levels. The monitoring of supplier lead times relies upon a proper record of past lead times being set up and close liaison between the stock manager and supplier. The 'just-in-time' concept highlights the importance of the relationship between suppliers and stock managers.

When scientific systems are first introduced, stock controllers, accustomed to the traditional approach based on using their market knowledge and experience to prepare forecasts, find it difficult to accept that the computer can in most cases do as good a job. There is always a tendency to try to override the mathematical forecast without good reason. Unless some exceptional situation arises, overriding the mathematically prepared forecast can often increase the size of forecast errors. Most demand patterns are more or less random so that the actual demand for a particular week or month cannot be predicted precisely and attempts to improve accuracy are self-defeating. (See Chapter 8 in Moroney, 1958, for a discussion of the Poisson distribution.)

An important part of introducing any stock control system is to provide users with careful and sympathetic training and the opportunity to familiarize themselves with the 'scientific' approach, preferably sometime before the new system goes live. Various training systems which can be run on PCs are available for this purpose.

Case study 1: Distribution of hospital supplies

The West Midlands Regional Health Authority (RHA) wanted to introduce a modern inventory control system in order to improve customer service. The wind of change in the Health Service has brought commercial competition into hospital supplies: a self-governing hospital from 1990 can choose commercial suppliers in place of the supplies organization of the RHA. This RHA did not intend to have its hospitals and clinics shopping elsewhere.

Service level has to be particularly high in hospital stores and consistently reliable. For critical medical supplies, service levels must be pretty nearly 100 per cent. At the same time budgetary constraints are stringent.

West Midlands RHA began its review of its supplies operation in 1986. It was decided to centralize twelve divisional stores which supply twenty-two District Health Authorities in one regional supply centre in Birmingham. This will handle well over 6,000 stock lines from many suppliers, and distribute them to over 12,000 transfer (local stock) points in 211 hospitals, 500 clinics and administrative centres.

The system chosen

The NHS uses McDonnel Douglas computers with the PICK operating system. The inventory control system chosen — SLIM by Slimstock Systems Ltd — had to be specially rewritten for this system in the 'ENGLISH' computer language.

While development was taking place, the intending users were taught the principles of the system in a series of seminars. The Director of Logistics claims that the use of techniques which staff learned at those seminars was responsible for a dramatic reduction of stocks which was achieved even before the SLIM system became operational.

Forecasts are based on analysis of product usage. The system takes account of expected seasonal peaks, automatically adjusts for changes in patterns and trends, regularly updates the forecasts and adjusts the size of buffer stocks to counter the effects of forecast error. A special facility allows management to alter the forecasts to meet unusual circumstances, such as the introduction of new products.

With the chosen system, the stock controller can know the cost consequences (in terms of stockholding) of specifying a particular level of service. As each successive improvement in service requires proportionately more stock, this is vital for budgetary forecasting. It is also important to the NHS that the specified level of service will always continue to be achieved with this system, no matter what circumstances change in terms of trends in demand, suppliers' lead times, seasonal peaks and other changes in patterns.

Results

The main financial benefit to be expected in the RHA is a reduction in stock levels. Because of the high service levels needed, present stocks were also very high, and trial runs on sample data showed an overall expected saving of 50 per cent under the existing supply conditions. In effect stocks which stood at £6.8m in 1986 were reduced to £4.2m in 1989. A reduction of £2.5m financed at 12 per cent is a cash saving of £300,000 per annum, i.e. the system has paid for itself several times over in its first year. Meanwhile, of course, turnover is increasing. Stock turnover nearly doubled in the three years to permit an increasing throughput of health service supplies. Although further reductions in stock are targeted, the prime aim now is a better and more reliable service level to end users, and getting the right balance between service levels and costs for each item.

For most items, the target customer service level, defined as the proportion of demand which on average can be met immediately from stock, will be 97.5 per cent. In the SLIM system a different target can be set for every single item if desired. There is a feedback from better service levels to ward and department transfer points. As users develop confidence that supplies will be delivered when they are wanted, they cease hoarding against shortages. This alone is the source of considerable savings.

Because the system permits the centralization of twelve divisional stores into one, there will in the long run be important savings in staff and other resources.

The system also permits consolidation of orders in particular ways. Many items can be ordered at the same time from one supplier, by scheduling their reviews at the same time. More standing orders can be confidently placed. Suppliers can be given a forecast of future requirements up to many months ahead. Complaints of orders which were promised and then not placed are now a thing of the past. To some suppliers these improvements are worth so much that they will offer a substantial additional discount to any Health Authority which uses the SLIM system.

To the staff themselves, operating this system means improved working conditions. Past purchasing methods and stock replenishment systems left a lot of room for personal interpretation by the stock buyers who had to exercise their judgement and risk errors which could have had serious consequences. Now that this function is automated, they can devote more time to talking to their suppliers and looking for better purchasing deals. Stock buyers did not need much training to use the system — hardly more than one hour. The information which is produced automatically for management is much more comprehensive than the old stock replenishment reports.

In a parallel development, the RHA introduced an automatic data capture system which will become standard at the ward and other local stock points throughout the region. A hand-held computer with a bar-code reading pen attached is used to check the stocks and quantities actually used in requisitions. Nursing staff are rid of the paper-work chores which took up valuable nursing time and the system has helped staff to agree on the stock levels and requisitions needed.

The next step will be to extend the stock control system to ward stocks. The real end users who generate demand are the doctors, surgeons, nursing staff and even patients. While the divisional stores have been treated as the end users, in practice the wards, laboratories, etc., need to be advised on how much stock they ought to hold, how often to order and what the lead times are. When SLIM is extended to ward stocks, a heavy burden will be taken from the nursing staff. The whole system will work better and human error in over- and under-ordering will be minimized. SLIM will then be working as a linked and integrated two-level system.

Finally, the RHA is looking for enhanced profitability. It estimates that the cost of the supplies service, now some 6.7 per cent of stock turnover, can be kept to this level and even reduced with the use of the new system.

Case study 2: Spare parts for maintenance and repair

Alcatel — a French group — is a major force in communications systems and information technology. The Alcatel Business Systems Division accounts for about a quarter of the turnover of the group and its distribution centre in the United Kingdom supplies equipment to more than 110 countries throughout the world; some of this equipment is manufactured in Alcatel's own factories and some by factories outside the group. Whatever the source, the equipment is maintained by a spares and services division.

From the customer's point of view, it is important that when their equipment goes wrong, a service engineer visits them quickly and that he has the necessary spare parts so that repairs can be effected as soon as possible. At the time the project was initiated, Alcatel's central warehouse carried 32,000 unique part numbers in stock valued at over £2.25m. Despite this level of investment, service to service engineers and hence to customers was far from satisfactory. In May 1988, only about 70 per cent of spares requested were available immediately ex-stock.

Slimstock Systems Ltd was invited to install a new system with the aim of significantly improving services to customers without increasing investment. Because of the very large number of parts carried and the expectation that this number would increase, it was required that the majority of parts replenishment orders should be placed automatically and management would only be asked to intervene when something unusual occurred.

The structure of the system supplied closely follows the principles outlined in earlier sections and comprises the following main groups of computer programs:

1. *Start-up* — there are two programs under this heading. The first identifies and determines seasonality profiles, and the second classifies products according to their demand characteristics and sets up forecast and stock control parameter values.
2. *Routine update* — the first of this group of programs updates demand forecasts using seasonal, double exponential smoothing or other techniques as appropriate. The second determines inventory requirements in the light

of the forecast updates and then calculates purchase orders. The third program provides the supplying factories with forecasts of future requirements.

3. *Exception reports* — in addition to the normal range of exception reports, the system includes one which identifies those items whose forecasts are sufficiently inaccurate to call for management intervention.

After a year's experience the features of the system which have impressed the users most are the better control of stocks and purchasing procedures. Every part is looked at each week, and where the computer indicates an unsatisfactory state of affairs for whatever reason, a management review is carried out. Management time is therefore used selectively on only those parts which need attention. Nevertheless, because of the way the system has been designed, a very close level of control can now be exercised over the whole of the inventory.

Because the Alcatel Group has been changing so rapidly in the period reviewed — with the introduction of new products, a wide variety of marketing promotional campaigns, taking on of new dealers and the bringing of other companies into the group — it is difficult to compare like with like. However, comparison of the changes in the two years from May 1988 to May 1990 has shown that the number of unique parts has increased by 25 per cent, part movements per month have increased by 12.5 per cent, customer service level has improved from 70 to 85 per cent and back-orders have been halved. Nevertheless, the average stock level has been reduced by 2 per cent.

In a modern inventory system the user is free to select the customer service level he aims to achieve. Alcatel has taken the opportunity provided by the introduction of the new system to improve the availability of the spare parts to its service engineers (and hence to the customers) in preference to reducing inventories. For many businesses much greater benefit in terms of improved profits is obtained by improving service to customers rather than in reducing stocks and hence bank interest charges.

Conclusion

The last few years have witnessed the maturing of stock control as a practical technology. When OR is applied systematically to any field of endeavour, there must come a time when the theoretical pioneering is over and the practicalities of the situation become the dominant issue. As we have tried to show in this and the preceding chapter, the practical use of inventory theory raises a wealth of issues — some too complex (or too expensive) to be resolved by the application of OR and other formal methods. Rounding up (or down) stock replenishment order quantities to suit pack sizes, etc., is a fine example of how the rough and tumble of everyday life can ride rough-shod over the fine tuning of the OR analyst: to what avail is debate over whether the normal or the gamma distribution is the correct one to use when a calculated order quantity of 160 units is increased to a round 250?

Experience has shown that inventory control packages have almost always to be customized if the needs and characteristics of an individual business are to be properly taken into account. In this respect OR-based 'scientific' inventory control systems differ significantly from the many stock recording computer packages which are on the market. There is a wide gulf between merely supplying information and using it to take decisions automatically. As the second of the case studies above demonstrates, it is possible to make a modern inventory control system over 95 per cent automatic. Building up management confidence to entrust the majority of their decisions to a computer is however, a task that few have so far attempted. On the few occasions when this has been successful, the benefits to the company concerned have been considerable.

References and further reading

Burgin, T.A. (1975) 'The gamma distribution and inventory control', *Operational Research Quarterly*, **26**, 3(i), 507−25.

Croston, J.D. (1972) 'Forecasting and stock control for intermittent demands', *Operational Research Quarterly*, **23**, 2.

Lines, A.H. (1983) *Inventory Control*, Financial Times Business Enterprises, pp. 14−16.

Moroney, M.J. (1958) *Facts from Figures*, Penguin.

Rosenbaum, B.A. (1981) 'Service level relationships in a multi-echelon inventory system', *Management Science*, **27** (8), 926−45.

Silver, E. and R. Peterson (1985) *Decision Systems for Inventory Management and Production Planning*, John Wiley.

Winters, P.R. (1960) 'Forecasting sales by exponentially weighted moving averages', *Management Science*, **6**, 324−42.

– 9 –

Project management

J.B. KIDD

Introduction

Project management has been of importance since the earliest times — most likely since man became a social animal and several persons co-operated for the good of all. More recently we find that analytic and practical tools to aid project managers derive mainly, but not solely, from the Polaris Project of the mid 1950s in the United States. The US Government found it suddenly had to control and schedule thousands of contractors to meet deadlines of research, testing and production. Independently, two groups of consultants created two systems of control: the critical path method (CPM) was proposed by the Du Pont group; and the project evaluation and review technique (PERT) was offered by the consulting group Booz, Allen and Hamilton.

Both methods have been used with considerable success, but too many projects still have escalating times and costs and thus fail to meet their specified goals. Some of these failures are due to lack of use of the appropriate tools, and some to the lack of a project manager. Sometimes blame must rest with the client, as too often projects are badly specified and the specifications are changed midway through.

Managing with networks

We will use a simple example to show how the application of networking can clarify the project management process and how developments following on from the basic method below can lead to the analysis of strategic opportunities.

This example contains only the core activities of a more extensive real project.

A regional motor parts factor (Parts Factoring Company plc: PFC for short)

136

decided to link up several of its local dealer operations directly to the database of parts held centrally by PFC. There were several reasons for this: it was seen to be a strategic move to tie in dealers to PFC by offering better service, and it was to be a pilot operation before opening the service to its national dealer base.

Two software-generated screens which were used for data input in-house had to be redesigned for remote use. To help the dealers further a new enquiry screen was to be designed. This was to let the dealers access the database to check the probable delivery date of a part at an instant when they may have a customer waiting at their own service counter. Naturally, as the database of PFC was to be opened to the 'world', several security barriers had to be programmed: essentially this was to be a remote dial-back system with password control. Each of these changes had to be tested as they were completed. Afterwards, field testing would be undertaken to check if the dealers could understand what may seem 'obvious' to the systems programmers! In parallel a new telephone line had to be ordered for the computer services centre of PFC and this in turn linked to their internal network so that dealers on dialling would get instant access to the database. Finally the microcomputer systems of the dealers would have a communications module added and a small batch program installed so that the link to PFC would be automatic. The users, of course, had to be trained in the use of the newly extended systems capabilities.

This project was assigned to three people: two systems programmers, Nancy and Jane, and one communications specialist, Bob. They were instructed to consider the tasks needed to develop the project network using a microcomputer package and to present their schedule of work to senior management for approval.

The tasks were evaluated by the project team and are displayed in Table 9.1. Some of the tasks have been given rather short names — for instance, 'net' refers to network and 'logon' is the activity of presenting a password to the computer for validation. Similarly, 'Func. traps' describes the programming of the security validation traps against database access by 'hackers' and other unauthorised persons.

The derivation of the detail of the project — the activities, the persons to undertake each task and the durations of each task — were all obtained from internal discussions and through subjective feelings about previous work that each person had completed. While each understood that many more detailed activities had to be undertaken, the tasks as presented were thought to capture the essence of the work. For ease of presentation we have not considered any cost structures though the real project contained both fixed and variable costs assigned to each activity, as may be seen in later figures.

Network diagrams as in Figure 9.1 are very useful since they illustrate accurately the logic of the task flows. The numbers in circles denote 'nodes', the beginnings and ends of tasks. Thus task 8 'test net' takes place between

--- **Table 9.1** ---
Project data

ID[1]	Task	Person[2]	Optimistic duration[3]	Usual duration[4]	Pessimistic duration[5]	Average duration[6,8]	SD[7,8]
1	Screen 1	Nancy	3	6	11	6	1.33
2	Screen 2	Nancy	3	5	10	6	1.17
3	Comms	Bob	3	6	11	6	1.33
4	Eng. Screen	Nancy	2	4	8	4	1.00
5	Test 1, 2, 4	Nancy	5	8	13	8	1.33
6	Order phone	Bob	1	1	3	1	0.33
7	Install net	Bob	1	2	4	2	0.50
8	Test net	Bob	3	5	10	6	1.17
9	Logon change	Jane	2	4	8	4	1.00
10	Func. traps	Jane	5	8	13	8	1.33
11	Test 9, 10	Jane	3	5	10	6	1.17
12	Field test	Nancy	5	8	13	8	1.33
13	Train users	Jane	4	5	12	6	1.33
14	Field installation	Bob	11	15	26	16	2.50

[1] A unique numerical code for each named task.
[2] The resource assigned to each task.
[3] The estimated duration if all goes well.
[4] The estimate of the typical time for the task.
[5] The estimated time if the task goes badly.
[6] The calculated average duration.
[7] The standard deviation of the task average time.
[8] See below for details of the average and SD in PERT.

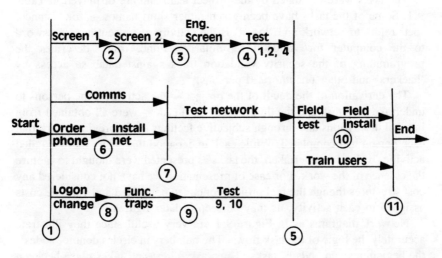

Figure 9.1 'Link-up' — the project network

nodes ⑦ and ⑤. We see here that task 11 (testing logon change and func. traps) cannot occur until Jane has completed two tasks — programming of the logon revisions (task 9) and setting up the traps (task 10). Each member of the project team knows these activities have to occur, but the logic diagram — the network — shows clearly the interactions to someone who may not be familiar with the work to be undertaken. As such it is a powerful management tool, lending itself to the open exchange of models of the real world for discussion by those concerned with a project and those involved in wider issues — for instance, the firm's legal department responsible for the work contracts and for agreeing penalty clauses against time, cost and quality of workmanship.

Derivation of the critical path

The identification of the critical path is one of the major contributions of networking techniques. This is defined as the path linking those tasks on which any delay which occurs will be added to the overall project duration. Conversely, where there is some free time ('slack' or 'float') available on a non-critical task its start may be delayed up to the limit of its free time before it affects the overall project duration.

Calculating the critical path is easy, though we may note a rule of thumb that has existed for a long time which says 'if the network consists of 500 jobs or more then a computer is needed to calculate the critical path; and if one has to undertake resource usage calculations this number falls to 150 tasks.'

Given the availability of microcomputer-based programs it is unlikely that any network needs to be calculated by hand. However, the procedure is as follows. First find the date that the project will begin. Then add the durations of each task in turn, with each commencing at its earliest start time, to find the accumulated time through each chain of tasks. From time to time an adjudication is needed when there are multiple inputs to a node — in this case choose the latest of the incoming times. Continue to the end of the network. Having found the duration for the project, the calculation process is reversed: commencing the calculations at the end of the project, all tasks are assumed to begin at their latest start times and individual task durations are subtracted successively. From time to time in most networks an adjudication is needed when there are multiple tasks exiting a node. Choose the task with the smallest of the latest start times and continue working backwards towards the beginning of the network. We define tasks as being 'critical' whenever their earliest start times are equal to the latest starts: the 'critical path' is the linked set of critical tasks passing right through the network. Other tasks exhibit some 'float' or 'slack', thus their starts may be altered according to resource availability — they are defined as sub-critical.

While the calculation of the critical path and the associated slack times is simple, we should also bear in mind that in practice there may be limited resources to do these tasks, even using a computer. After the time-based calculation we have to rearrange the actual timing of the tasks to cope with the reality of Bob, Jane or Nancy not being able to perform more than one task at the same time. Doing this by hand and eye was found to be a time-consuming task, so computer software for this resource allocation process was developed soon after the original CPM or PERT methods were announced.

In this example, if one schedules the three workers at the earliest opportunity the critical path can be seen to be forty-six days long. Table 9.2 shows the critical tasks, and also introduces the two components into which total float may be divided. 'Free float' is the amount of time the task may be delayed without affecting the start of the following task. 'Dependent float' is float which is shared between two or more tasks. One or the other may be delayed by that amount, but not all. Float usually occurs after the scheduled start time, but sometimes before.

To list the calculated information in this way is impossible and too messy for any real network. Most PC software for network analysis will carry out the computations in the form of a Gantt chart. In this the tasks are displayed as they are scheduled in time and given different shading (or colours) so we can note the two types of float, and for how many days this is available. Most software packages also will allow 'editing' of the schedules as presented in

—— **Table 9.2** ——

Critical tasks — no slack time

Tasks   1, 2, 4, 5, 12 and 14
Usual times   6, 5, 4, 8, 8 and 15 = 46 days' total
              critical path

Free float

Task 11: 6 days after scheduled time
Task 8: 9 days after scheduled time
Task 13: 18 days after scheduled time

Free and dependent float

Task 3: 3 days free and 6 days dependent float —
          all after the scheduled time

Dependent float

Task 6: 6 days before schedule, and 9 days after
Task 9: 6 days after scheduled time
Task 10: 6 days after scheduled time
Task 7: 9 days after scheduled time

the Gantt chart. This facility is very useful as there are limits to the information one can feed into a computer, and a little bending of fixed rules can materially modify the network. This is of use when the network is critically dependent on one resource — for instance, if the schedule has to be calculated on a fixed time-base it may be possible to see where some re-allocation of resources or of durations between activities may allow a particular bottleneck to be overcome.

The weakness of the Gantt chart lies in its failure to portray the logical interlinking of tasks that the network diagram does so well. In practice both forms of output are needed by management — some people in the team may not be familiar with the logical progression of the tasks so will need the network, and all need it to ensure they maintain the correct logic when they wish creatively to alter a tight schedule using the framework of a Gantt chart. What is very important of course is that the drudgery of hand recalculation following a change is minimized by the use of the computer — if it is a desktop system, the results can be ready in a few minutes, even for large networks. At one time recalculating changes were done infrequently (if at all) for hand-derived schedules, and projects analyzed by a central services computer may have had turn-round times measured in days — too long for many projects.

Resolution of uncertainty

Uncertainty within a project may be of two forms: (a) it may be simply that the durations and/or costs are a bit fuzzy, or (b) there may be some doubt as to the structure of the network. Both these conditions have been known for years — and both have been handled in an *ad hoc* fashion. Sometimes this is done by adding a contingency factor. In other situations, especially in maintenance work, the project manager knows of a history of having to undertake extra work packages, X, Y or Z, any of which may be represented as a network, but cannot be incorporated easily into the project, except as explicit add-on networks. In this case one is implying that sub-project X, Y or Z *will* take place, which does not reflect the underlying uncertainty.

Estimating task durations

The designers of PERT allowed for the incorporation of uncertain task durations into the network calculations. They argued that if tasks were repeated, a distribution of durations would be seen to be somewhat like Figure 9.2.

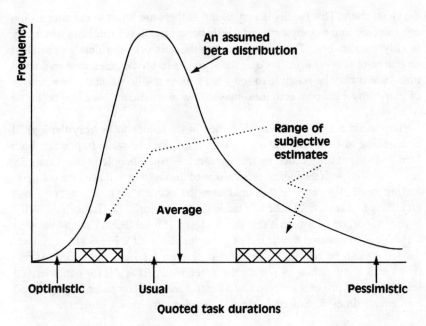

Figure 9.2   Duration of estimates

Following logical and theoretical arguments, they said the durations could not be less than zero, the distribution would exhibit a single mode (the most frequently seen time) and the distribution would have a distinctly long tail, since many aspects of any job have a likelihood of being difficult to complete and so delay the overall completion time. These requirements would best be met by a mathematical form known as the beta distribution. Since that time there have been many arguments for or against the use of the beta distribution; but its statistical formulation is embedded in PERT calculations as a *de facto* standard.

To use this feature of PERT fully one has to obtain three time estimates for each task. The 'optimistic' time (opt) reflecting the shortest duration when everything goes well, the 'pessimistic' duration (pes) when all does not go well and the 'usual' time (us) indicating how one would expect the time to be in normal circumstances. The opt, pes and us times are shown in Table 9.1 and along the horizontal axis of Figure 9.2. Given these raw estimates, PERT calculates two parameters for each task — the average time and the variance (var):

$$\text{Average} = \frac{(\text{opt} + 4 \times \text{us} + \text{pes})}{6}$$

$$\text{Var} \quad = \frac{(\text{pes} - \text{opt})^2}{6}$$

and we should note: standard deviation = $\sqrt{\text{variance}}$.

These parameters are used within the PERT system as follows: first the critical path is calculated as in CPM, but using the derived average times, not the usual times, and the total of the average times is calculated. The sum of the variances of the tasks on the critical path gives the variance of the overall project duration. As can be seen in Figure 9.2, and from the data, the calculated average durations will be greater than the usual times since the effect of the pessimistic times will 'drag' the averages to the right.

Statistical theory says (roughly) that provided there are a large number of tasks in a project and their actual durations are not 'correlated' (i.e. affected in the same direction by weather or other common influences), we can assume the following: the total project duration will follow a normal distribution with a mean equal to the sum of the task average times and variance equal to the sum of the individual task variances. In this case we can calculate the overall project standard deviation (the square root of the variance) as 4 days. Assuming a normal distribution therefore, 68 per cent of project durations will be within one standard deviation (± 4 days) of the average. We would also expect 97.7 per cent of durations to have occurred on average by $+8$ days, and almost all durations (99.9 per cent) to be less than $+12$ days above the average time. From this knowledge we can assess the probability of having to pay penalty clauses, and management can address issues such as 'what is the chance of exceeding 52 days for this project?'

The answer for our example is 16 per cent, and it is calculated as follows, using the table in Appendix 1. The critical path using the 'usual' times is 46 days, but when we take into account the uncertainties, its average time is 48 days. As the SD = ± 4 days, the probability of completion by day 52 (i.e. mean + 1SD) is 84 per cent. The risk area is the remaining part of the distribution up to 100 per cent, that is 16 per cent. Whether this is important to the management depends on many factors, not least the size of the penalty.

There are two underlying problems. The first is that the theory supporting PERT demands that the estimates of the optimistic and the pessimistic durations are at the 1 per cent and 99 per cent points of the distribution. In only one case in a hundred should the real duration exceed the quoted figures; but we are very limited in our ability to imagine rare events and so tend to under-estimate their occurrence. Conversely, the estimate of the usual time is reasonably accurate — because we have more experience of the usual! Research on subjective estimating has shown that our conservatism leads to estimates too close to the usual time, roughly as given in Table 9.3.

The quoted subjective estimates support the PERT method of calculating the average duration, since the ratio of usual to pessimistic, and usual to

------ **Table 9.3** ------

Duration	PERT theory	Subjective research
Usual	50 pt1[1]	50 pt1
Optimistic	1 pt1	25–45 pt1
Pessimistic	99 pt1	65–75 pt1

[1] pt1 = one-hundredth of the distribution range or 'percentile'

optimistic is similar in both theory and practice. However, the calculation of the variance by the PERT method is a gross underestimate since the quoted range (optimistic to pessimistic) is too narrow. We have illustrated these ranges of subjective estimates in Figure 9.2.

The second problem also lies within the computer programs that calculate the aggregate PERT results. As we saw above, the standard deviation of the overall project was derived as the square root of the sum of the variances of tasks along the critical path. This is correct, but the PERT method totally ignores all sub-critical paths. By chance one or more of the other sub-critical paths may have a longer duration than expected which may cause that path sequence to become the critical path. A calculation of 'what is the chance of exceeding 52 days?' would have to take into account the combination of all sub-critical paths and their probability of affecting this question. Thus, when we multiply probabilities

$$P \text{ (path A)} \times P \text{ (path B)} \times P \text{ (path C)} \ldots$$

we lower the overall probability of success. Consider the lower path of the network in Figure 9.1: its average duration is 44 days and its standard deviation is 3.5 days. We are interested in the chance of completing the project in 52 days or less. Fifty-two is average $+ (52 - 44)/3.5 = 2.3$ standard deviations. From the table in Appendix 1 we see that this chance is about 99 per cent, which may be combined with the probability of the earlier path as follows:

$$P \text{ } (\leq 52 \text{ days}) = 0.84 \times 0.99 = 0.83$$

This shows the overall risk has risen to 17 per cent through considering these two paths. The other paths in the network do not have large variances nor long total durations relative to the critical path so are not likely to affect the overall risk greatly. We have made an estimate in Table 9.4.

Handling structural uncertainty

Two forms of structural uncertainty may be envisaged; the first we mentioned above when there is some probability of having to add X, Y or Z sub-projects.

—— **Table 9.4** ——

Network type	Chance of paying-out penalty after 52 days working
CPM	None: finish in 46 days
PERT (critical path)	16%: finish in 48 days (average)
PERT (all paths)	20%: finish in 48 days (average)

This aspect may be resolved using the GERT (graphical evaluation and review technique) software. The reader is referred to an early paper by Samli and Belas (1971) in which they consider the workings of a market research agency.

The second form of structural uncertainty occurs when the completion of tasks or sub-projects has to be evaluated according to criteria other than time alone (for instance in evaluating competing R&D projects). This difficulty may be addressed by the venture evaluation and review technique (VERT, from Venture Analytic Associates, Bettendorf, IA, United States). In some ways this is similar to GERT, being based on simulation methods, though it is likely to be of more general use in strategy analysis. These points are fully discussed in Lee *et al.* (1982). For instance, we could allow in our example network for each task to carry three types of uncertainty — time, cost and technical performance — which is typical of the real world. And within the simulation numerical values for each uncertainty parameter may be assigned by one of the following:

1. One of fifteen standard statistical distributions embedded in the VERT program.
2. A histogram of observed performance.
3. A mathematical relationship of the time or cost or performance which may be derived for any activity, or which may be carried onward from (or be dependent on) earlier tasks or nodes.

The output from the simulation runs is a set of graphs showing appropriate aggregate distributions. From these we can look at the probability of achieving targets, or we may note the chance of having a 'successful' project given the data and the constraints.

To obtain VERT outputs we introduced two small but significant changes to the example data given in Table 9.1. We carried out a first VERT simulation run in which each test task (i.e. tasks 5, 8, 11 and 12 of Table 9.1) has a failure chance of 10 per cent. If at any stage in the project one of the tests fails, then so does the whole project. This prompts a further question for the management — the likelihood of the project's failing. We then carried out a second run in which we extended the ranges of the optimistic and pessimistic estimates to compensate for the conservatism noted above. Figure 9.3, which is from this second run, shows the distribution of times that is to be expected of the

Network time distributions for node 11

Cumulative frequency distribution

0.1	0.2	0.3	0.4	0.5	0.6	0.7	0.8	0.9	1.0	

```
41.1529 ┌──────────────────────────────────────────────────────────────┐ Min.
        │                                                              │ 0.000
41.1529 │                                                              │
        │                                                              │ 0.009
42.6439 │                                                              │
        │ *                                                            │ 0.025
44.1349 │                                                              │
        │ ***                                                          │ 0.054
45.6259 │                                                              │
        │ ****                                                         │ 0.085
47.1169 │                                                              │
        │ *******                                                      │ 0.143
48.6079 │                                                              │
        │ **********                                                   │ 0.207
50.0989 │                                                              │
        │ **************                                               │ 0.278
51.5899 │                                                              │
        │ ******************                                           │ 0.370
53.0809 │                                                              │
        │ ***********************                                      │ 0.474
54.5719 │                                                              │
        │ ***************************                                  │ 0.562
56.0629 │                                                              │
        │ ********************************                             │ 0.660
57.5539 │                                                              │
        │ ************************************                         │ 0.739
59.0449 │                                                              │
        │ ****************************************                     │ 0.811
60.5359 │                                                              │
        │ *******************************************                  │ 0.857
62.0269 │                                                              │
        │ ***********************************************              │ 0.911
63.5179 │                                                              │
        │ *************************************************            │ 0.937
65.0089 │                                                              │
        │ ***************************************************          │ 0.962
66.4999 │                                                              │
        │ *****************************************************        │ 0.976
67.9909 │                                                              │
        │ *****************************************************        │ 0.988
69.4819 │                                                              │
        │ ******************************************************       │ 0.996
70.9730 │                                                              │
        │ ******************************************************       │ 0.996
72.4640 │                                                              │
        │ *******************************************************      │ 1.000
73.9550 │                                                              │
        │ *******************************************************      │ 1.000
73.9550 └──────────────────────────────────────────────────────────────┘ Max.
```

No. observations: 762   STD error: 6.0016   Kurtosis (beta 2): 2.77   Median: 54.9212
Coefficient of variation: 0.11   Mean: 55.2546   Pearsonian skew: 0.26   Mode: 53.7199

Frequency distribution

	0.05	0.10	0.15	0.20	0.25	
41.1529						Min.
						0.000
41.1529						
						0.009
42.6439						
*						0.016
44.1349						
**						0.029
45.6259						
***						0.031
47.1169						
*****						0.058
48.6079						
******						0.064
50.0989						
*******						0.071
51.5899						
*********						0.092
53.0809						
**********						0.104
54.5719						
********						0.088
56.0629						
*********						0.098
57.5539						
*******						0.079
59.0449						
*******						0.072
60.5359						
****						0.046
62.0269						
*****						0.054
63.5179						
**						0.026
65.0089						
**						0.025
66.4999						
*						0.014
67.9909						
*						0.012
69.4819						
						0.008
70.9730						
						0.000
72.4640						
						0.004
73.9550						
						0.000
73.9550						Max.

Figure 9.3 An example VERT graph of time distribution

end node (11). It shows both the cumulative frequency distribution and the probability distribution. As an aside, it has been noted by Kidd (1990) that the calculated duration of the network duration using PERT underestimates the real outcome time, whereas simulation methods like VERT give more accurate results.

Given the PERT-type data of run 1 of the simulation we see from Table 9.5 that the average time of the overall project duration has risen slightly to 48.5 days. However, using changed values for the optimistic and pessimistic estimates in run 2 the total project time increases to 55.3 days. The standard deviations of these durations were found to be 3.7 days and 6.0 days respectively.

It can be estimated by interpolation in the graphical output of Figure 9.3 that the probability of meeting the 52 days' target is only 40 per cent — quite a serious management issue; but of greater interest perhaps is the overall project success rate of 67.3 per cent which is obtained elsewhere in the VERT outputs. This is due to the cumulative effects of the individual failure rates of test activities 5, 8, 11 and 12 of Table 9.1, each of 10 per cent.

Management now has two interesting sets of statistics. Firstly, the fact that a project that at one stage looked to have no problems (critical path of 46 days, target time 52 days) now has an average time of 55.3 days and a chance of only 40 per cent of being finished before the 52 day target. Secondly, *above all*, the project has only a 67.3 per cent chance of ever reaching the final node if all the vital tests are to be passed.

Conclusion

The modelling techniques in VERT allow powerful analyses to be commissioned at the beginning of planning so that a good evaluation of the

—— Table 9.5 ——

VERT run 1		VERT run 2	
Duration (days)	Probability (%)	Duration (days)	Probability (%)
48.5	50.0	55.3	50.0
52.9	90.0	62.0	90.0
58.6	99.5	70.6	99.5
64.0	100.0	73.0	100.0

potential issues can be made well before the project itself is begun. Later, but prior to the project start, the network outline that provided the basis for the VERT analysis can be studied more finely using a standard network management package with the inclusion of resource demands so that the detail of task, cost and person scheduling can take place.

Using a network is far better than running the project from the back of an envelope without due consideration of task sequences or resource availability. We should accept also that a professional project manager can act as the focal point for the client and contractor alike and so smooth the way to a successful completion.

Finally, we should note that when the VERT analysis of issues is transposed to a CPM package it is easy to obtain schedules of resource and task timings from a PC. The PC is an ideal tool for instant rescheduling of tasks, whereas the minicomputer is better for the heavy number crunching required in the VERT simulations of all the 'what if' questions arising in the strategic analysis.

Figure 9.4 gives a comparison of the three methodologies. However, using VERT it is not possible to draw a line on the graph since the techniques are appropriate for calculating end points only — but end points which can show time and cost variation simultaneously. Figure 9.4 is also a graphic example

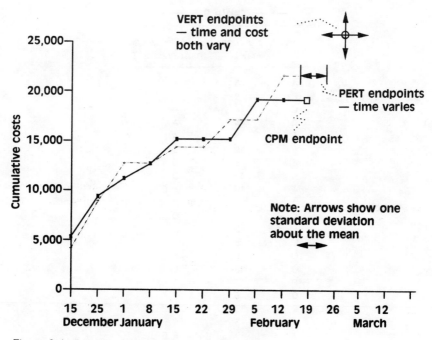

Figure 9.4 A comparison of three methodologies

of the following management dilemma: if we use CPM we will obtain results that suggest times and costs that are less than those obtained from PERT, and these in turn are less than the VERT results. But the derivation of the VERT-type results requires a greater time and resource application at the commencement of the project when there are pressures to 'get going — do something'. We suggest reflection and research will offer useful payoffs at this stage, and allow the analysis of the strategic issues.

—— Exercises ——

1. Compile a Gantt chart to illustrate the work schedules of the three persons involved on the project shown in Figure 9.1. In other words, a resource usage versus time graph. You will have to use the data of Table 9.1 and the calculations of earliest and latest start times of the activities are described on pages 139–41. You can check your results against the float figures shown in Table 9.2. (No answer is therefore given to this queston.)

2. Table 9.6 gives details of 20 activities which comprise a project where some must be completed before others can start.

—— Table 9.6 ——

Activity	Duration (days)	Activities which must precede it
A	5	—
B	9	—
C	4	—
D	4	A
E	3	A
F	10	B
G	6	D
H	12	D
I	10	F, G
J	3	C
K	4	C
L	5	J
M	5	J
N	8	K, L
O	18	M, N
P	3	H, I, O
Q	6	P
R	13	P
S	5	Q
T	7	R, S

(a) Draw a network diagram for this project.
(b) Calculate the critical path and explain its significance. What is the minimum completion time for the whole project?
(c) Calculate the earliest and latest start time for activity M.
(d) If time on activity F were cut to 6 days, how much sooner would the project be finished?
(e) If time on job K were lengthened to 9 days, by how much would the whole project be delayed?

3. Consider the data in Table 9.7 relating to a certain project.

(a) Construct the activity network for this situation.
(b) Calculate the critical path using the usual time estimates. Calculate earliest and latest start and finish times for each activity. How much float is there on non-critical activities?
(c) How confident would you be that the whole project would be completed in 15 days?

4. A jobbing contractor wins a contract to build concurrently five petrol stations along a motorway. He has to complete all five in 35 days. Each project has the characteristics in Table 9.8. (Assume no common resource constraints.)

(a) Could he complete a single project in 35 days?
(b) What are his chances of completing all five projects on time? (Hint: If p is the probability of success in a certain experiment, and if the experiment is repeated n times, then the (joint) probability of success in all n experiments is p^n.)
(c) What would be the effect of his losing control over these projects as indicated by (i) an increase in the mean job times; (ii) an increae in the variance of job times?

——— Table 9.7 ———

Activity	Immediate precedent(s)	Estimates of activity time (days): Optimistic	Usual	Pessimistic
A	—	0.7	1.0	1.3
B	A	3.8	5.6	9.8
C	A	5.2	7.6	12.4
D	B	2.1	2.7	5.1
E	B	2.0	6.8	12.8
F	C, D	0.7	3.4	3.7
G	E, F	0.7	1.0	1.3

—— Table 9.8 ——

Activity description	Activity name	Immediate precedents	Mean time (days)	Variance (days²)
Open up site	A	—	3	1
Civ. eng. work	B	A	15	3
Mech. eng. work	C	A	10	2
Mech. eng. work (in detail)	D	C	4	1
Instrumentation	E	D	4	1
Lay electrical circuits	F	C	4	1
Finish civ. eng. work	G	B, F	5	1
Run-up, check, close site	H	E, G	7	1

References

Kidd, J.B. (1990) 'A comparison between the VERT program and other methods of project duration estimation', *Omega*, **15** (2), 129–34.

Lee, S.M., G.L. Moeller and L.A. Digman (1982) *Network Analysis for Management Decisions*, Kluwer-Nijhoff.

Levine, H.A. (1986) *Project Management Using Micro-computers*, Osborne McGraw-Hill.

Meredith, J.R. and S.J. Manatel Jr (1989) *Project Management: A managerial approach*, John Wiley.

Samli, C.A. and C. Belas (1971) 'The use of GERT in planning and control of market research', *Journal of Market Research*, **8**, 335–9.

– 10 –

Queueing Theory

S.C. LITTLECHILD

Introduction

Everyone has stood in queues at banks, barber shops and bus stops and no doubt agrees that queueing is a nuisance. But how can a theory of queues be developed, and how is it likely to help a manager? A theory is possible because there are usually certain regularities about arrivals and service of customers; these regularities can be described by statistical distributions and the resulting performance of the system can to some extent be deduced by mathematical analysis. Queueing theory is useful because it embraces a much wider range of phenomena than the ones just quoted. It encompasses queues of machines or paper, not just persons, and it extends to the study of delay, whether or not a physical queue is observed. Queueing theory is therefore concerned with problems such as congestion in telephone systems, airports and harbours; machines out of action waiting for repair; stockouts in inventory systems; the design of appointments systems and production schedules, and so on.

Why does delay occur in these systems? Essentially because it is not possible or worth while exactly to tailor the supply of the required commodity to the demand for it. This may be because the timing of the demand is uncertain (for instance, one does not know exactly how many customers will arrive at any time of day) or because service can only be provided in 'lumps' (for example, one or two or three cashiers) or because peak demands last for a relatively short time and it is not worth providing extra capacity for them (in telephone systems or at airports).

Delay can be expensive. People standing in queues are precluded from doing more useful work; idle machines are not producing; aircraft circling over airports are burning up fuel; work in progress may be expensive to store; production held up may mean penalty payments or the loss of an order, etc. On the other hand it can be expensive to avoid delay: repairmen must be paid, airport and production capacity costs money. The problem for the managers of these various systems is thus to design the system in such a way that the total costs are minimized (or the total benefits maximized). Costs of providing better service must be weighed against the costs of *not* providing it.

In many cases, an adequate system can be determined by trial and error. For example, a bank manager will soon get to know the usual daily pattern and variation of customers and will work out in his head how many cashiers are appropriate. By contrast, other situations require large and irreversible investments where experimentation would be prohibitively expensive. One cannot design airports, roads and harbours by trial and error; once they have been built to a particular design, one has to live with that decision for many years.

In a wide variety of circumstances, queueing theory may be used to predict how different systems will operate. More precisely, it provides explicit expressions relating the design of the system to the length and frequency of queues, the average waiting time, the probability of no delay at all, etc. By the design of the system is meant the rate of arrival of 'customers', the number and speed of the 'servers' and the arrangements relating customers to servers. For example, simple formulae can be provided to predict how the average time spent queueing at a supermarket would vary with the number of checkout counters operated.

Queueing theory is useful only in a limited number of situations, but in those situations it is used quite intensively. In the early part of this century, pioneering studies were made in telephone engineering by the Danish engineer Erlang (whose name has subsequently been adopted as the standard unit of telephone traffic intensity), and queueing theory still lies at the core of this profession. One reason for this continued use lies in the application of computers to telecommunications. Kleinrock (1976, in Volume II) describes a very large number of applications of queueing theory to computers, satellites and other communications networks, including packet-switching.

Another early classic was the evaluation of standards of service at bridge and tunnel toll booths in New York (Edie, 1954). Queueing theory has also been used to study the maximum sorting capacity of a single clerk at airline ticket counters, where there was a danger that the whole passenger check-in area would have to be redesigned (Lee, 1966). It was used to calculate the capacity of London Heathrow Airport in terms of numbers of landings and takeoffs (Civil Aviation Authority, 1988), and is used regularly to calculate the staffing of Post Office counters (Monopolies and Mergers Commission, 1988).

Unfortunately, queueing theory can handle only relatively simple situations. Complex situations involving networks of queues (as in many production scheduling systems) or involving frequent human intervention based on the state of the system (for example, the provision of an emergency cashier for half an hour or the switching of men from one task to another or the adjustment of customer arrivals) are beyond the scope of queueing theory (at least, beyond present mathematical results). In these situations one often has recourse to simulation, as described in Chaper 12.

The difference between simulation and queueing theory is that the former involves the repeated trial of a particular system, under different patterns of customer arrivals or service performance, until one has built up an adequate picture of how the system behaves. Queueing theory gives an explicit picture, generally in the form of a mathematical function or graph, relating behaviour to certain system parameters. In this case, one may see immediately how the system would respond to changes in these parameters, whereas with simulation one would have to repeat a whole exercise. Simulation allows one to test ideas for different system designs but does not, of itself, lead to a 'best' design. Queueing theory thus has a distinct advantage in the limited number of situations where it can be applied, but simulation is a more flexible technique.

Elements of a queueing system

As remarked earlier, the main elements of a queueing system are the *arrival pattern* of the *customers*, the *queue discipline* for customers who cannot be served immediately, and the *service mechanism* itself. We shall briefly examine each of these elements in turn. It should be borne in mind that 'customers' and 'servers' are not necessarily people.

Arrival of customers

The arrival pattern may be known, or *deterministic*, as with an appointments system, or it may be uncertain, or *random*, as in a grocery shop. Even with appointments systems the customers are seldom exactly on time, so that actual arrival patterns are unknown. It is generally convenient to describe such arrival patterns by means of *probability distributions* (discussed in more detail in the next section). Customers may arrive singly or in bulk. The arrival date may be independent of the state of the system, or it may depend upon it — for example, customers may not enter the barber shop if there are several people already waiting (this is called *balking*); the rate at which machines break down will depend upon the rate at which broken machines are mended. Arrival rate may be constant or may vary over time, with peaks and troughs. Customers may be identical or different in relevant respects.

Queue discipline

The simplest situation is where the arriving customer joins a single queue until it is his turn to be served. Service may be on a *first-in, first-out* (FIFO) basis, or on a *last-in, first-out* (LIFO) basis (as often with goods drawn from stock), or even on a *random* basis. Servers may discriminate between different classes of customers (urgent hospital cases, or familiar restaurant patrons, or first-class passengers at airports). Instead of one queue there may be several, as at some Post Offices. In this case customers may jump from one queue to another (*jockey*) or they may be constrained to stay in the same queue. There may be *limits on queue size* (for example, because the telephone switchboard cannot record more than a specified number of callers, as described in the next chapter). Some customers may leave the system (or *renege*) if they are not served within a certain period of time. Increasingly in Post Offices (Monopolies and Mergers Commission, 1988) and banks a single queue is served by a number of counter positions working in parallel.

Service mechanism

There may be one or more servers; in the latter case they may be identical or they may differ with regard to the speed at which they work or the type of customers which they handle. The speed of working may be constant or it may vary around a given average rate. Again, it is convenient to use probability distributions to describe the service pattern. The number of servers and the average service rate may depend upon the time of day, or upon the number of customers who have already been served, or upon the number which remain to be served. Different servers may be alternatives for the customer (i.e. they work in *parallel*) or he may have to go through all of them (i.e. they work in *series*). For example, the sequence of operations in joining and trueing a wheel rim, adding, tightening and testing spokes and hub, etc., comprises quite a complex system of interrelated queues in series, where arrival rates at one queue depend upon service rates at another.

Thus, in describing a queueing situation one must specify every detail of the above three elements. Systems which appear to be identical may differ in some apparently small detail which may have significant implications for the way in which the two systems behave. On the other hand, two situations which appear to bear no relation to each other, such as the sorting of airline tickets and the serving of Post Office customers, may well be formally represented by exactly the same model.

Description of a simple queueing system

Consider the following simple example. Customers arrive at a self-service grocery shop at an average rate of twenty-four per hour. There is only one assistant. The time that is taken for the assistant to total up the bill and make change varies with the size of purchase, but the average time is two minutes. Are queues of customers likely to be the exception or the rule? What is the average number of customers waiting to pay? What is the average time spent waiting to pay?

This is one of the simplest kinds of problem that queueing theory can handle. The answers can be obtained from formulae in a matter of seconds, but before we give the answers the reader might like to hazard guesses of his own in order to test his intuition.

It seems reasonable to assume that the system in this example involves a single queue operating on a first-come first-served basis, with no limits on the size of queue, and no balking, reneging or jockeying.

We need to specify a little more closely the arrival and service patterns. Although the average arrival rate is twenty-four per hour (or 0.4 per minute) this does not mean that one customer arrives every 150 seconds. Five customers may arrive in one five-minute period then ten minutes may elapse before another customer arrives. In principle it is possible to measure how often 0, 1, 2, 3, ... customers arrive in each interval of, say one minute. In this way one could build up a *frequency distribution*, and measure the *mean* (or *average*) arrival rate and the *variance* or *standard deviation* of the arrival rate.

Let us suppose that customers arrive completely at random, so that (given the average arrival rate) the probability of a customer arriving in any short interval of time, T, depends *only* upon the length of that interval, and *not* upon the time of day or upon the number of customers who have already arrived. In this case it may be shown mathematically that the number of arrivals in any time interval of length T is given by the *Poisson probability distribution:*

$$P\{n \text{ arrivals in time } T\} = \frac{(\lambda T)^n e^{-\lambda T}}{n!} \quad \text{for} \quad n = 0,1,2, \ldots$$

where λ denotes the average arrival rate in time T. In our example, setting $T=1$ minute and $\lambda=0.4$ yields

$$P\{n \text{ arrivals in any minute}\} = \frac{0.4^n e^{-0.4}}{n!} \quad \text{for} \quad n = 0,1,2, \ldots$$

These probabilities have been calculated and expressed in tables such as Table 10.1. This shows that, in any given minute, the chances of 0, 1, 2 or 3 customers

—— **Table 10.1** ——
Poisson probabilities: a table of $e^{-\lambda} \lambda^n/n!$

λ	n = 0	1	2	3	4	5	6	7	8	9	10	11	12
0.1	0.9048	0.0905	0.0045	0.0002	0.0000								
0.2	0.8187	0.1637	0.0164	0.0011	0.0001	0.0000							
0.3	0.7408	0.2222	0.0333	0.0333	0.0002	0.0000							
0.4	0.6703	0.2681	0.0536	0.0072	0.0007	0.0001	0.0000						
0.5	0.6065	0.3033	0.0758	0.0126	0.0016	0.0002	0.0000						
0.6	0.5488	0.3293	0.0988	0.0198	0.0030	0.0004	0.0000						
0.7	0.4966	0.3476	0.1217	0.0284	0.0050	0.0007	0.0001	0.0000					
0.8	0.4493	0.3595	0.1438	0.0383	0.0077	0.0012	0.0002	0.0000					
0.9	0.4066	0.3659	0.1647	0.0494	0.0111	0.0020	0.0003	0.0000					
1.0	0.3679	0.3679	0.1839	0.0613	0.0153	0.0031	0.0005	0.0001	0.0000				
1.1	0.3329	0.3662	0.2014	0.0738	0.0203	0.0045	0.0008	0.0001	0.0000				
1.2	0.3012	0.3614	0.2169	0.0867	0.0260	0.0062	0.0012	0.0002	0.0000				
1.3	0.2725	0.3543	0.2303	0.0998	0.0324	0.0084	0.0018	0.0003	0.0001	0.0000			
1.4	0.2466	0.3452	0.2417	0.1128	0.0395	0.0111	0.0026	0.0005	0.0001	0.0000			
1.5	0.2231	0.3347	0.2510	0.1255	0.0471	0.0141	0.0035	0.0008	0.0001	0.0000			
1.6	0.2019	0.3230	0.2584	0.1378	0.0551	0.0176	0.0047	0.0011	0.0002	0.0000			
1.7	0.1827	0.3106	0.2640	0.1496	0.0636	0.0216	0.0061	0.0015	0.0003	0.0001	0.0000		
1.8	0.1653	0.2975	0.2678	0.1607	0.0723	0.0260	0.0078	0.0020	0.0005	0.0001	0.0000		
1.9	0.1496	0.2842	0.2700	0.1710	0.0812	0.0309	0.0098	0.0027	0.0006	0.0001	0.0000		
2.0	0.1353	0.2707	0.2707	0.1804	0.0902	0.0361	0.0120	0.0034	0.0009	0.0002	0.0000		
2.2	0.1108	0.2438	0.2681	0.1966	0.1082	0.0476	0.0174	0.0055	0.0015	0.0004	0.0001	0.0000	
2.4	0.0907	0.2177	0.2613	0.2090	0.1254	0.0602	0.0241	0.0083	0.0025	0.0007	0.0002	0.0000	
2.6	0.0743	0.1931	0.2510	0.2176	0.1414	0.0735	0.0319	0.0118	0.0038	0.0011	0.0003	0.0001	0.0000
2.8	0.0608	0.1703	0.2384	0.2225	0.1557	0.0872	0.0407	0.0163	0.0057	0.0018	0.0005	0.0001	0.0000
3.0	0.0498	0.1494	0.2240	0.2240	0.1680	0.1008	0.0504	0.0216	0.0081	0.0027	0.0008	0.0002	0.0001
3.2	0.0408	0.1304	0.2087	0.2226	0.1781	0.1140	0.0608	0.0278	0.0111	0.0040	0.0013	0.0004	0.0001
3.4	0.0334	0.1135	0.1929	0.2186	0.1858	0.1264	0.0716	0.0348	0.0148	0.0056	0.0019	0.0006	0.0002
3.6	0.0273	0.0984	0.1771	0.2125	0.1912	0.1377	0.0826	0.0425	0.0191	0.0076	0.0028	0.0009	0.0003
3.8	0.0224	0.0850	0.1617	0.2046	0.1944	0.1477	0.0936	0.0508	0.0241	0.0102	0.0039	0.0013	0.0004
4.0	0.0183	0.0733	0.1465	0.1954	0.1954	0.1563	0.1042	0.0595	0.0298	0.0132	0.0053	0.0019	0.0006
5.0	0.0067	0.0337	0.0842	0.1404	0.1755	0.1755	0.1462	0.1044	0.0653	0.0363	0.0181	0.0082	0.0034
6.0	0.0025	0.0149	0.0446	0.0892	0.1339	0.1606	0.1606	0.1377	0.1033	0.0688	0.0413	0.0225	0.0113
7.0	0.0009	0.0064	0.0223	0.0521	0.0912	0.1277	0.1490	0.1490	0.1304	0.1014	0.0710	0.0452	0.0264
8.0	0.0003	0.0027	0.0107	0.0286	0.0573	0.0916	0.1221	0.1396	0.1396	0.1241	0.0993	0.0722	0.0481
9.0	0.0001	0.0011	0.0050	0.0150	0.0337	0.0607	0.0911	0.1171	0.1318	0.1318	0.1186	0.0970	0.0728
10.0	0.0000	0.0005	0.0023	0.0076	0.0189	0.0378	0.0631	0.0901	0.1126	0.1251	0.1251	0.1137	0.0948

arriving are 67, 27, 5 and 1 per cent, respectively. The chances of 4 or more customers arriving in any minute are negligible.

If customers arrive according to a Poisson distribution with mean λ (per minute), it may be shown mathematically that the probability distribution of time intervals *between* successive arrivals is described by the *negative exponential distribution:*

$$f(t) = \lambda e^{-\lambda t}$$

which has both mean and standard deviation equal to $1/\lambda$ (minutes). In our example, the mean inter-arrival time is $1/0.4 = 2.5$ minutes. From this function one may calculate by integration the probability of, say, more than five minutes elapsing between the arrival of successive customers or the probability of two customers arriving within ten seconds of each other, etc.

Are these distributions likely to characterize the arrival behaviour of the customers in the grocery shop? There are reasons to believe that arrivals would not be completely at random: there are likely to be more customers at lunchtime or coffee break, and fewer customers when it rains, and people may come shopping with their friends, and so on. Nevertheless, it is remarkable that, in practice, these two theoretical probability distributions of arrivals (which are, in fact, two aspects of one distribution) *do* provide very good approximations to actual behaviour.

It also happens that exactly the same probability distributions can be used to characterize the service mechanism. In other words, it is often reasonable to describe the service time by a negative exponential distribution with mean $1/\mu$ (minutes) where $1/\mu$ is the average time to serve a customer (in minutes). Equivalently, one might describe the number of customers capable of being served (in one minute) by a Poisson distribution with mean μ. In our example, average service time is $1/\mu = 2$ minutes so the average number of customers capable of being served in a minute is $\mu = 0.5$.

An additional property of the negative exponential distribution is that the probability of a customer arriving at any time is independent of the time already elapsed since the previous arrival. Similarly, a service which has already taken three minutes is no more likely to be completed in the next five seconds than one which has taken only one minute.

The symbols λ and μ are used throughout queueing theory, as is the symbol ρ, meaning *traffic intensity*, defined by

$$\rho = \frac{\lambda}{\mu} = \frac{\text{average arrival rate}}{\text{average service rate}}$$

Here $\rho = 0.4/0.5 = 0.8$. One important condition of the model we shall describe is that the traffic intensity ρ be less than one; equivalently, the average arrival rate should be less than the average service rate (as in the present example). If this were not the case, queues of ever-increasing length would build up.

Results

The queues in a shop one minute after it opened would not present a fair picture of the day's operations because there would be insufficient time for any queue to build up. The following results describe the performance of a system once it has settled down into so-called *steady state*. (It is not entirely clear how long this takes in practice: one theoretical study has suggested that half a day would be necessary.)

Recall that the situation consists of a single server and a single queue with first-in, first-out queue discipline, Poisson or negative exponential arrival and service distributions with average arrival rate λ and average service rate μ (per unit time).

The probability of n customers in the system (i.e. being served or in the queue) is denoted P_n. In the present situation, this is given by

$$P_n = \left(1 - \frac{\lambda}{\mu}\right)\left(\frac{\lambda}{\mu}\right)^n = (1 - \rho)\rho^n \quad \text{for} \quad n = 0,1,2, \ldots \quad (10.1)$$

Since there is only one server, one person at most is being served at any time; any other customers in the system must be in the queue. As might be expected, the probabilities of all possible states of the system sum to unity ($\Sigma_{n=0}^{\infty} P_n = 1$), since $\Sigma_{n=0}^{\infty}\rho^n = 1/(1 - \rho)$ for $\rho < 1$. It is easily shown by induction that the probability of N or more customers in the system is

$$\sum_{n=N}^{\infty} P_n = \left(\frac{\lambda}{\mu}\right)^N = \rho^N \quad (10.2)$$

A customer has to wait for service whenever a queue exists, which is whenever there are one or more customers already in the system. The probability of this is one minus the probability of there being no one in the system, hence

$$\text{probability of a queue} = 1 - P_0 = \frac{\lambda}{\mu} = \rho \quad (10.3)$$

The following results are quite easily obtained. Average number of customers in the system:

$$\frac{\lambda}{\mu - \lambda} \quad \text{or} \quad \frac{\rho}{1 - \rho} \quad (10.4)$$

Average number of customers in the queue:

$$\frac{\lambda^2}{\mu(\mu - \lambda)} \quad \text{or} \quad \frac{\rho^2}{1 - \rho} \quad (10.5)$$

Average time a customer spends in the system:

$$\frac{1}{\mu - \lambda} \quad \text{or} \quad \frac{1}{1 - \rho} \times \frac{1}{\mu} \quad (10.6)$$

Average time a customer spends in the queue:

$$\frac{\lambda}{\mu(\mu - \lambda)} \quad \text{or} \quad \frac{\rho}{1 - \rho} \times \frac{1}{\mu} \quad (10.7)$$

The last two expressions are in the same units of time as the arrival and service rates. Various other results are also available for this system.

We may now answer the questions posed at the beginning of the last section for the shop with $\lambda = 0.4$ and $\mu = 0.5$. The probability of a customer having to wait for service (i.e. having to queue) is $\rho = 0.8$, so that queues will be observed about 80 per cent of the time. The average number of customers in the queue will be $0.8^2/(1-0.8) = 3.2$. The average time spent waiting in the queue will be $0.4/0.5(0.5-0.4) = 8$ minutes. This is a surprisingly 'bad' performance for a shop which originally appeared to have more than enough capacity to deal with its customers. But notice how the average time a customer spends in the system depends crucially on the traffic intensity, and increases rapidly as ρ tends to one.

It is instructive to plot how the various aspects of performance depend upon λ and μ. Figure 10.1 illustrates for the average time a customer spends in the system as given by Equation (10.6).

Sensitivity analysis and optimization

Queueing theory formulae are useful in exploring how system behaviour is likely to respond to changes in the parameters. In our simple example, one

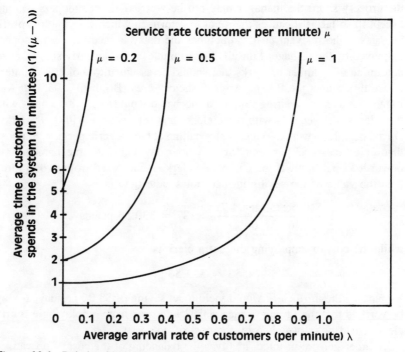

Figure 10.1   Relationship between arrival rate (λ), service rate (μ) and average time in system ($1/(\mu - \lambda)$)

might ask: how fast must the single assistant work in order to reduce below
0.5 the probability of a customer having to wait for service? The probability
in question is given by λ/μ, where $\lambda = 0.4$. In order that $0.4/\mu$ be less than
0.5 the service rate must exceed $0.4/0.5 = 0.8$ customers per minute, or 48
per hour (an average service time of $1/0.8 = 1.25$ minutes). Alternatively,
if the assistant doubles his speed to $\mu = 1$ customer per minute we might ask
how high an arrival rate could be handled before average time in the system
exceeds six minutes. From Figure 10.1 the answer may be read off as $\lambda =$
0.83 customers per minute.

In this way, the models may be used to help design the system, showing
how performance depends upon number of servers, queue discipline, etc. The
manager wants to design the 'best' system; this may mean the cheapest system
which will function adequately, or the system yielding the least delay for a
specified cost, or the system which minimizes cost of delay plus cost of
providing service. Typically, as the quality of service improves, the cost of
delay falls but the cost of providing the service increases: the problem is to
strike the right balance. Some simple optimization models are described by
Hillier (1965).

In practice, just as it is difficult to measure the cost of stockouts (Chapters
7 and 8), so it is often difficult to measure the costs of delay. In the case of
the grocery shop, the manager may not be worried about shoppers waiting
except in so far as it causes them not to return, in which case the lost profit
on sales is the relevant cost. Sometimes the delay is incurred by personnel
employed by the manager himself. For example, a classic early study was to
determine the number of clerks that should be assigned to tool crib counters
in use throughout the Boeing Aircraft factory area (Brigham, 1955). It was
found that average waiting time of a mechanic would be 33.8 seconds with
two clerks, 4.7 seconds with three clerks and 0.8 seconds with four clerks.
On average there were 540 mechanics calling at the tool crib per day. Suppose
that a clerk costs \$3 per hour for a $7\frac{1}{2}$ hour day and that a mechanic's time
is worth \$7 per hour. If the number of clerks is increased from two to three
then the value of the saving in mechanics' idle time is

$$\frac{540 \times (33.8 - 4.7)}{60 \times 60} \times \$7 = \$30.56 \text{ per day}$$

while the cost of employing the extra clerk is:

$$7\frac{1}{2} \times \$3 = \$22.50 \text{ per day}$$

Employing the third clerk would yield a net saving of \$8.06 per day. It may
be verified that the saving in mechanics' idle time from employing a fourth
clerk would be outweighed by the cost of doing so.

Another general problem involves the balancing of the cost of operatives
against the lost profit from machine down-time (see exercise 6). This is known

as the *machine interference* problem. The manager has to decide how many operatives to employ and whether to organize the machines into separate groups with their own operatives or to let all machines be tended by all operatives. This is a familiar problem in the textile industry and queueing theory is used to tackle it. Page (1972) describes the following problem which arose in a study by Ashcroft (1950). Contrary to first impressions, it is formally the same as the machine interference problem.

Ingots of steel are heated to the temperature required for rolling in soaking pits. The time taken to heat the ingots is very variable and can be assumed to have a negative exponential distribution. There is one rolling mill which reduces the ingots to slabs. The time taken to roll the ingots from a soaking pit is constant. On continuous working sufficient pits must be provided to ensure that the mill is not delayed by more than one hour a week on average because there are no ingots ready to roll in the soaking pits. The average time to heat a pit of ingots to be ready for rolling is three hours. The time taken to roll the ingots in a pit is twenty minutes. What is the smallest number of soaking pits needed to provide the specified utilization of the mill?

Treating the mill as the operative, and the pits as machines, the problem becomes a machine interference problem with constant repair time of twenty minutes (the rolling time for a pit) and exponential running time (the heating time). A single operative (the mill) looks after the machines, and the requirement is that the operative must be busy for not less than $167/168 = 99.40$ per cent of the time. Results for this model are tabulated in Ashcroft (1950) and the number of soaking pits required is calculated as fifteen. Many queueing studies such as this, and simulation of the types described in Chapter 12, showed very clearly to managers in the steel industry how high was the cost of variation in time to carry out all production processes. The aim these days is to study the reasons for the variation and by getting rid of the causes, get closer to constant operation times, thereby speeding up the output of the system even though average operation times may not change at all. The result can be seen theoretically too. If in equation (10.7) service time is supposed to be constant instead of exponentially distributed, the equation becomes

$$\frac{1}{\mu} \times \frac{\rho}{2(1-\rho)}$$

or exactly half its previous value.

Extensions of the simple queueing model

The model described so far has involved negative exponential (or Poisson) arrival and service distributions and a single server. Similar formulae may

—— **Table 10.2** ——

Average waiting time of customers in a simple Poisson queueing
system (expressed in units of average service time)

Utilization	Number of servers (n)								
ρ/n	2	3	4	5	6	7	8	9	10
0.1	0.0101	0.0014	0.0002	0.0000	0.0000	0.0000	0.0000	0.0000	0.0000
0.2	0.0417	0.0103	0.0030	0.0010	0.0003	0.0001	0.0000	0.0000	0.0000
0.3	0.0989	0.0333	0.0132	0.0058	0.0027	0.0013	0.0006	0.0003	0.0002
0.4	0.1905	0.0784	0.0378	0.0199	0.0111	0.0064	0.0039	0.0024	0.0015
0.5	0.3333	0.1579	0.0870	0.0521	0.0330	0.0218	0.0148	0.0102	0.0072
0.6	0.5625	0.2956	0.1794	0.1181	0.0819	0.0589	0.0436	0.0330	0.0253
0.7	0.9608	0.5470	0.3572	0.2519	0.1867	0.1432	0.1128	0.0906	0.0739
0.8	1.7778	1.0787	0.7455	0.5541	0.4315	0.3471	0.2860	0.2401	0.2046
0.9	4.2632	2.7235	1.9693	1.5250	1.2335	1.0285	0.8769	0.7606	0.6687

be deduced for the same model with multiple servers. It is often easier to present these formulae in the form of tables. Table 10.2 shows how average waiting time is related to number of servers (n) and traffic intensity (ρ). Consider the previous grocery shop example where average service time is $1/\mu = 2$ minutes and traffic intensity is $\rho = 0.8$. If there were now $n = 2$ servers then utilization would be $\rho/n = 0.4$. Average time spent waiting in the queue would be 0.1905×2 minutes $= 0.38$ minutes, a substantial reduction from 10 minutes.

Formulae are available for a variety of other arrival and service distributions, and for various queue disciplines, e.g. situations involving balking, and where the servers give priority to different classes of customers (as at many computer installations; Kleinrock, 1976). Work was also carried out some years ago on the problem of designing an optimal price schedule for different grades of service provided (Turvey, 1971).

One of the most common situations involves a maximum limit on the queue size. This is typically the case on telephone switchboards, where only a limited number of calls can be held. The next chapter describes such a situation at British Gas West Midlands and the model used to analyze it; exercise 6 at the end of this chapter gives some of the relevant formulae.

—— **Exercises** ——

1. If customers arrive according to a Poisson distribution with mean of 2 per minute, what are the probabilities that in any one minute the number of arrivals is (a) 0, (b) 3, (c) between 1 and 3 inclusive, (d) 4 or over?

2. In the simple example of the grocer's shop discussed in the text, calculate the performance of the system if a different assistant is hired instead of the present one, where the new assistant can work at twice the rate of the previous one.

3. In the same simple example, with the original assistant, how far would customer arrival rate have to fall before average waiting time reduced to three minutes?

4. A telephone switchboard receives an average of 40 calls per hour and each call lasts two minutes on average. If it is required that there should be a line free at least 90 per cent of the time, how many lines need to be installed? (Assume inter-arrival times and holding times are distributed exponentially.) *Hint:* use the equation in question 6 for $q = 0$.

5. A set of machines breaks down in a Poisson fashion at an average rate of two per hour. Machine idle time is assumed to cost £5 per hour in value of lost output. The repairman can service machines in an average time of 15 minutes (from the time he starts on the machine) where repair time is distributed exponentially. A new testing gauge is available which will cost £1,000 but will cut average repair time to 10 minutes. Should the gauge be purchased? (Assume an 8 hour day, 5 day week, 50 week year.)

6. For the system of c servers described in the next chapter, where there is a limited queue length q, Syski (1960) has shown that the steady state probabilities are given by

$$P_n = \begin{cases} \dfrac{\rho^n}{n!} P_0 & 0 \le n \le c \\[2ex] \dfrac{\rho^n}{c!c^{n-c}} P_0 & c \le n \le c + q \end{cases}$$

P_0, the probability of the system being empty, is obtained by solving for

$$\sum_{n=0}^{c+q} P_n = 1$$

hence

$$1/P_0 = \sum_{n=0}^{c-1} \frac{\rho^n}{n!} + \sum_{n=c}^{c+q} \frac{\rho^n}{c!c^{n-c}}$$

Calculate the probabilities of there being 0, 1, 2 and 3 customers in the system when there are 2 servers and a maximum queue length of 1. Assume $\lambda = 0.8$, $\mu = 1.0$.

References

Ashcroft, H. (1950) 'The productivity of several machines under the care of one operator', *Journal of the Royal Statistical Society, Series B,* **12** (1), 145–51.

Brigham, G. (1955) 'On a congestion problem in an aircraft factory', *Operations Research,* **3** (4), 412–28.

Civil Aviation Authority (1988) *Demand, Capacity and Traffic Management,* DORA Report 8809, CAA.

Edie, L.C. (1954) 'Traffic delays at toll booths', *Operations Research,* **2** (2), 107–38.

Hillier, F.S. (1965) 'Cost models for the application of priority waiting line theory to industrial problems', *Journal of Industrial Engineering,* **16** (3), 178–85.

Kleinrock, L. (1976) *Queueing Systems,* Vols I and II, John Wiley.

Lee, A. (1966) *Applied Queueing Theory,* Macmillan.

Monopolies and Mergers Commission (1988) *Post office Counters Services,* Chapter 9, HMSO.

Page, E. (1972) *Queueing Theory in OR,* Butterworths.

Syski, R. (1960) *Introduction to Congestion Theory in Telephone Systems,* Oliver and Boyd.

Turvey, R.L. (1971) *Economic Analysis and Public Enterprises,* Allen and Unwin.

—11—

Manning the telephone enquiry bureau at British Gas West Midlands*

L.B. SPARROW

Introduction

All telephone enquiries to British Gas West Midlands are dealt with by a team of specialist clerks in two centralized enquiry bureaux. Customers anywhere in the region can contact a bureau at local call costs. At all times it is essential to maintain a high standard of answering service, not only because this is expected by the customer for any type of enquiry but also to ensure that emergency calls relating, perhaps, to gas leaks are accepted and dealt with.

In about 1970 the enquiry bureaux were finding it difficult to maintain the servicing of customers' calls at peak periods with the existing monitoring equipment. It was decided to set up a queueing theory model of the telephone answering system. The aim was to derive the relationships between traffic level, grade of service, waiting time and manning levels within the bureaux. The model would be used as a planning tool, both for indicating peak manning requirements and for optimizing number of staff at off-peak times. This chapter describes the model which was developed and the results which were obtained.

Description of the system

The automatic call distribution system (ACD) installed at West Midlands Headquarters at Solihull operates as follows. Incoming calls pass through the

* This paper describes the work of Mrs P. Bishop who was a member of the Corporate Planning Department at British Gas West Midlands, formerly West Midlands Gas Board, from 1964 to 1971.

automatic call queueing device in strict order of arrival and are allocated in cyclic order to those service positions which are manned. If there are no free positions, the caller waits in the queue, where he hears a ringing tone until he is answered by the next available operator. If the calls in the system equal the combined capacity of the operators and the queue, the incoming call is rejected and the caller receives an 'engaged' tone. The maximum queue length can be set to suit the operating conditions.

Application of queueing theory

The situation is quite evidently a queueing system with many servers and a limited queue length. The ACD system ensures a single queue with a strict first-come, first-served queue discipline and full availability of operators to all calls, i.e. calls cannot be rejected or queued while any operator is available to answer the call.

It was assumed that calls arrived at random from an infinite number of sources, so that the inter-arrival times had a negative exponential distribution and the number of calls within a given time interval had a Poisson distribution. This was a reasonable assumption, since there was a large number of customers acting independently of each other, as long as the grade of service achieved was good enough to ensure few repeated calls.

The service time was assumed to be negatively exponentially distributed, i.e. the probability of a call finishing at any time is independent of the duration of the call up to that time. Figure 11.1 illustrates the nature of this assumption. The histogram was drawn from data on call durations taken at an off-peak time. The exponential fit is a good one. At peak times the exponential fit is not so good, but there is still a long tail to the distribution and the average call duration is not significantly different. Call duration here includes any paperwork which might be necessary immediately after the call, since the operator is not available to the ACD system while this paperwork is being carried out.

Using the notation introduced in the previous chapter, let λ denote the average calling rate, measured in number of calls arriving per minute; let μ denote the average serving rate, measured in number of calls dealt with per minute ($1/\mu$ is the average call duration measured in minutes); let $\rho = \lambda/\mu$ denote the traffic intensity, that is, the average number of calls arriving in the average service time; let P_n denote the steady-state probability that there are n calls in the system, either being dealt with or waiting in the queue; let c denote the number of telephone operators and let q denote the maximum capacity of the queue of calls being held.

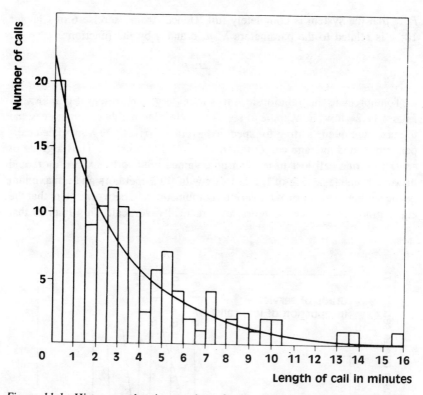

Figure 11.1 Histogram showing number of calls of a given length at half-minute intervals. The curve shows the expected number of calls of a given length from a negative exponential distribution with mean call length 3.322 minutes

The steady-state probabilities P_n for this system may be expressed in terms of the parameters ρ, c and q (see exercise 6 in Chapter 10).

There are two important criteria in the management of a telephone system: grade of service and waiting time. The next task is to obtain expressions for these in terms of the system parameters λ, μ, c and q.

Grade of service

Grade of service, denoted by g, is defined as the proportion of calls which are lost, i.e. the ratio of lost calls to calls offered. Lost calls are those which receive the engaged tone.

It may be shown that grade of service is numerically equal to the probability

P_{c+q} that the system is completely full. Hence (from exercise 6 of Chapter 10) g is related to the parameters λ, μ, c and q by the function

$$g = \frac{\rho^{c+q}}{c!c^q} P_0$$

To appreciate this relationship, it is necessary to represent it graphically. Figure 11.2 shows how grade of service is related to number of operators and to maximum queue setting for specified average arrival rate λ = fifteen calls per minute and average call duration $1/\mu$ = 3.322 minutes. Thus a grade of service of one call lost in ten can be obtained with forty-six operators and maximum queue setting of ten calls, or with fifty operators and a maximum queue setting of zero, or with various combinations in between. Note that the equal grade of service contours are practically vertical. This implies that

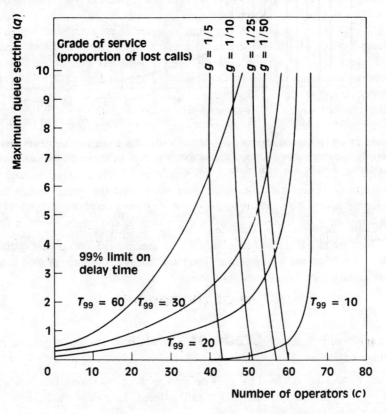

Figure 11.2   Graph showing contours of constant g and T_{99} for λ = 15, $1/\mu$ = 3.322

changing the queue setting has a negligible effect on grade of service compared with the effect of changing the number of operators.

The grade of service predicted by the model was compared with actual values measured on the ACD system, and a good correspondence was found.

Waiting time

Waiting time, T, is the length of time that a caller is kept waiting in the queue before he is allocated to an operator. It is not possible to obtain T as an explicit mathematical function of the various system parameters. However, it is possible to obtain an indirect expression for the probability that the waiting time of accepted calls will exceed any specified time t. Let T_{99} denote that waiting time which is not exceeded in 99 per cent of the accepted calls (hence is suffered by only 1 per cent of the accepted calls).

Using Newton's method of iteration, a computer program was written to calculate values of T_{99} as a function of the parameters λ, μ, c and q. Figure 11.2 plots the contours of constant T_{99} (in seconds) against number of operators and queue setting for the previously specified values $\lambda = 15$ calls per minute and $1/\mu = 3.322$ minutes. Thus, the contour for $T_{99} = 30$ shows that 99 per cent of the calls accepted will wait less than thirty seconds if there are about fifty-seven operators with a queue setting of ten calls, or about fifty operators and a queue setting of four calls, or about twenty operators and a queue setting of one call. The slopes of these curves show that when a low waiting time is specified (say, less than ten seconds), the required number of operators is quite rigid (somewhat over sixty) and the queue setting has negligible effect. When a long waiting time is allowed (say, one minute) there is a fairly constant trade-off between queue setting and operators, with five operators compensating for an increase of one call in the queue setting.

Use of the model

It is apparent from Figure 11.2 that, for a given queue setting, increasing the number of operators improves both the grade of service and the waiting time. However, for a given number of operators, an increase in the queue setting improves the grade of service but worsens the waiting time (because more calls are accepted but they have to wait longer to be answered).

It was decided that the grade of service should be maintained at one lost

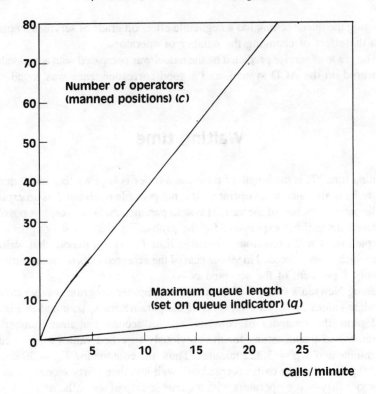

Figure 11.3 Planning graph, showing values of *c* and *q* for different call rates such as to give *g* = 1 lost call in 25 and T_{99} = 20 seconds

call in twenty-five and that 99 per cent of the accepted calls should not have to wait longer than twenty seconds. The intersection of the *g* = 1/25 contour and the T_{99} = 20 contour in Figure 11.2 shows that, for the specified traffic conditions λ and μ, a maximum queue setting of three calls is required with at least fifty-five telephone operators.

The model was originally designed to indicate staff requirements at various times of the day. Using a computer, it was possible to plot out in Figure 11.3 the queue settings and operator requirements against the average call rate λ for any chosen performance criteria, and for specified average holding times 1/μ. Figure 11.3 shows such a planning graph for the criteria *g* = 1/25 and T_{99} = 20 seconds, with 1/μ = 3.322 minutes as before. Thus, if call rates fell to five calls per minute during slack periods the queue setting should be reduced to one or two and less than twenty operators would be required. For an average call rate of twenty per minute about seventy operators would be required.

Reservations

Certain reservations on the use of the model must be borne in mind:

1. The graph shows the number of positions manned, not the staffing of the ACD system. Work study measurements must be used to make allowances for rest periods, etc., to give a ratio between operators available and positions manned.
2. Some calls require the operator to hold them and make an enquiry of another department. Any increase in manning should be matched on these other departments so that no extra delays are caused, otherwise the mean call length will increase. Under such circumstances, Figure 11.3 would no longer be valid. The need for referral of calls to other departments can be reduced by widening the competence of the telephone operators and providing them with a comprehensive information system via a visual display console connected to the mainframe computer.
3. It is essential to ensure that an adequate number of lines from the Solihull telephone exchange is provided, otherwise calls may be lost while some operators within the bureau are free. Under those circumstances, the first assumption on page 168 is not valid. In practice, extra external telephone lines are provided based on the forecast growth in traffic and the overall system is kept in balance.

Further developments

We have described the initial study of the ACD system as it existed in 1971. Since that time, telephone traffic has increased considerably and this has entailed extensions to the system. A two-stage ACD is now in operation which allows the maintenance of answering standards throughout the day and throughout the year with varying traffic levels, while ensuring the efficient use of manpower. Automatic management control equipment has been installed which continuously monitors the grade of service, line occupancy, call duration and waiting time and indicates the number of operators that is required to maintain the target standards of service. Currently, 148 positions are provided at Solihull and a further 38 positions at the second bureau; the number of these positions which are manned is adjusted depending on the telephone traffic. The two bureaux are connected by a thirty line megastream link so that their use can be optimized. All calls received are dealt with in the same manner to the same high standard, although consideration is being given to the provision of a separate telephone number for emergency calls which would receive priority in the queueing system. The chapter has attempted to show how queueing theory has played a useful part in the successful development of this system.

–12–

Computer simulation methods

M. PIDD

Simulation defined and considered

There are times when an OR/MS specialist can neither carry out useful experiments in 'real-life' nor can a useful mathematical model be formulated. In such cases, computer simulation offers one way of probing the consequences of alternative policies and options. The essence of computer simulation is that the system of interest is mimicked by computer programs which then become the basis for experimentation. Figure 12.1 gives the general idea. The model, or computer program, is used almost as if it were a video game. The modeller controls the running of the computer program to see how it performs when subject to whatever policy needs to be simulated. The expectation is that the behaviour of the model will mimic the behaviour of the system of interest when subject to the same policy. Automatic warehousing is a suitable case for simulation.

Many businesses have invested in large-scale automated warehouses which are intended to house a wide range of stocks for delivery to customers. Typical automated warehouses have the items stacked on racks which may reach from the floor up to twenty feet (6 m) high. The stock items are not collected manually but by computer-controlled handling equipment which glides along the aisles between the racks and moves to the correct locations to find the stock. The items are then moved to some other point in the warehouse where the order is assembled and prepared for despatch to the customer. The entire operation is overseen by a central computer system which monitors orders, instructs the handling devices to pick the items, oversees the assembly of an order and controls the stocks and their locations.

Such automated warehouses are not cheap to build and are very reliant on correct design, both of the materials handling equipment and of the controlling computer software. Computer simulation methods can be of great value in designing these warehouses, since they offer the opportunity to experiment with alternative designs *before* construction. Hence the designer might examine

174

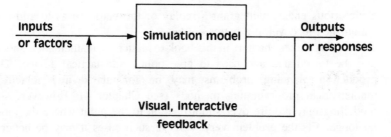

Figure 12.1 Computer simulation as experimentation

how much handling gear is needed, what stock control policy might be followed and how stock location should be organized. With suitable simulation software, this can be done quickly and cheaply.

There are many reasons why computer simulation methods are used. Some of the more sensible ones are as follows:

1. *Cost*: compared with experiments on a real system, computer simulation experiments can be much cheaper as there is no possibility of damage to the system itself. The costs incurred in simulation amount to the provision of a suitable computer and some programs to mimic the system being simulated.

2. *Control of the time-base*: many systems are simulated because the modeller wishes to speed up or slow down an experiment. As computers operate so quickly, an experiment can be run in much less time than would be the case with the real system. For example, a year or more of orders on a warehouse might be simulated in a few minutes of computer time. Sometimes the modeller may wish to slow down an experiment, for example to follow the detailed progress of an item through a factory to check that it follows the correct path. Again, this is often impossible in the real system.

3. *Safety*: some experiments are very dangerous, especially if they go wrong. Nobody would want to be on the jumbo jet that attempts to land just as airport capacity is stretch to its limit in an experiment. Simulated aircraft cause less damage when they fall from the simulated sky.

4. *Legality*: sometimes it is important to carry out an experiment which is strictly illegal. For example, a company may wish to investigate whether it would be worth lobbying for a change in legislation. Simulated experiments do not break the law.

5. *Repeatability*: often the point of an experiment is to find the best way of doing something and this means comparing the options under the same conditions. Examples might be attempts to find the most suitable production control strategy, the best algorithm for placing stock in a store or even the deadliest strategy in a battle. In all of these cases, the various possibilities need to be tried and compared. In the military arena, it seems unlikely that

a victorious enemy will grant a replay of the battle so as to allow the vanquished to develop a better policy.

6. *Tractability*: other chapters in this book explain how mathematical models may be formulated and used to give policy and tactical advice. Thus production planning problems may be formulated and solved by mathematical programming methods (see Chapter 4). However, such modelling may require over-simplification to the point where the model no longer fits the problem very well. In such cases it may be better to simulate the system of interest — especially when it is non-deterministic (see pages 177–8).

Hence computer simulation methods are most useful when policies need to be developed for systems which are dynamic, variable and involve complicated behaviour for which direct experimentation may be expensive, time consuming or dangerous. But, like any other aid to good management, computer simulation methods are not panaceas and are, sometimes, used inappropriately. Perversely, the availability of good software makes this misuse more likely, but that is hardly an argument for banning good software. Instead, it serves to underline the argument which runs throughout this book, that OR/MS is not just the use of mathematical techiques. OR/MS practitioners need to be skilled enough to recognize when particular methods are appropriate. This chapter should give enough information for the reader to understand how computer simulations work and to appreciate their limitations. For more information on specific applications of simulation methods, especially in manufacturing, the reader should consult Carrie (1988) or Hurrion (1986).

Continuous, discrete or mixed?

Approaches to computer simulation are often divided into *continuous* and *discrete*, with the latter being much more common in OR/MS. In fact the division between the two is artificial, since many systems require a mixed approach if they are to be simulated successfully. Table 12.1 lists the essential differences.

1. A *discrete* simulation is one which focuses on the behaviour of the individual, discrete objects which make up the system. These are usually known as *entities* and their behaviour must be modelled explicitly by rules which the modeller must devise. The entities are considered to move from state to state; for example, an order might move from the state 'Received' to the state 'In process' to the state 'Assembled' to the state 'Despatched'. Similarly, handling gear might be 'Idle', 'Moving empty', 'Picking', 'Moving loaded' or 'Under repair'. The full list of states through which an entity may pass will define its entire life cycle or

——— **Table 12.1** ———
Continuous and discrete
simulation compared

Continuous	Discrete
'Continuous' variables	Discrete entities
Equations	System rules
Values	System and entity states
Time slicing	Next event technique
Deterministic	Deterministic/stochastic

process. To build a discrete simulation model, the analyst must decide which are the essential entities of the system and must then determine the rules which govern their state changes. A computer is then programmed to mimic these rules.

2. A *continuous* simulation operates at a rather different level. It concentrates on variables which can take a continuous set of values rather than the discrete states occupied by discrete entities. Examples might be the number of orders received in a time period such as a week or a month. Strictly speaking, this would not be a continuous variable as it may only take integer values; however, such variables are often the type included in continuous simulation models. Examples of genuinely continuous variables might be liquid levels in the tanks of a chemical process. These can clearly vary freely between empty and full. To build a continuous model, the analyst must compose equations that describe how the variables behave. As these equations cannot usually be solved mathematically, a computer is used to run them again and again through time to see what they imply in the way of system behaviour.

3. A *mixed* simulation will include both discrete entities which occupy discrete states, and variables which are, in some sence, continuous. Mixed problems are common in some manufacturing systems in which variables such as temperature may be used to control a production process.

Rather than attempting a general overview of all three approaches, the rest of this chapter will concentrate on discrete simulation methods. Reference will be made to the other methods when appropriate.

Stochastic variation

Though an entity may be considered to move from state to state, this does not mean that its behaviour need be considered as deterministic. Various aspects may indeed be *stochastic*, that is, they may only be known probabilistically. For example, the time which it takes to process an order may depend on a whole host of factors which lead to a significant variation in order processing time. Thus it may not be possible to say precisely how long order processing will take, but it may be possible to represent it by a probability distribution. Similarly, the time interval between the receipt of successive orders may vary and it may be possible to model this variation by random sampling from a probability distribution such as the negative exponential $y = e^{-x}$ (see Figure 12.2).

Another common type of stochastic behaviour is when a class of entity (e.g. orders) is known to exist in different types according to certain proportions. Thus there may be 10 per cent of type A, 15 per cent of type B, 20 per cent of type C, etc., and the sequence in which these arrive may be random. In this case the random sequence of arrivals — which may be the key to the behaviour of the system — may be simulated by taking random samples from the histogram which defines the proportions of each type. Thus, many discrete simulation models involve many random samples, which, taken repeatedly and combined, serve to mimic the non-deterministic behaviour of a system.

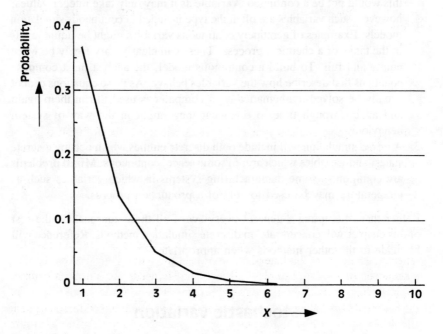

Figure 12.2   A negative exponential distribution with mean = 1

Pseudo-random sampling

There are many methods of taking random samples from probability distributions and they all have in common the use of so-called *random numbers*. As employed in computer simulations, random numbers are not random at all. They merely look as if they are, if we pretend not to know how they were produced. Such *pseudo-random numbers* are produced by mathematical methods which are entirely predictable, yet which produce a sequence of numbers which pass tests designed to check for randomness.

These pseudo-random numbers are preferable to truly random numbers for two reasons. First, they can be generated very quickly by simple algorithms. Secondly, they have the major advantage of repeatability — the same sequence may be used each time to test a different policy. This repeatability is one of the main bonuses of computer simulation and allows us to compare different policies under the same conditions. For example, it would be unfair to compare different order picking rules while using quite different sets of orders. Instead, it is crucial to ensure that the same samples are used in simulating each policy.

To take a sequence of random samples from a probability distribution, well-established methods are used. These methods employ transformations, either mathematical or via some kind of look-up table, to produce the required sequence of random samples. The simplest such transformation is the technique known as 'top hat sampling', which illustrates the general principles of all random sampling.

Top hat sampling

Consider a simple order sequence in which there are six different types of order — A, B, C, D, E and F and suppose that the proportions in which they occur are shown in Table 12.2. Suppose that, as part of a simulation, it is necessary to generate the pattern of the first twenty orders.

Consider a simple analogy of a hat (preferably a Topper) into which a hundred counters are placed, each counter bearing one of the letters A to F in this example. To sample correctly, the letters should be assigned to the counters in proportion to the order types. Thus 10 per cent should bear the letter A, 15 per cent the letter B, 20 per cent the letter C and so on. To take a sequence of random samples, all the sampler needs do is draw a counter from the hat, write down the value and then return it to the hat. To be safe, the hat should be shaken thoroughly each time. This sampling with replacement should, with a large enough sample size, provide a sample which is in the correct proportions and is in a random sequence.

——— **Table 12.2** ———
Order pattern

Order type	Percentage
A	10
B	15
C	20
D	20
E	25
F	10
Total orders	100

Top hats are scarce nowadays and shaking and writing are slow processes, thus (pseudo) random numbers are used instead. Suppose that the sequence of random numbers (see Table 12.3) has been produced by an approved method. It can then be used to generate a sequence of random samples. There are fifty numbers, each somewhere on the range of 00 to 99 inclusive. If Table 12.3 contained many thousands of such numbers then, to be considered as a random number series, these numbers must pass several statistical tests. These tests check whether the sequence is *uniformly distributed* — that is, that all values occur with approximately the same frequency in the table and *independent* — that is, that any value is equally likely to occur anywhere in the table. Thus there are no recurring sub-sequences of particular values. In addition, it is useful if the sequence includes all possible values in its range (in this case all values in the interval 00 to 99 inclusive).

In any random sampling, the aim is to produce a set of samples which have the same parameters (such as the mean and variance) as the distribution from which the samples are taken. In addition, the samples should occur in a random sequence — hence the use of (pseudo) random numbers. To do this, the possible random number values must be related to the distribution in some way.

For top hat sampling this can be done by the use of a simple look-up table based on the distribution. In the case of the order pattern shown in Table 12.2 it is clear that the orders occur in particular proportions. Thus, the trick is

——— **Table 12.3** ———
A short random number sequence

22	10	94	05	58	60	97	09	34	33
50	72	56	82	48	29	40	52	42	01
13	74	67	00	78	18	47	54	06	10
36	76	66	79	01	90	36	47	64	93
91	82	60	89	28	93	78	56	13	68

to divide the random number range into the same proportions as shown in Table 12.2. This is done in Table 12.4. Hence 10 per cent of the random numbers will correspond to an order of type A, 15 per cent to an order of type B and so on.

To generate a sample of twenty orders, all that is necessary is to take a sequence of twenty random numbers, for example from Table 12.3 and use Table 12.4 to decide which orders they represent. This is done in Table 12.5, using the first twenty numbers of Table 12.3.

Sampling from common distributions

There are many other standard methods for sampling from common probability distributions. The detail of these is beyond the scope of this introductory

—— **Table 12.4** ——
Look-up table for top hat sampling

Order type	Proportion (%)	Random number sub-range
A	10	00–09
B	15	10–24
C	20	25–44
D	20	45–64
E	25	65–89
F	10	90–99

—— **Table 12.5** ——
Twenty orders simulated by top hat sampling

No.	Random no.	Order type	No.	Random no.	Order type
1	22	B	11	50	D
2	10	B	12	72	E
3	94	F	13	56	D
4	05	A	14	82	E
5	58	D	15	48	D
6	60	D	16	29	C
7	97	F	17	40	C
8	09	A	18	52	D
9	34	C	19	42	C
10	33	C	20	01	A

chapter, but their broad approach is similar to top hat sampling in that they apply the following procedure:

step one: generate one or more random numbers.

step two: use some method to transform this number or numbers into a sample from the desired distribution.

The particular transformation method will depend on the mathematical function which represents the distribution in question.

Commercial simulation software will include suitable algorithms for generating samples from all the common probability distributions, by using one or more random number generators. For more detail see Pidd (1988) for information about sampling in computer simulation, and for sampling methods in general, see Knuth (1971).

The next event technique: moving time

Most systems which are simulated display dynamic behaviour, that is, the behaviour varies through time. Thus some way must be found to ensure that the state changes of the model occur at the right simulated time so that the model's dynamic behaviour will mimic that of the real system. The most general way of doing this is to use a *next event technique* in which the interval between state changes is variable.

To implement a next event approach (often known as event scheduling), the simulation program includes a *clock* amongst its variables. This serves as an indication of the passage of simulated time as the model runs. In addition, the program maintains what is in effect a diary, though it may be more formally known as an *event list, time list* or *timing tree*. As the simulation proceeds and the clock is moved forward, entries are made in this diary which tell the simulation program to execute certain activities at the times indicated in the diary. As a result of activity at a particular clock time, another entry in the diary may be made for a later time. For example, a crane may start to move and if it is possible to predict when it will stop, then this stop time may be entered into the diary. The simulation program scans through the events listed in the diary and moves from one event time noted there to the next until the simulation is complete.

The alternative approach is to use *time slicing* in which the clock is moved forwards in equal intervals regardless of the action within the simulation. This is simpler, in that there is no need to maintain a diary of future events, but there are two snags. The first is that the time slice needs to be fixed in advance

— not always straightforward — and if the slice is too large then some action may be missed. The second is that many systems exhibit irregular behaviour and it is simply wrong to force them into a regular mould.

The difference between time slicing and the next event technique can easily be understood by imagining the task of making a cine film of activity in a twenty-four hour car-park. Suppose that there is not enough film to leave the camera running all the time. The camera operator then faces a choice. He can either film short bursts at regular intervals (time slicing) or watch what is happening in the car-park and film whenever something interesting happens. Just as the camera operator must be more alert in the second case, so the simulation program must be slightly cleverer to employ a next event technique.

Most discrete or mixed discrete-continuous simulation software employs a next event technique. If the system being simulated displays regular behaviour, the software will autmatically generate regular events, because it is the events that drive the simulation. Simulations that use graphics screens to display their results as they proceed may be difficult to follow if they use a next event technique. This is because time will move forward in unequal jumps. A person watching the simulation needs to be aware of this, or else the software needs to have some way of smoothing the display of time events on screen as the simulation proceeds.

Capturing logical interactions: Activity cycle diagrams

In a discrete simulation model, the analyst must identify the important entities of the system, must describe their state changes and interactions and must capture this information in a way which a computer can understand. There are many ways of doing this. One simple way is to use *activity cycle diagrams*. These are simple flowcharts, popularized by Hills (1971) and described in detail in Pidd (1988). They employ only two symbols: a rectangle which represents an *active state* and a circle which symbolizes a *dead state*. Some writers, rather confusingly, call these symbols activities and queues. Each entity class has its own cycle which represents the states through which an entity may pass during its time in the system. It is normal to ensure that all cycles consist of alternate active and dead states.

It is important to realize that these diagrams are not intended to be ends in themselves; rather they are a useful aid to understanding how a system operates. They permit the analyst to sketch out some of the links between the various entities in the system and should not be regarded as permanent records of the system.

As an example of a simple activity cycle diagram, consider Figure 12.3 which relates to a simplified pub. There are three classes of entity in this system:

1. *Customers*: who arrive, wait for service, are served, leave the bar and drink their beer and then leave the pub. None (in this unrealistic case) goes back for second or subsequent drinks.
2. *Bar staff*: who are idle, serve customers, wash glasses or collect empty glasses.
3. *Glasses*: which are clean (and ready for use behind the bar), full (in use), dirty or waiting to be washed.

For simplicity's sake, this model assumes that customers drink only beer and that the pub never runs dry.

Several things are apparent from this simple example. First, entities of two or more classes may share the same active state, whereas dead states belong to particular individual classes. In the case of active states, this is only to be expected as an active state such as 'Serve' involves the co-operation of three classes of entity. Maintaining separate dead states for each class of entity simply makes it easier to know their current state when not engaged in an active state.

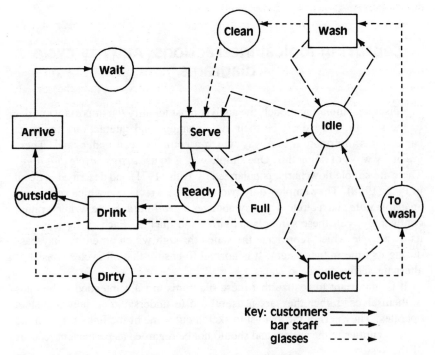

Figure 12.3 An activity cycle diagram for a simple pub

The second feature of this diagram illustrates its main purpose — it shows how the entity classes interact and the result of that interaction. For example, consider the active state 'Serve' which involves the co-operation of three classes of entity:

1. There must be at least one *glass* in a 'Clean' state.
2. There must be at least one member of the *bar staff* who is currently 'Idle'.
3. There must be at least one *customer* who is 'Waiting' to be served, having arrived at the bar.

This simple logical map of the system can be used as the basis for writing a formal computer program which might contain expressions such as:

If (customer in queue) and (bar staff in idle)
and (glass in clean) then
    Take customer from queue
    Note that bar staff member no longer free
    Reduce number of clean glasses
    Sample service duration and note termination time.

Alternatively it can be used as a starting point for the provision of data to a program such as HOCUS (see pages 186—7) which simulates a system from a description of an activity cycle diagram.

Why is it that activity cycles consists of alternate active and dead states? The answer is to make clear the logical interactions of the entities in the model. An active state is one whose duration can be directly determined at its outset. Consider for example the active state 'Serve' which, like all states has a definite start and finish. If the conditions listed above are satisfied, then the service can begin — but when will it end? Most such states have a stochastic duration which can be determined by sampling from some appropriate probability distribution. The sample taken shows how long the service will last, and thus its expected termination time can be noted in the event list (see page 182). When the simulation reaches this time, the program takes the action necessary to end the service — it frees the bar staff member to idle, notes that the drinker is ready and that the glass is full. A dead state is, by definition, one which an entity occupies until entering another active state. How long it must wait to do so depends on the durations of the active states in the simulation and thus cannot be determined at the start of the dead state itself.

The principle of parsimony

Only very simple systems can be fully modelled in an activity cycle diagram, but that does not mean that they, and other, flow diagram methods are useless.

They are useful for establishing the basic structure, or skeleton, of the system to be simulated. It is crucial to establish this skeleton and to validate it before attempting to model the full complexity and detail. Simulation modelling is best done incrementally; that is, the analyst should begin with a deliberately simplified view of the system which can be easily simulated on a computer. Once the simplified model is working, enhancements can be added one at a time until the simulation is considered valid enough for its intended purpose. This approach, sometimes known as the *principle of parsimony* is valid in most OR/MS modelling, but especially so in computer simulation. Activity cycle diagrams provide one way of getting a simplified model established quickly.

Discrete simulation software

Surveys of the use of OR techniques and methods frequently show that computer simulation methods are amongst those most commonly used. There are two reasons for this. First, almost anything can be simulated — though whether it should be is another issue altogether. Secondly, there is a wide selection of high-quality computer software which is designed to aid the rapid development of valid computer simulation models. This section considers the types of discrete computer simulation software that are available and identifies recent trends. It is not a complete survey, for such surveys are quickly out of date. For a thorough review of the types of software available, see Mathewson (1989) and Pidd (1988).

Different types of application require different types of software, and two extreme types of software are commonly used, with other options between the two extremes. The first of these two types of software is *data driven* which is suitable for less complex applications. Examples of data-driven simulation software are Witness, from Istel, and HOCUS, from PE International. To use data-driven software, the analyst has no need to write a computer program in any formal sense, but interacts with a pre-written computer program to develop a working model. The basis of HOCUS is an activity cycle diagram which the analyst produces and then describes, using a formal syntax, to the HOCUS system. These data include the entity classes which will compose the simulation and the states through which they pass (called activities and queues in HOCUS), together with information about activity durations and queueing disciplines. Hence the analyst provides a formal system description as data to the HOCUS system which then runs a simulation based on the data. In this way, reasonable applications can be developed in a few hours and the model can be run directly at any stage — as long as all of the cycles are logically complete. Thus parsimonious modelling is encouraged.

Witness, originally intended for use in manufacturing, takes a rather more contemporary approach and employs a graphical user interface. The analyst places entities on-screen as icons and links them into a network through which they pass or in which they may operate. Hence, an engine may be taken from a machining centre by a robot to an inspection area and thence to a 'just-in-time' buffer. As entities (known as machines and parts) are defined and linked, so the analyst is prompted for information about activities and the rest. As with HOCUS, Witness requires no conventional programming for many applications and allows a competent analyst to produce a working model in a few hours. Also, like HOCUS, Witness allows the user to run a partial model, as long as the parts are fully defined. Thus the partial model might not contain the full complications needed for a proper simulation, but may be enough to check whether such a detailed model will be worth while. In this way it encourages parsimonious modelling.

For HOCUS, Witness and similar products, there is no computer program for the analyst to edit — the analyst needs only to provide a data description of the system to be simulated. Thus, each time the simulation is run, a copy of HOCUS or Witness needs to be present in the computer being used. Thus multiple applications may require multiple copies to be purchased.

Unfortunately, not all systems can be simulated in this data-driven way. Sometimes some very detailed programming is needed. This is the case when there are many entity classes each with many members and with complex interactions between them. For such applications, data-driven systems lack power and the analyst needs to be a skilled programmer and must write a *bespoke program* either in one of the simulation languages (such as Simscript, Simula, Ecsl or Siman) or in a general-purpose language such as Pascal, C or Fortran. These applications can take much longer to develop than using data-driven systems such as HOCUS or Witness, but may be the only way to simulate some types of system in anything like a satisfactory way. If the application is to be written in a general-purpose language, then the analyst should sensibly make use of one of the libraries of simulation routines available in that language (see Pidd (1989) for more details). Writing bespoke software requires more discipline to achieve parismony, but has the advantage that the program may be easily moved from computer to computer.

Attempts have been made to combine the ease of use of data-driven systems with the flexibility of bespoke software. Two broad approaches are evident in commercial products which attempt to do this.

The first permits the analyst to descend into bespoke programming for the tricky parts of a data-driven simulation model. Thus Witness allows a very skilled analyst to do some coding in Fortran and, it is rumoured, will soon allow this in C. Obviously, to do this, the analyst needs to be a skilled programmer in Fortran or C and must have a full understanding of the data-driven system itself.

The second approach is that taken by systems such as GENETIK, from Insight Logistics, which forces the user to code the model in a simplified language of its own which is forgiving in structure and which is linked directly into a graphical user interface. The disadvantages of this approach are that the user must always do some 'programming', albeit in a simple language, and also that the GENETIK system is required before any model can be run. The advantages are that model development may still be parsimonious and that there is no need to be concerned with possible bad links between the analyst's coding and a data-driven program's own logic.

Experimentation

The whole reason for building a simulation model is to carry out some experiments on it. The first section highlighted the reasons for doing so, and now we consider how such experiments are to be undertaken. Nowadays, most simulations are run either on workstations or on single-user computers. In both cases, the user has control over the running of the program (how much control will depend on the particular program and the operating system of the computer). Also, the program may display graphics and/or text output on-screen as it runs.

Whatever the form of experimentation, it is as well to be aware that the results of stochastic simulations are more difficult to interpret than those from deterministic models. This is because a stochastic simulation is, in effect, a complex sampling experiment in which samples from various distributions are combined as the model runs. Hence, the sampling processes themselves need to be well controlled so as to reduce the effect of sampling errors. At the very least, the use of pseudo-random numbers allows the experimenter to compare a set of policies, each using approximately the same random samples. Two different types of experimentation may be used: interactive or classical.

As argued earlier, the applications which are best suited to simulation are complicated, highly variable and dynamic. This dynamic behaviour may be represented on-screen as the simulation runs by careful use of icons, diagrams and graphs. The changing state of the entities can be represented by icons which may change position, colour, orientation or size. The icons can be displayed against a backcloth of some stylized plan of the system being simulated and can be used to give a convincing representation of the system on screen. As an extension, state variables, such as waiting times, queue lengths and throughputs, can be displayed in a graphical form and accessed through multiple windows.

Using such devices, the analyst can observe the dynamics of the simulation as it runs. Thus it is possible to see the build-up of queues, the movement of jobs, the delays suffered and the utilization of the entities without waiting until a simulation run is complete. Of course, such observations can be misleading because the on-screen behaviour will be a function of the samples taken, if there are stochastic elements in the model. If the samples are unrepresentative, then so will be the observed behaviour. Despite this caveat, the ability to view the dynamics as the simulation runs is a real benefit since it links with the possibility of interacting with the simulation and operating it in a 'gaming mode'.

To provide interaction, the simulation software must permit some way in which the analyst can halt the simulation, vary some of the parameters and continue the run under these new conditions. This visual interactive simulation (VIS) is now the norm in OR/MS and makes it easier for the analyst to experiment, to see logical errors (where did that crane go just then?) and to convince the client that the simulation is valid. Visual interactive modelling (VIM) is enjoying increasing use in a variety of OR/MS applications and simulation was the first area in which it was applied. A substantial discussion of VIM applications is given in Chapter 15.

Sometimes, the VIS approach is not powerful enough, possibly because the system is simply too stochastic or because there are too many entities and variables to display meaningfully on-screen. Thus some classical form of controlled experiment is needed which must be carefully planned and executed.

The subject of experimental design is beyond the scope of this book, but the basics are simple enough. The experiment must be planned so that the various factors which may influence the results can be disentangled. In this way, the experimenter can determine statistically which factors give rise to which effects and may be able to draw appropriate conclusions about the effect on the system of the policies being simulated. To do this requires the experimenter to consider how long the experiment should be run in order to achieve statistically significant results. It also requires the investigator to be familiar with the appropriate statistical methods.

Summary

Computer simulation methods allow experimentation on a computer-based model of some system. The model is built by carefully describing the ways in which the system changes state and the rules wich govern its dynamic behaviour. Modelling is best planned on an incremental and parsimonious basis, with the expectation that the model will need to be enhanced as knowledge about the system develops. Once built, the model is used for experimentation, either interactive or classical or both.

References

Carrie, A. (1988) *Simulation of Manufacturing Systems*, John Wiley.
Hills, P.R. (1971) *HOCUS*, PE International.
Hurrion, R.D. (1986) *Simulation*, IFS Publications Ltd.
Knuth, D. (1971) *The Art of Computer Programming, Vol. 2 Semi-numerical algorithms*, Addison-Wesley.
Mathewson, S.C. (1989) 'Simulation support environments', in M. Pidd (ed.) *Computer Modelling for Discrete Simulation*, John Wiley.
Pidd, M. (1988) *Computer Simulation in Management Science*, John Wiley.
Pidd, M. (ed.) (1989) *Computer Modelling for Discrete Simulation*, John Wiley.

– 13 –

Decision analysis

J.B. KIDD

International differences

There are vast differences between the life-styles of oriental and occidental peoples: their general expectations differ and their modes of decision support differ — often the oriental person will consult decision-aiding mechanisms that are very subjective and which rely upon a high degree of individual interpretation or, at least to the Western person, this would seem to be so. Thus, by consulting the oracle and reviewing the sayings therein they come to an understanding of the way forward in some business or personal issue. Naturally one must have a question to ask in the first place, otherwise such a consultation is frivolous. There are several decision aids that are in this category, which are also used in the West: astrology, graphology, Tarot, I'Ching (Damian-Knight, 1986) and the sayings of Sun Tzu.

The notion of the 'question to ask' is important. Whether we are studying strategy, new technology, organizational structures or the implementation of change, two questions must be asked — 'What are we to do?' followed by 'How?' The use of I'Ching, for example, is no different — we have to be aroused enough to be able to discern an issue and to formulate a question about it. The resulting sayings should cause reflection on their inner meaning and how they interact with the perception of the issue as you, the decision-maker, see it. The outcomes should be perceived unfolding through one or more courses of action.

In the West, we seem happier with decision aids that appear more clinical and which have a theoretical rationale supporting their structure and use. This is not to say that Westerners reject the subjective Eastern decision aids; far from it: their use, as shown by a wider range of accessible books, reflects a growing interest in the subject, and is an acknowledgement of their use in business and in personal guidance systems.

Single-stage decision models

The simplest type of decision is that which consists of a single stage. Suitable models of this process are often represented as a table showing the decision options and the outcomes that may occur. The problem is to find the decision option that is 'best' in the circumstances: we may wish to maximize income, or minimize costs, or the outcomes may be subject to varying degrees of uncertainty. Various models have been proposed to accommodate these aims and they are usually well described in more advanced operations research texts, or decision analysis texts such as Taha (1982), or Cooke and Slack (1984).

It is, even so, interesting to study Figure 13.1. In this diagram all the possible action choices (A) and all possible outcomes (O) are listed — beginning with the first A(1) and O(1) up to the end of the list beyond the $(m+1)$th alternative. Each of these has to be mutually exclusive (no fuzzy overlaps to cloud decision-making) and the list has to be exhaustive (no options or feasible actions omitted).

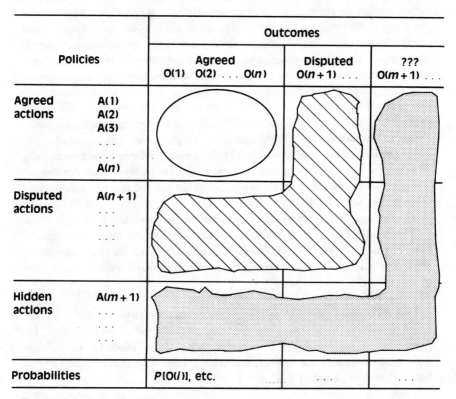

		Outcomes		
Policies		**Agreed** O(1) O(2) . . . O(n)	**Disputed** O($n+1$) . . .	**???** O($m+1$) . . .
Agreed **actions**	A(1) A(2) A(3) . . . . . . A(n)			
Disputed **actions**	A($n+1$)			
Hidden **actions**	A($m+1$)			
Probabilities		$P[O(i)]$, etc.	. . .	. . .

Figure 13.1   A generalized payoff matrix

Where each action and outcome meets in the table there is a cost or payoff: this represents the income or loss to the decision-maker if this result occurred in practice. The methods of analysis try to find the decision that would yield the 'best' result not knowing which outcome will finally take place.

The majority of methods in the textbooks consider only the upper left section of this table. That is, only those choices and outcomes that are agreed between all parties. But there are several instances where there is not a total agreement — such as in confrontations or negotiations: both sides have their own choices (and outcomes), but they also have their own beliefs about alternatives not accepted by the 'other side'. If each is using this type of payoff table it may be clear that they could agree on a compromise — they may even find they have the same constructs, but are using different words to describe them! Traditional methods concentrate on the 'agreed' portion of the table. Newer methods, such as Metagame analysis move into the 'non-agreed' area of the table (see Bennett and Huxham, 1982), as does COPE (software developed by Eden et al., 1979) or the soft systems methodology of Checkland (1981) — though the last two do not aim to reach optimum answers; they focus on exploration.

Naturally the third area at the bottom and in the leftmost column of the table is unapproachable. It must remain hidden until after the event as we cannot out-guess the future. All we may do is to set up decision processes that are 'robust' and allow us some freedom of action over the unfurling days, weeks or years of the decision horizon. This approach is well explained by Rosenhead (1989).

The concept of a robust decision incorporates the notion of multiple decisions that are not addressed in the above analysis of single decision methods. In practice we are often faced with a rolling sequence of conscious decisions followed by their natural evaluation which leads to further conscious decisions. This concept is embedded in the technique known as decision tree analysis.

Multi-stage analysis methods

There are many instances when we are faced with a set of decisions that unfurl over time and are dependent on how intermediate decisions are affected by chance as we move from the initial decision to some desired end state. One basic difficulty is that the feasible decisions, costs and relevant probabilities must be known before we may evaluate the optimum decision sequence. Although this sounds to be a large task, it is not too formidable. A point in favour of the technique is that we still can make the calculations even if the data set is not fully available. We can use estimates of costs and probabilities which, through analyses of the sensitivity of the result to changes in the raw data, can show that the project is either sensitive or insensitive to these changes. If it is found to be insensitive we may be confident in the 'correctness' of the derived decision sequence, even if based on imprecise data.

An example of a decision tree is given below. It is hypothetical, though it follows from the project network example given in Chapter 9 (Figure 9.1). In that network we saw three main task sequences:

1. To reprogram the screen images.
2. To order and install new communications links.
3. To revise the security traps.

We concentrate now on the third aspect and note that management has established that there are three options available for the development of security traps.

OPTION 1   This is a manual checking system for access to the database by remote clients. Some software modifications are needed so as to divert access calls to one of the firm's personnel who would grant access to the database for bona fide clients.

This is deemed to be a weak option, though secure. It has been given a cost rating of five money units.

OPTION 2   This is preferred by management. It involves software modifications which will automatically grant access to the database for bona fide clients without the intervention of their own personnel.

In the time available for system development it is felt that the software traps will be limited, and that some 25 per cent of all calls received by the system will be by hackers, and these will get to access the database.

Before the current development, strong traps were placed on the database access for users internal to the firm. These traps will remain in place, so that invalid access by hackers will close down the database to a fail-save mode, so incurring a cost of fifteen money units to reinstate its operation after an 'attack'. A valid client will invoke a zero cost in this option.

OPTION 3   A firm of hardware engineers has offered to develop an access validation process based on hardware. Its purpose is to reject all false calls on the system and it would have a rental charge of one money unit per access call.

This was thought to be a fair cost — but management has noted that tests of the hardware have shown that it is fallible: there is a probability of 0.10 of falsely allowing unauthorized access to the database, and a probability of 0.20 of falsely rejecting bona fide clients. The hardware simply notes the calls as 'pass' or 'fail'.

At this stage management wishes to find the best of these options. It has drawn a decision tree (Figure 13.2) which shows all the options and potential decisions. Some of these potential decisions may look odd. For instance, after using the hardware trap of option 3 it is possible to revert to the manual verification method of option 1. We will see in the following analysis that this decision, while feasible, is not optimal and will be rejected. It should be noted that the 'Total cost' is the sum of all costs incurred along each route through the tree, and the terminal condition of the tree is that there is a valid database access by a valid client.

In Figure 13.3 we note the probabilities of reaching any point of the tree. We have expressed these probabilities numerically as well as symbolically — for instance, at the top right of the tree we are saying 'the probability is 96 per cent that the access is truly valid (i.e. good), given that it has passed the hardware test and been labelled as 'pass'. This is more neatly expressed as $P(G|P) = 0.96$, where the '|' represents the condition of passing the hardware test, and being in this case, pass. $P(B)$ is the probability of the access being truly unauthorized, i.e. bad.

The derivation of these probabilities is relatively straightforward using the

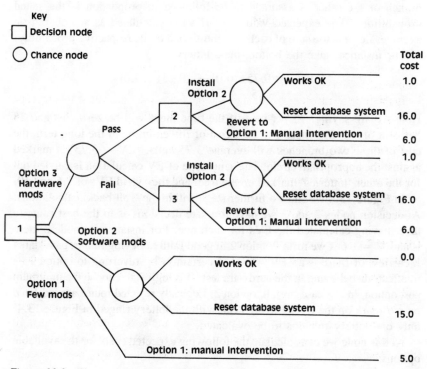

Figure 13.2 The security trap decisions

basic laws of probability, including Bayes' theorem. For instance, the probability of the hardware giving a 'pass' is given by

$$P(\text{pass}) = P(G).P(P|G) + P(B).P(P|B)$$
$$= (0.75)\ (0.8) + (0.25)\ (0.1)$$
$$= 0.600 + 0.025$$
$$= 0.625$$

And the $P(G|P) = 0.96$ is derived by the following formula:

$$P(G|P) = \frac{P(G).P(P|G)}{P(G).P(P|G) + P(B).P(P|B)}$$

$$= \frac{0.600}{0.625}$$

$$= 0.96$$

The other probabilities may also be calculated using this form of Bayes' theorem.

Figure 13.3 also indicates the beginning of the so-called 'roll-back' procedure. Each of the ringed sections of the tree represents a 'lottery'. One branch or the other is assumed to be followed in proportion to the stated probabilities. The expected value cost (EV) is calculated as a probabilistic average, i.e. it is the sum of each cost multiplied by its respective probability.

For instance, take the bottom-most lottery:

$$EV = (0.75)\ (0.0) + (0.25)\ (15.0)$$
$$= 3.75$$

Here we are saying: 75 per cent of the time there will be zero cost and 25 per cent of the time there will be a cost of fifteen units; in the long term the cost of these two branches will average 3.75 units. 'EV = 3.75' is marked against the appropriate circle. The same type of EV calculation is carried out for the other 'lotteries' marked on the tree, and they yield EVs of 1.6 and 10.

In Figure 13.4 we show a further stage within the 'roll-back' calculations. At decision nodes 2 and 3 we have to make decisions as to the best route to take, having calculated the EVs for each one. For instance, at node 2 there is an EV = 1.6 if we install option 2 in good faith believing in the 'pass' label it carries; or there is an EV = 6.0 (a certainty) by reverting to option 1 — in effect, disbelieving in the hardware test. It is logical to choose the minimum cost option, in this case 'install' option 2. Logically rejected routes are indicated by a // mark on the tree. Having dealt with the lottery ringed in Figure 13.4, only one lottery remains to be evaluated.

At this node we can calculate the following expected costs for the available options:

Option 3:   hardware modifications   3.25 monetary units

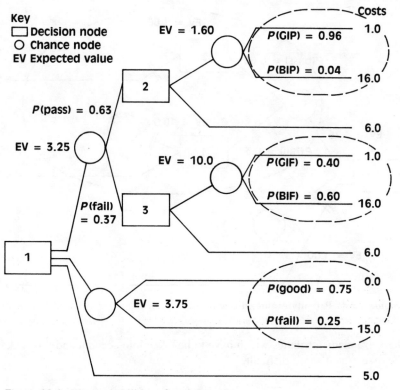

Figure 13.3 The probabilities of each branch

Option 2:	software modifications	3.75 monetary units
Option 1:	few changes	5.00 monetary units

To minimize the expected costs it is optimal to follow the hardware modification route of option 3; if the trapping shows the access to 'fail', the management should then revert to option 1 and invoke a manual verification. But if the test indicates the access is 'pass', they should bet on it being from a valid client, which it will be in 95 per cent of the cases. If the access is not from a valid client the database will have to be reset when it crashes.

These procedures may look difficult to set up and analyse, but even very complex decision systems follow the same rules that were used to evaluate the above tree. There is no greater complexity, save that of dealing with a larger problem — and there are computer packages, such as Arborist (Texas Instruments, 1984), to aid these analyses. For an introduction to the use of decision analysis see Hogarth (1987), or for more depth and rigour see Keeney and Raiffa (1976).

It is important to note that the above decision tree analysis was based solely on a single assessment criterion — the minimization of expected cost. In practice

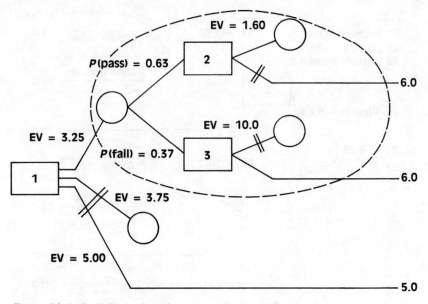

Figure 13.4 Partially evaluated tree

there are many attributes which have to be taken into account and this makes the assessment more difficult.

General multiple attribute analysis

The earlier example had only one attribute — cash flow — but as the illustration of Figure 13.5 shows we may be considering attributes a, b, c, such as cash flows and/or the profit/earnings ratio, market penetration, R&D results and media image, to name but a few of many attributes that characterize business decisions. In this type of analysis we must ensure that each individual attribute is measured consistently within its own scale, be it a money scale, a ratio scale or a subjective, descriptive scale. We must also find an equation that binds all the attributes together. This will allow the calculation of a single utility value with which to commence the roll-back procedure as before. In Figure 13.5 the vertical shading highlights the need for internal measurement consistency, while the horizontal shading indicates the scope of a multi-attribute equation which will generate one value to be derived from each measurement of the attributes in each outcome set.

By way of illustrating this decision situation we will consider briefly a tendering problem. It concerns a general difficulty for many firms — when

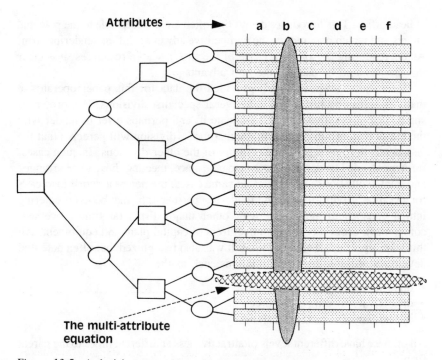

Attributes ———▶   a   b   c   d   e   f

The multi-attribute
equation

Figure 13.5   A decision tree with multiple terminal attributes

an offer to submit a tender is published, should the firm tender for this offer, or wait for a better situation? For most large contracts the tender cost is itself very expensive. It can be shown that the application of multi-attribute decision analysis can offer a solution: it will adjudicate upon the uncertainty inherent in the situation so that a rapid decision may be made. If the decision is in favour of tendering, this will allow the maximum time for the firm to create and develop the tender document. In other words, the method will maximize (hopefully) the chance of winning the tender by allowing more development time, and it will in turn minimize the chance of wasting the money spent in generating the tender.

The paper by Kidd and Prabhu (1990) is concerned with the tendering process: it may be summarized as follows. The marketing and business development representatives of major construction firms operating abroad experience difficulties from being remote from their decision-making executives. Even with modern communications the physical distances involved, with their attendant time zone differences, present many problems for decision-making. One objective of these representatives is to identify business opportunities and pursue these through all phases, including that of tendering competitively. Managerial policy has called for major decisions to be referred to head office. This introduces delays that often are unacceptable to the potential clients and which may reduce the competitive advantage of the tendering firm. As the tendering personnel are one of the firm's scarce resources, it is clear that they should be used to the best advantage.

The major enterprise which provided the data for this paper operates in many overseas countries and has several specialist divisions. If a project is small, one of the divisions will evaluate it, and perhaps offer to tender with the aid of a local sub-contractor. Sometimes a division will perceive that the task needs the services of one or more of the other divisions. In such cases, further extended tender analysis has to take place, meetings have to be arranged and joint evaluations undertaken. In some cases, the potential work-load calls for the total group to be in the tendering partnership, maybe even entering into a consortium agreement with other major firms (at times, overseas companies), especially the manufacturers of capital plant and equipment. All this takes up valuable analysis time. It was also recognized that often potential developments have built-in attractions such as the

- opportunity to generate cash
- opportunity to utilize resources
- opportunity for further business

All of these have different levels of attractiveness at different times to the parent firm.

It was suggested that systematic analysis could help identify the range of uncertainty within which contractors had to work, and could evaluate factors such as:

- uncertainty about the facts at hand
- the subjective assessment of these facts
- the future consequences of present decisions based on the facts

Initially, and usually with the help of a consultant, the decision-maker has to ascertain which variables are within his control and which are extraneous to the firm. A small number of controllable variables have to be selected so as to describe the problem properly, while not including surplus detail. Following this selection there is an initial analysis to check that the attributes of the decision are independent and do not 'colour' each other through the ensuing discussions. If there is some overlap in the decision-maker's mind between these attributes it will not be possible to determine the importance of variation in a particular attribute when the others are also varying in magnitude. Once independence is proven, the way is clear to the development of an equation that links all attributes to the utilities which the decision-maker perceives that they possess, individually and in total. The derivation of this equation is the objective of a long elicitation process, since once found it may be used as a fast decision support tool, or even as a surrogate decision-maker if the responsible manager is absent for some reason and the client is pressing for an answer.

It is not the purpose of this chapter to go into the depths of the analysis — merely to give a flavour of its power. If we consider the three attributes mentioned earlier — the chance to generate cash, the chance to use the firm's resources and the chance of future business — we find these are complex and interrelated matters. In the real tendering situation there were even more attributes that had to be included.

The full analysis comprising five lengthy, time-consuming processes is outlined in Kidd and Prabhu (1990). Theoretical justification is given by Keeney and Raiffa (1976). Through the process of eliciting the decision-makers' preferences we derived an equation which expressed their feelings about the attributes they considered to be pertinent to the problem. This allowed us to create a graph for managerial decision-aiding similar to Figure 13.6 in which the total of the raw utility scores for each individual attribute is plotted against a single scaled utility for each project. The scaling was carried out via an equation developed by Keeney and Raiffa.

There are two uses for the graph and the underlying equation. First, the decision-maker can use it directly when he or she sees a tender on offer and

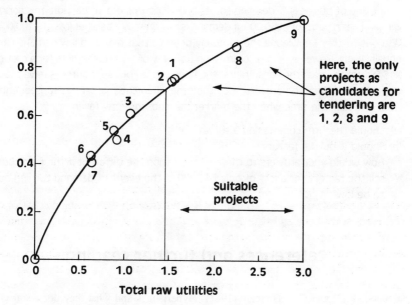

Figure 13.6 Combined utility decision-aiding graph

can feed in the appropriate measures on each attribute scale to compute if the final value lies in the 'go' or 'no go' region of the graph. Secondly, in the absence of the decision-maker, it can be used by the departmental staff themselves. If the answer to their computations is in the affirmative, they may begin the process of tender evaluation ahead of a final confirmation by the chief. This mechanism clearly leads to more time being available for better research into the tender evaluation rather than the alternative of having to wait for the return of the decision-maker and so risking a hurried tender evaluation.

—— Exercises ——

1. Consider the variability inherent in option 2 of Figure 13.2. If there is more time available for software development it is expected that the illegal access by hackers will be trapped more efficiently, perhaps even totally.

Reconsider the optimal decisions available to management: firstly, if this software option development was hurried so there was a 60 per cent chance of hackers getting to the database system; secondly, if there was ample time given to its development so the chance is reduced to only 5 per cent.

2. A firm is considering whether to build a new factory in order to increase capacity in one line of business. If demand for its product turns out to be high, this action will yield net returns of £250,000. If demand is low there will be a net loss of £100,000. Without further knowledge the company believes that high and low demands are equally likely. However, it can commission a survey of likely customers for a cost of £15,000. In the past the consultants who have carried out such surveys have made correct predictions three quarters of the time when the market has subsequently risen and half the time when the market has subsequently fallen.

(a) Should the firm commission a survey?
(b) Should it build a factory?
(c) How would your answers to these two questions be different if the firm could sell the factory for a loss of only £10,000 in the event of demand turning out to be low?

References and further reading

Bennett, P.G. and C.S. Huxham (1982) 'Hypergames and what they do: a soft OR approach', *Journal of the Operational Research Society*, **33**, 41–50.
Checkland, P. (1981) *Systems Thinking, Systems Practice*, John Wiley.

Cooke, S. and N. Slack (1984) *Making Management Decisions*, Prentice Hall.
Damian-Knight, G. (1986) *The I'Ching on Business and Decision Making*, Rider.
Eden, C., S. Jones and D. Sims (1979) *Thinking in Organisations*, MacMillan.
Hogarth, R. (1987) *Judgement and Choice*, John Wiley.
Keeney, R.L. (1980) *Siting Energy Facilities*, Academic Press.
Keeney, R.L. and H. Raiffa (1976) *Decisions with Multiple Objectives*, John Wiley.
Kidd, J.B. (ed.) (1985) *Managing with Operational Research*, Philip Allen.
Kidd, J.B. and S.P. Prabhu (1990) 'To bid or not to bid? A practical example of a multi-attribute decision aiding technqiue', *Omega*, **18** (2), 139–49.
Rosenhead, J. (1980) 'Planning under uncertainty II: a methodology for robustness analysis'. *Journal of the Operational Research Society*, **31**, 331–42.
Rosenhead, J. (ed.) (1989) *Rational Analysis in a Problematic World*, John Wiley.
Taha, H.A. (1982) *Operations Research: An introduction*, MacMillan.
Texas Instruments (1984) *Arborist: Decision Tree Analysis Package*, Texas Instruments Inc.

– 14 –

Operations research and artificial intelligence

G.I. DOUKIDIS

Introduction to artificial intelligence

Artificial intelligence (AI) has seen, during the last fifteen to twenty years, a rapid development in its theory, techniques, applications and client acceptance. This has been accelerated in the 1980s with the announcement of the Japanese fifth generation project and the national and international response to it.

Artificial intelligence can be viewed from two standpoints. The first is the scientific standpoint aiming at understanding the mechanisms of human intelligence, the computer being used to provide a simulation to verify theories about intelligence. The second standpoint is the engineering one, the object of which is to endow a computer with the intellectual capabilities of people. Most researchers adopt the second standpoint, aiming to make the capabilities of computers approach those of human intelligence without trying to imitate exactly the information processing steps of human beings. In both cases, researchers and practitioners are facing problems in creating models of complex and sometimes partially understood systems. Just presenting the reality (i.e. the various objects of the real system, their attributes and their interactions), however, is not enough to model reality. It is further required to represent the dynamics of the system, for example, how new properties are proved, how objects change their behaviour, etc.

The main domains to which AI has been applied are game playing and theorem proving (in the early days), natural language processing, perception (speech and vision) and expert systems (ES). The main characteristics of AI programs are that on a conceptually high level they deal mainly with symbolic representations, they use heuristics, they cope with incomplete data, they often show learning abilities and they are written mainly in Lisp or Prolog (Barr and Feigenbaum, 1981).

One of the major application areas of AI is that of natural language processing, which started in the 1950s with translation systems, followed in the 1960s by impressive language understanding systems on 'toy' fields (with no relation to real life) and followed from the mid 1970s by limited (in terms of syntax and semantics) systems to be used in real-life applications. The purpose of the last 'generation' is to make computers easier to use and fit more naturally into people's lives.

The main AI application area is that of ES which are computer programs that assist a user by providing information about a particular field. An ES does this by manipulating information about the field that has been provided by a number of 'experts' in the field. Another important feature of an expert system is that it has the facility to explain and justify the methods used to provide the information (Chorafas, 1987; Harmon *et al.*, 1988).

Various authors (Doukidis, 1987; Simon, 1987) have identified various similarities betwen AI and OR in the problems they tackle and the techniques they use. Both the OR and AI approaches build models which consist of three major components: excitation or input, system or model structure, and response or output. Both face the problem of model validity. Therefore, the same problems are being considered by these two disciplines, each in its own way, using sometimes the same approach.

This chapter reviews the topic of AI, with special reference to its main research area of ES, by outlining its main features and its use in business and management. It examines also the relationship between AI and OR by presenting their integration, the various AI concepts used in OR and the actual and potential gains from AI. Finally, it identifies trends by analyzing the actual AI activity that takes place at the practical level within the OR community.

Expert systems: basic concepts

As modern industrialized society becomes more specialized the need to have 'expert advice' increases rapidly. This trend is visible in all forms of life. At present, most of this 'expert advice' is provided by humans. Storing expertise in humans, just as having humans doing certain physical tasks, has both advantages and disadvantages. On the positive side humans have initiative and intelligence; they can adapt to new surroundings automatically and make decisions based on new data rapidly. Humans, however, become ill, move to different jobs, get tired, make irrational decisions, become preoccupied with other matters, die, take a long time to learn things and can only perform one complex task at a time.

The traditional solution to these problems has been to encode this knowledge in manuals and guidebooks. The use of these is often laborious and expensive and the books take up valuable storage space, so for some of the reasons mentioned above many firms have attempted to use the technique of ES to store the knowledge of an expert (or group of experts) about a particular problem area in a computable form and then use this stored information if a problem arises.

There are a number of reasons for doing this — first the knowledge of an expert who is going to retire soon can be stored so that his knowledge is not lost to the company forever. This can also apply if there is a strong possibility of experts changing jobs, particularly if they take a long time to train. A second reason for implementing ES is to lighten the load on the specialists — if an ES can be created to solve the easier problems in a particular domain, the specialist will be left with the more demanding and rewarding problems to solve.

When one is dealing with ES it is easy to get carried away with the thought of a computer system that can solve all one's problems by making it as intelligent as a human. Unfortunately, this is not the case, if only because human knowledge makes use of patterns of characteristics that cannot be explicitly defined.

Models of expert systems

The simple expert system model consists of only four parts. These are the *knowledge base*, the *inference engine*, the *user interface* and the *working memory*. A diagrammatic way of representing the relationships between different parts is shown in Figure 14.1. The knowledge of the expert is stored in a set of files known as the knowledge base. The most common form of knowledge consists of 'if . . . then' production rules. An inference engine manipulates the knowledge in the knowledge base to provide new information. Typically in a production rule system, the inference engine uses some form of logical deduction to provide the answers. The user interface enables the expert system to communicate with the user — this is done either directly via the screen and keyboard, or indirectly via external links to machines and monitoring devices, etc. Finally the working memory contains details of the state of the system's knowledge at a particular time.

A typical example would involve the user calling up the expert system through the user interface. The expert system then uses the inference engine to manipulate the rules in the knowledge base. If the system needs to know some facts, it will ask the user (again through the user interface) and then store these facts in the working memory. Any new facts that the inference engine derives are also stored in the working memory. This process continues until either the system provides the user with an answer to his query, or until there are no more rules that can be used.

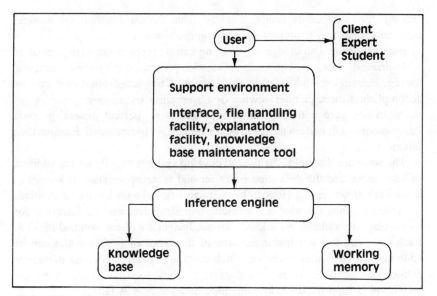

Figure 14.1 The simple expert system model

Expert systems which are currently available differ quite markedly from the traditional picture that has been described above. The differences lie not so much in the contents of the expert system. Rather they highlight the movement towards an integrated development environment, complete with an (implicit or explicit) development methodology. The first point to note is that the support environment is considerably larger than in the simple model — both in absolute size and relative importance.

The support environment is now much more than simply a user interface and explanation facility. It now contains a sophisticated knowledge base maintenance tool, a knowledge base handling facility which deals with those items that have become standard on large-scale database systems, for example security, data integrity, restart capabilities, etc. An external interface is available to connect the expert system to conventional databases, simulation and statistical packages, etc. The support environment may also contain a natural language processor, a time mechanism, networking and distributed processing facilities as well as graphic and linguistic programs.

Knowledge engineering

A computer is inherently ignorant. Therefore, the know-how of an expert has to be fed to it. The task of doing this is called 'knowledge engineering'. The 'knowledge engineer' typically 'extracts' from the experts their knowledge, rules of thumb and strategies for solving problems.

Four phases of knowledge engineering can be recognized: selection of an appropriate domain; the knowledge elicitation process; coding the system; and testing, debugging and refining the system. Knowledge elicitation can be accomplished through interviewing or observation techniques.

As in any case with programming, there is no perfect general-purpose development tool; certain tools are better for certain projects and domains than others.

The software that helps the user to develop systems rapidly by the addition of knowledge and the definition of a user and systems interface is known as a 'shell' (Harmon *et al.*, 1988). The characteristics of a shell are a ready-made inference engine, knowledge representation structures and an interface for users. Current examples include XI, Savoir, Insight 2 +, Leonardo and PESYS. Each one specifies particular features of the types of problem that can be addressed, a particular order in which tasks are undertaken, and particular methods to be used to express expertise. They usually assume a simple 'prototyping' approach — do something and see how it fails.

An alternative to the shell approach is to use either conventional high-level languages or AI languages. Very many working systems in the general business world, are written in conventional languages such as Pascal, Fortran or C. The advantage is in efficiency and the secure programming environment they provide, as well as portability and the possibility of integration with other conventional systems software.

The AI languages, dominated by Lisp and Prolog and their derivatives, do of course provide something more in that they contain some supporting features that give particular appeal in developing applications; yet they are not without drawbacks.

While both the shell and the programming language approach are currently developing strongly, there is a move in each case to increase functionality and provide more help to the developers of systems. The result is that shells acquire more and more 'features', and users approaching ES via programming languages get support in the form of extensive libraries of system routines for knowledge representation, etc.

The future for these tools must be in a fusion of their particular strengths, and the development of what are increasingly known as 'environments', 'tool-sets' or 'large, hybrid system-building tools'. Examples of such developments include KEE, ART and LOOPS. They focus on the skilled knowledge engineer, they are potentially able to provide support to the sysem in its environment and through its life cycle and they are often linked to special-purpose hardware or high-powered workstations. The environments developed recently indicate that there is a slow move towards increasing functionality and providing more help to the developers of systems.

Expert systems applications in management and business

Expert systems applications can be data driven or goal directed depending on whether causes or consequences of known facts are to be inferred (Chorafas, 1987). Examples of the former include interpretation, prediction and monitoring. Goal-directed expertise involves putting together actions, events or objects to build up a plan or solve more complex problems. Planning and designing, but also assembling and repairing, are examples. Computer-aided instruction and process control are examples of both types. Expert systems can also be used as front-end and interfacing tools. In such applications they help to ensure that all proper questions are asked and a two-way communication is effectively established between system and user.

Harmon *et al.*, (1988) argue that ES could be used when people need to analyze and solve problems and when they need assistance to make decisions. They could be used when people need to communicate information about problems involving analysis and decision-making. They could be used to store and communicate knowledge. All businesses face numerous situations requiring decisions that result from problem analysis. Expert systems could provide managers throughout organizations with a means of formalizing these decision processes and effectively communicating the results to everyone faced with similar decisions.

Mockler (1989) lists ES which have been developed by operating managers covering such decisions, tasks, or problems as the following.

Configuring computer systems (operations).
Capital investment planning (finance).
Personal investment planning (finance).
Customer service representative training (marketing).
Sales management quota setting (marketing).
Commercial loan application screening (finance and banking).
Tax planning (accounting and taxation).
New venture decision-making (marketing and management).
Career planning (management).
Auditing (accounting).
Strategic planning (management and business policy).

Financial expertise has been a major target of ES developers because the market is huge at both ends. The financial world is facing a time of increasing competition and there is a definite need to employ new strategies to lower operating costs, to increase productivity and to standardize services and profits.

Some typical financial applications in use include (Chorafas, 1987; Harmon *et al.*, 1988): *Taxadvisor* designed to make tax planning recommendations for businessmen and other users; *Lending Advisor* assists credit managers in analyzing commercial loan applications and structuring appropriate loan packages; *Underwriting Advisor* evaluates risk in insurance applications to determine pricing, and is for use by field underwriters in commercial property, workers' compensation, inland marine, general liability and commercial auto insurance; *PlanPower* helps financial institutions analyze personal needs of clients in offering investment or other financial advice.

Evidence to date suggests that the most successful systems have been those that are least abstract, such as systems for credit evaluation and giving tax advice. Early over-optimism in this field has now given way to an approach which is more conscious of the basic limitations of ES in this area.

One of the main problems is that ES have been developed in parallel with, yet independently of, decision support systems (DSS). Both systems operate in the same area of application: that in which technology-based systems provide advice and support for a range of human activities from diagnosis and fault finding, to planning and decision-making. Doukidis *et al.*, (1989) show that much can be gained from integrating the ES and DSS approaches. Such systems are labelled 'knowledge based management support systems'. However, to be truly effective the integration has to be taken a step further. The technology-based approach of the management support systems has to be integrated with the human activity systems which they serve. The association and integration of the two techniques with human-based problem-solving skills in conditions of uncertainty, could have a synergetic effect, if the complementary nature which each component brings to the managerial decision process is recognized.

The spread of expert systems world-wide

An international survey carried out in 1988 (Griendley, 1989) shows that progress with ES is slow (see Table 14.1). On average only 19 per cent of companies surveyed in leading IT countries have put any ES to use. All these

―――― **Table 14.1** ――――
Present use of expert systems (%)

Country	Developed at least one ES	Put at least one ES into use
United States	28	25
Japan	27	23
Australia	26	22
United Kingdom	15	11

companies have well-organized IT departments. There is no evidence to show that ES have captured the imagination, or the purse strings, of many IT executives. Indeed, a number of them did not know what an ES was. However, nearly three-quarters of companies in Japan and the United States state that electronically dispensed knowledge will, eventually, become a main computer application in their businesses.

In the United States, 58 per cent of those involved with ES use the easy approach of the shell. This contrasts sharply with Japan, where 70 per cent of businesses trying out the new technique are gaining much more detailed experience by writing their own programs. There is some evidence to show that an 'easy come, easy go' attitude prevails. The drop-out rate of systems developed, but not actually used, is 46 per cent world-wide for shell-based ES, but falls to 33 per cent for systems where companies have invested the time and effort to develop them from scratch.

The top five problems preventing widespread use of expert systems are shown in Table 14.2. The top problem preventing the take-off of ES, for Australia, the United Kingdom and the United States alike, is the failure of management to appreciate the potential. Japan, however, does not even list this problem amongst its top five.

The second problem has to do with the ES experts who know all about producing ES but have serious problems in suggesting what these systems should do for the company. The main solution here is to create momentum within the users' groups and make them identify suitable applications and often develop them.

Expert systems represent a challenge to the technicians, hence availability of technical skills is an important world barrier. Programmers brought up in a traditional DP department can find the rigorous separation of the rules from the programming procedures, the mathematical modelling involved and the new jargon used not to their taste.

There was general agreement that the real payoff from ES only comes when

—— **Table 14.2** ——

The top five problems preventing widespread use of expert systems

	Corporate awareness	Finding applications	Availability of skills	Cost/benefit justification	Integration with IS
Australia	1	2	3	4	5
Japan	—	1	—	—	3
United Kingdom	1	2	4	3	5
United States	1	4	—	5	2

No. 2 problem for Japan: validating the results
No. 3 problem for United States: acceptance by users

they are integrated with the existing data processing applications of the company. Computer-based expertise has to work with facts which are often in existing databases. Getting an ES to integrate with today's database systems is a problem, especially if an ES shell is used.

It is quite clear that all these problems are ones which OR practitioners are already used to solving.

The evolving expert systems market

In the early 1980s, apart from those pushing the ES technology in order to provide a market for their products, the primary ambition for most involved with ES was to engage in learning, rather than in the construction of operational systems.

From the late 1980s though, we began to see the emergence of four distinct classes of ES products. These are the tailor-made system, the generic system, the knowledge base itself and information systems which incorporate some intelligent elements.

Tailor-made systems

The applications of tailor-made systems are often experimental and contain proprietary knowledge. They are developed using shells and are initiated usually by non-technologists. A limited, though increasing, number of these are 'fully engineered', often in technical or medical fields. A fully engineered system is one that has found a mainstream role in the organization, contains many person-years of development, and has been through a number of cycles of development. The classic example here is the DEC XCON system (Chapter 18 of Doukidis *et al.*, 1989). This system has been designed to replace the technical editor in computer manufacturing plants by providing information on the mix of components required by a particular application and on the ways in which these components had to relate to each other. As ES prove their value they will most likely take their place in the general portfolio of DP systems.

Generic systems

A recent entry into the market is the generic system, otherwise known as a 'packaged' expert system. The essence of a generic is that it is a true product, containing a knowledge base in a field of general interest. Examples from the

United Kingdom include products that advise on employment law, welfare benefits and taxation — applications which attract many potential users. The intention in general is to complement or replace the skills of professional advisers.

For such systems the knowledge base is the principal attraction to the purchaser, and the supplier will be expected to keep it up to date. Thus we see here a start of the move from an industry based on software skills to one based on knowledge or information. The generic will be used more as a reference tool than as a way to capture specific knowledge or skills.

Knowledge bases

The third product, as yet only in its infancy, is the knowledge base itself. The existence of a market in knowledge is universally acknowledged, and large multinational corporations are committed to exploiting it, and yet today we can identify only a few knowledge base products that are available separately from operational software. Expertech, a large UK shell developer, has entered into the knowledge base market selling knowledge bases to run with its software in domains such as employment law. One of the limitations to a wider market is clearly that there are no agreed standards for what a knowledge base should look like, though the emergence of dominant shell products and, in particular, production rule systems might drive this process to a point equivalent to the ubiquitous Lotus 1-2-3™ spreadsheet format.

Information systems incorporating intelligent elements

Most existing ES are stand-alone systems with few, if any, linkages back into the organization's information systems (IS) of databases and programs. At the same time today's IS are primarily concerned with well structured, procedurally defined applications.

Using the new technology and concepts acquired from work in AI, designers of standard IS applications could incorporate more intelligence into systems as an aid to users. In so doing, they may well use techniques derived from the ES movement to carry out procedures which previously used conventional programming techniques. The knowledge incorporated in DEC's XCON system is of a kind which has been used for many years in product explosion and production and material scheduling applications. By holding that knowledge, not in the form of the classic 'product specification' database, but in the form of deterministic rules, the designers of XCON have made a significant gain in flexibility. As a result it has been possible for DEC product engineers to devise new methods of configuring and building VAX computers. These developments are reflected in the growth of the knowledge base from a few hundred rules, defining VAX configurations, to more than 3,000 rules.

Thus the development of expert systems ideas within the IS community is twofold. One leading to the increased possibility of applications incorporating elements of the intelligence; the second permitting IS to become flexible by using some of the new tools of expert system technology.

Artificial intelligence and operations research

The Committee on the Next Decade in Operations Research (CONDOR, 1988), set up by part of the US National Science Foundation, proposed a range of research topics suggestive of the possibilities that could arise from the integration of OR and AI. The committee proposed these topics because, as they stated, this will improve problem solving:

> The primary objective shared by OR and artificial intelligence (AI) is to provide methods and procedures that support effective problem solving and decision making. The two disciplines approach this common objective in fundamentally different but complementary ways: AI problem solving techniques tend to be inferential and to rely on expert knowledge and heuristics: OR uses algorithmic, mathematically based approaches. Artificial intelligence emphasizes qualitative aspects of problems; OR emphasizes the quantitative. A careful integration of these two approaches to problem solving shows significant promise for improving the capability and, notably, the acceptability of problem solving systems.

Further support for the increasing role of AI in OR is given by Simon (1987), who suggests that the AI toolkit can be used by OR practitioners on 'ill-structured, knowledge-rich, nonquantitative decision domains that characterize the work of top management and that characterize the great policy decisions that face our society.'

Integrating artificial intelligence and operations research to solve operations research problems

A number of possible applications for the integration of AI and OR to solve traditional OR problems have been suggested recently and a few have been tried. Production planning is one suggestion because OR methods in this area have lacked credibility in the past, partly because they need a great deal of precise data. A successful prototype system was developed for the scheduling of a feed mill in Thailand. The system integrates ES, databases, mathematical programming and simulation models in generating daily shop-flow schedules based on weekly master plans.

AI applications to assist in the construction and validation of simulation models have also been developed. The complexity of the problems faced in real applications enables simulation to use AI in two ways. First, the art of simulation modelling itself can possibly be enhanced by adding AI software applications to the analysts' tools. Second, parts of a simulation might be modelled by an AI application. Examples of such environments include the CASM simulation environment at the London School of Economics, the visual interactive simulation environment of Warwick University and the KBDSE (knowledge-based design and simulation environment) developed at the University of Arizona.

Artificial intelligence concepts used in operations research

Intelligent front ends to operations research packages

Defining an OR problem is a manual task, and is largely an art. It requires a lot of communication between the analyst and the client which is often ineffective. Because of these characteristics the computing aids that help the analyst formulate the problem with the customer could have the form of a natural language understanding system (NLUS). Such systems are considered as intelligent front ends since their outcome, which is the semantic representation of the problem, can be used as input to a standard OR software package such as a simulation program generator or a mathematical programming package.

One of the first intelligent front ends is SPIF (Doukidis, 1987) (simulation problem intelligent formulator), designed to reduce the total time needed to produce the logic model which the client requires in a simulation project. Similar systems have been developed in the areas of multi-criteria decision-making and mathematical programming, except that they operate on very specific problem areas. The fact that all these systems remain in a prototype form shows the difficulty in drawing up an informal specification of an OR problem even in a specific application area.

Expert systems as aids in operations research projects

Expert systems can assist a user to develop his computer model. Such a system is SIPDES (Doukidis, 1987) which helps users to discover the location of compilation errors occurring within their simulation programs and to propose possible solutions. Expert systems are also used to analyze the output from mathematical programs and to analyze data required for the experimentation of a simulation project.

Artificial intelligence software tools in operations research

From the mid 1980s AI languages have been widely used within OR since it is possible to use the if . . . then or condition–action rules to describe state transitions in the OR application areas discussed above. Artificial intelligence languages and environments can also help rapid model development. Special-purpose workstations which provide efficient graphic and interactive support to the user, are obviously of prime importance for computer-aided algorithmic design in complex OR domains such as factory scheduling, vehicle routeing, simulation, etc.

Operations research computer models with learning abilities

Designing programs that exhibit learning capabilities has always been an important aspect of AI. Production system models have been used to study the learning aspect by investigating how new rules can be generated automatically. In OR models learning has never been investigated in an organized way, although it has potential because many OR models (for example, in simulation or scheduling) are modular and use aspects of production systems modelling. Lately, though, there have been a few attempts, as in the area of factory scheduling.

Gains for artificial intelligence from interaction with operations research

Most ESs now either use some simple calculations to assign values to variables or ask the user to do so. It is becoming obvious that this simple mode of operation is not enough. In many real-life situations a value for a variable cannot be calculated directly but can only be found by calling an OR module embedded in the ES. For example, one of the largest financial-based ES developed to date, which is designed to assist public accounting auditors in their analysis of the collectability of loans, has an embedded integer programming module.

Visual interactive modelling (see Chapter 15) is a major aid in an OR project because the decision-maker increases his confidence in the model by interacting with it and experimentation becomes easier (since the pictures help the user to determine and to evaluate appropriate experiments). Equally visual interaction modelling has much potential in the area of ES (especially when the knowledge base concerns physical systems).

Simulation has been used to evaluate expert systems for flexible manufacturing. Artificial intelligence programs which involve reasoning about systems which change over time can also use particular simulation techniques, such as the three-phase method, to calculate when important events are going to occur.

A survey of artificial intelligence activity at the practical operations research level

What is not clear from the many publications on the subject of AI and OR is just how much activity is actually taking place at a practical level, and what the nature of this activity is. A recent study at the London School of Economics (Doukidis and Paul, 1990) tried to quantify this activity through a survey carried out using OR Society members in the United Kingdom. The purpose of the survey was to establish how far ideas from AI have infiltrated the work of members of the Society, at what level, their practical significance and the prospects for future use. It is suggested that the type of application and the tools employed by surveyed users might indicate areas for fruitful investigation by non-users of AI techniques.

The sample was found to be representative of the membership generally. Just over a fifth (21.5 per cent) of the sample were involved in AI in some way or other, but they expected to double their involvement (45.5 per cent) in future. The first main conclusion of the survey was that professional and organizational motivation was the main reason for using AI, since it seemed to relate to securing the position of the OR profession and of the individual OR worker.

The survey found that 85 per cent of the applications were ES. More generally, AI meant ES for most respondents to the survey. The remaining applications ranked in order of popularity were of intelligent interfaces with computers, intelligent planning systems, program generators and intelligent tutorial systems.

Most systems were used as support for decision-making. Typical OR application areas such as production and transport scheduling and planning ranked only fifth in the list. As one might expect, most systems were assessed for use by a client department; they helped to improve OR's image. Very few were developed for use within the OR department itself.

Of the applications, 62 per cent were based on the use of shells on PCs, reflecting the fact that OR scientists are developing systems in order to help themselves learn. Prolog dominates as the European AI language, although Lisp is quite popular.

The time taken to implement an ES is felt as a strong constraint in the practical development of systems. Other strong constraints were the cost, the lack of practical use, technological limitations and lack of expert help when implementing an ES. It is evident that ES is still far from being a 'user-friendly' technology.

Although the practical benefits appeared to be limited, the vast majority of respondents had a positive attitude towards ES in future. About 40 per cent of UK organizations with OR members are involved to some extent in developing or using ESs, and this figure includes 21.5 per cent where the OR community in the United Kingdom is directly involved.

As we have noted above, well over three-quarters of respondents were not involved in AI at all. The reasons are mostly the same as given by those who were involved but not doing more. The broadest interpretation that can be given to these results is that AI/ES has still a long way to go before it will be widely applicable in OR, and that OR departments and societies should provide more responsible information on the potential of AI/ES.

Two typical examples developed in operations research departments

The Health Service Indicator (HSI) Analyst is an ES developed by the OR service of the UK Department of Health to support the interpretation of key management information in the context of performance reviews. The specific ES brings together knowledge bases and databases to provide a more focused use of information by managers. The ES is now in use in seventy or so health authorities. It examines performance indicators which provide some 450 items of comparative data on each of the 190 district health authorities, to identify areas of unusual performance. For example, it can analyze potential waiting list problems to help identify possible contributory causes. The system, written using the Crystal shell, reads in indicator data from prepared data files, filters out extreme values and, according to the combinations it finds, provides a written report. It has easy and quick to use facilities for the user to interrogate the logic.

Lately the ES is being substantially rewritten to relate directly to the issues faced by managers in individual health authorities, rather than being data driven. Technical changes include the development of an interface into a relational database system, which will allow much easier access to a wide range of local management information. These developments open up the possibility of a wider decision support function, with modules of the system being directly linked to a range of management information systems, thus providing an interpretative facility for health service managers.

The OR department of BICC Technologies Ltd (a large multinational group of companies involved in construction, engineering and electronics) has developed a totally different system which is the result of European co-operation in the ESPRIT programme. This OR department provides a typical example of involvement in AI R&D projects in the areas of scheduling and simulation. Their effort is high, they use sophisticated hardware and software, they are very experienced on AI matters and they have valuable direct contacts with leading edge developments in Europe.

The system operates as a real-time planning system that bridges the existing gap between the business system and the factory shopfloor; it also supports many different manufacturing philosophies concerned with machine grouping and scheduling. The developed software uses a combination of an AI object-oriented paradigm and an OR scheduling approach based on a heuristic model.

As a package addressing production simulation, planning and scheduling in small to medium batch manufacture, the approach using the combination of OR methods and AI techniques provides a number of advantages over either of them applied separately. These are that the user's expertise is captured, systems may be easily configured for particular conditions, systems can easily be kept up to date to reflect changing requirements of production, the range of scheduling-related applications in small to medium batch production may be covered, the system is easy to use and ergonomic and the latest concepts for rapid system development are incorporated.

As its AI skills were developed and knowledge about AI tools and techniques acquired, the status of the OR department became that of a centre of excellence for AI within the company. Besides production planning and scheduling, the department is now developing ES in areas that are not in the traditional sphere of OR.

Conclusions

Expert systems are an attractive idea. Although progress is slow, it is steady. We begin to see a move from technology research to research and development grounded in a firmer appreciation of the wider needs of business and management. Although organizations are constructing operational systems, they are facing serious problems that could be solved reasonably well by OR practitioners.

There are attempts to integrate AI and OR to solve OR problems mainly in simulation and scheduling. The most promising are intelligent simulation environments, sophisticated software and hardware AI tools, intelligent front ends to OR packages and the inclusion of learning in OR models. The gains for AI, from using OR models and techniques, are substantial.

Although their potential for application is recognized, ES as aids in OR projects are at an early stage of development. It seems that there are currently few systems for providing routine assistance. One of the major problems is the lack of anything resembling general knowledge in specific OR techniques. There are experts who can provide practical and theoretical views, but these often disagree about what constitutes good OR practice, how to get good results, how to recognize a reasonable solution, and so on. There is no agreed body of facts or rules which could form a knowledge base. The alternative to generalized systems is to build customized systems for each application. Technically this can be achieved but costs would be prohibitive for most organizations.

There are considerable areas of work in common where each group of practitioners would benefit from a closer relationship with the other. Furthermore, for the efficient solution of complex problems, a combination of the two approaches is clearly called for: objective models for those parts of a system capable of mathematical descriptions, together with human-style heuristic reasoning for the more complex and behavioural parts.

We should keep in mind that the motivations which led to OR involvement in AI/ES are diverse, even though there is common agreement that it is a new technology that one should keep an eye on and that it is adequate to tackle certain kinds of problems. These ideas are supported either by specific policies of companies which try to follow recent developments in IT or by the individual effort of OR professionals who have identified some potential applications of AI within their work. In both cases, the initial efforts have been devoted to developing expertise in the field, to promoting AI ideas and to demonstrating AI applications. In many cases they are still doing that. In addition, there are AI developments which started simply when a specific part of a project was better tackled by an AI approach.

The findings of the survey of members of the OR Society confirm the growing interest in the possible uses of ES in problem solving by OR practitioners. The main involvement of OR departments has to do with the development of simple ES. Professional and organizational motivation is the main reason for developing ES, but it is premature to abandon the methodological motivation. The findings indicate enthusiasm by practitioners and clients for trying ES, but the benefits have yet to be demonstrated. There also appears to be growing confidence that there are still more benefits to be gained and anticipation of greater participation in the future.

—— Exercises ——

1. Describe the conditions under which it might be appropriate and feasible for a business to develop an ES application. What is the role of a non-technical manager in ES development?

2. Describe two or three situations in which, whilst the development of an ES would be possible, it would be better to use a specific OR approach.

3. Describe the role that an OR practitioner can play in ES, as a user and as a developer. Examine the potential impact of AI on a specific OR technique or application area.

References and further reading

Barr, A. and E. Feigenbaum (1981) *The Handbook of Artificial Intelligence*. Vol. 1, Pitman.
Chorafas, D. (1987) *Applying Expert Systems in Business*, McGraw-Hill.
CONDOR, (1988) 'Operations research: the next decade', *Operations Research*, **36**, 619–37.
Doukidis, G.I. (1987) 'An anthology on the homology of simulation with artificial intelligence', *Journal of the Operational Research Society*, **38**, 701–12.
Doukidis, G.I., F. Land and G. Miller (eds) (1989) *Knowledge-based Management Support Systems*, Ellis-Horwood.
Doukidis, G.I. and R.J. Paul (1990) 'A survey of the applications of artificial intelligence techniques within the OR Society', *Journal of the Operational Research Society*, May, **41** (5), 363–75.
Griendley, K. (ed.) (1989) *Managing Information Technology International Survey — 1988/89*, Price Waterhouse.
Harmon, P., R. Maus and W. Morrissey (1988) *Expert Systems Tools and Applications*, John Wiley.
Mockler, R. (1989) *Knowledge-based Systems for Management Decisions*, Prentice Hall.
Simon, H.A. (1987) 'Two heads are better than one: the collaboration between AI and OR', *Interfaces*, **17**, 8–15.

— 15 —

Visual interactive modelling

E. FIDDY, J.G. BRIGHT and K.J. JOHNSTON

Why?

As we have seen in Chapter 2, OR is a problem-solving activity. But it is also an advisory activity: the OR worker is focusing on someone else's problem — not his own. This fact has led to different styles of OR. At the extremes these styles could be caricatured as:

Approach A — providing *the* answer to *the* problem on a golden plate;

Approach B — providing a process for solving the problem which the problem-owner can use himself to find his own solution.

Over the last thirty years the emphasis of OR has changed from A to B. Approach A is applicable to a small fraction of tightly specified problems which the OR worker is occasionally called on to answer: for example, 'Given the chemical analysis of a set of raw materials, specify the minimum cost mix required to give a finished product which meets a given specification.'

This approach obviously assumes that the OR worker can quickly get to a state of being sure what the problem is and what the objectives in solving it are. Alas, this is rarely the case for the majority of more 'open' problems which are the usual lot of the OR worker. Attempting to use approach A on these latter problems is almost bound to give rise to some or all of the following responses from the problem-owner when the solution is proffered:

'I forgot to tell you something about the problem'

'Now I see the answer I realize that I want to give more emphasis to objective P rather than Q'

'I think we're tackling the wrong problem'

'That solution is just not practical'

and, perhaps, for the less enlightened problem-owner

'I'm not going to implement your solution' (no reasons given)

The truth is that the investigation of such problems uncovers new questions which would not have occurred to anyone at the outset (almost as quickly as it reveals answers to the questions originally asked).

Problem and solution are opposite sides of the same coin: 'If that's the solution I can tell you what the problem is!' Clearly the golden plate approach is not the best, particularly if some of the variables of the problem are 'political' or emotional ones, and therefore unquantifiable. Approach B is better.

Approach B also has its variants. At one extreme it merges with approach A, the OR worker trying to 'keep the problem-owner in touch' by providing glimpses of the data and techniques he is using, and even being susceptible to the problem-owner's refreshed views of what the problem really is! At the other extreme the OR worker merges himself chameleon-like into the problem-owner's psyche, acting as a catalyst, occasionally steering the problem-owner into an advantageous direction or pointing out inconsistencies of thought. The technique of cognitive mapping (Chapter 16) is an example.

Visual interactive modelling (VIM) comes between these two extremes. It is concerned with providing a solution process. It faces up to the fact that in many problems some variables are quantifiable, and some important variables are not. It attempts to parallel the changing perception of what the real problem is. It not only allows but demands the involvement of the problem-owner in key aspects of designing the solution method, and it ensures that the solution method can be used by the problem-owner himself in finding his own answer. What more could be asked for?

What?

Visual interactive modelling has been developed primarily to help the problem-owner help himself, as we have said, but its development has been facilitated by new technology such as colour graphics and fast interactive computer software — normally implemented on microcomputers.

The essence of the VIM approach is to represent an initial solution to a problem in *picture form* and in *colour*. The underlying model is specified in the normal way by defining relationships between variables. The solution shown on the computer screen at any time is the result of choosing particular values for certain *decision variables* in the model. The underlying model is not the essence of the VIM approach and may take any form. For some problems it might be a linear program (Chapter 4) or a simple heuristic (e.g. 'least-cost first', Chapter 3). The key feature is the picture form of the solution which stimulates two questions in the mind of the user:

1. Is this a good solution?

2. If not, what is wrong with the solution and what new choice of values of the decision variables could improve the solution?

The approach stands or falls by the extent to which the pictures really do stimulate these thoughts. Moreover, the decision-maker can take himself through not just successive solutions to one problem, but by adding further variables and other features he can redefine the problem itself. For example, consider the following:

1. Perhaps labour requirements were first ignored as being of little importance in a capital investment problem. With VIM it is simple to add them as another picture, linked to the first ones used, and to present them automatically to the user as part of the process of judging whether the final solution is satisfactory.
2. Some constraint can be removed and a study made as to whether the resulting improvement to the solution is more valuable than the cost of removing the constraint in the real world.
3. The model may highlight that the problem, as originally perceived, really results from, say, an unsatisfactory flow of material from an earlier process, not so far modelled. This extra process can easily be grafted into the model, and the results presented in the form of modified or additional pictures.

The reader will observe that much of the foregoing could be accomplished by conventional modelling methods. So what is the advantage of VIM? The answer is simple — speed. Providing the appropriate software is used (more about this later), VIM allows very rapid model evolution, and this is its most powerful feature.

So VIM is a species of 'what if' computing, the results of which are displayed pictorially in order to prompt better ideas. It contrasts with optimizing approaches whose starting point has to be a clear definition of the problem, a knowledge of the alternative means of solving it and a clear statement of the objectives to allow the best solution to be determined. For the VIM zealot, none of these is ever known at the start: *the model is being built in order to discover them!* A false pretence that all this knowledge is available a priori, leading to a highly structured model in which it is firmly embedded, provides no defence when the solution is not accepted by the client. The VIM approach allows the relatively little understanding available at the start of modelling to be stated loosely, and to become harder as understanding evolves.

In carrying out a study using VIM four steps are involved:

1. A first attempt at defining the boundary of the problem, the objectives or performance measures (normally multiple), and the main decision (or 'control') variables which could be manipulated in practice.
2. A definition of the causal links between the decision variables and the performance measures.

3. The design of suitable pictures to display the outcome of experimenting with different values of the decision variables.
4. The design of interactions to allow the values of the decision variables to be changed easily.

All the thinking behind these steps is carried out in reality by the problem-owner, aided by the OR worker. As a result of the experience gained by the problem-owner, some or all of the following will occur:

1. New performance measures will be thought of and pictures derived to illustrate them.
2. A richer understanding will evolve on how to choose values of the decision variables in order to improve these performance measures. This often leads to the learning of an efficient heuristic.
3. The assumed causal relationship between decision variables and the objectives or performance measures will come under close scrutiny. This will often demonstrate the need for more detail in parts of the model.
4. The boundary of the problem area will be reconsidered and the scope of the model changed.

Again it is the speed with which (a) results can be viewed after a change in the value of a decision variable is made, and (b) a required change to the model in any of the ways outlined above can be made which distinguishes VIM from the more usual approaches, and which makes it so successful in operation. This depends on the VIM software which is used, as we shall see later.

Examples of the visual interactive modelling approach

Three examples are discussed to show the VIM approach in action. They are based on actual VIM projects, simplified somewhat for ease of understanding, but nevertheless retaining those features that show the advantages of the VIM approach.

As we have said, VIM produces coloured pictures, sometimes moving like a cartoon. It is extremely difficult to convey the immediacy of VIM by means of printed words and static non-colour pictures. This perhaps is one of the reasons why VIM is not even more well known.

The examples are as follows:

1. Scheduling the transportation of sulphuric acid to final customers.
2. Designing a system of robots to insert electronic components into printed circuit boards.

3. Planning the strategic allocation of products to markets subject to manufacturing limitations and profitability considerations.

Each example is presented in four parts:

1. A statement of the problem as originally perceived.
2. An example of the picture(s) designed to present potential solutions.
3. The interactions built into the model to allow experimentation.
4. The evolution of the model resulting from the greater understanding promoted by the VIM process.

Sulphuric acid distribution

The first example concerns the distribution of a by-product of zinc production — sulphuric acid.

THE PROBLEM   AD Limited produces zinc at its three plants. One of the by-products is concentrated sulphuric acid. This acid is diluted to four different strengths before being sold to customers. There are fourteen customers, all remote from the production plants. Each of these customers has a constant rate of demand for one or more of the four acid strengths.

The acid is delivered by three modes of transport — ship, rail and road — but not all plant/customer combinations can be serviced by all three modes. The transport cost per tonne by each of the three modes is known.

The problem was to devise a forward schedule for transport, which was both feasible and least-cost. Such a schedule had to recognize that each plant and customer had minimum and maximum storage levels for each acid strength. At the outset, it was unclear who made the decision when to change the dilution strength at each producing plant. This decision, which had a major influence on the transport schedule because it closed off a number of distribution options, was believed to be outside the remit of the transport scheduler.

THE PICTURE   Figure 15.1 shows a typical schedule in the form of a timechart, with time running horizontally. The bars on the chart fall into three categories:

1. The customers (fourteen rows)
2. The plants (three rows)
3. The transport schedule (six rows: three trains, two road tankers and one ship)

INTERACTIONS   There are no optimizing algorithms to solve the above problem and produce the desired transport schedule. Clearly an efficient heuristic must be discovered, but it is unlikely that this could be achieved sitting at a desk with only paper and pencil!

Using the VIM approach, a schedule can be built up manually on the screen.

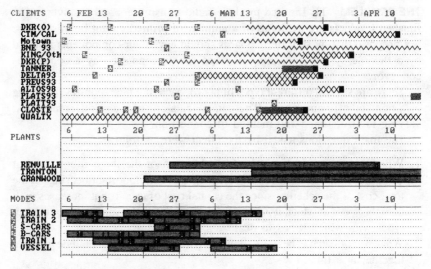

Figure 15.1   Transport schedule

Here the computer can help. At any stage during the process of creating the schedule, the immediate customer demands that need to be satisfied can be displayed, the alternative transport possibilities shown and the 'player' can decide which alternative to introduce into the schedule. All the arithmetic — and there is much of it — is performed automatically, leaving the player to concentrate on 'looking beyond the end of his nose' in making individual decisions.

This is a discovery process which brings to the surface many 'hints and tips'. For example, the following was quickly discovered: 'if delivery A can use ship, road or rail, and delivery B, slightly later, can use ship only, beware of committing the ship to delivery A even if — at the time — it is the lowest cost alternative'.

EVOLUTION   A natural progression from this manual scheduling is to begin the development of a heuristic, using the rules learnt during manual operation.

After the transport scheduling system had been refined over a period of time, it became apparent that the decisions made at the producing plants on when to change dilution strengths needed to be integrated into the scheduling system.

Printed circuit board component insertion

The second example is a discrete event simulation of a robot system for the insertion of components into printed circuit boards.

THE PROBLEM   TE Limited produce radio transmitters and receivers. The finished products are made up of a number of printed circuit boards. There is a proposal that most of these boards should have their components inserted by a flexible system consisting of three robots connected by a continuous conveyor.

There are several different types of board, each of which requires the fitting of a number of components. The components are of many different types, varying in size, shape and method of connection.

The main questions asked by the client were as follows:

1. Which components should be fitted by each of the three robots, and at what speed should each robot work? This has an important bearing on the total cost of the scheme, since the capital cost of each robot increases with both the speed at which it is required to operate and the variety of component types with which it has to deal.
2. What size of batch is best, i.e. how many identical boards should be grouped together at a time?
3. Is the overall production rate affected by the time between batches? It is possible that the system will become blocked if too many boards are present.

There are many subsidiary questions, including one of the classical questions for which simulation is a good technique for giving an answer: 'what size of buffer should be provided on the input and output sides of each robot?'

THE PICTURE   Figure 15.2 shows an outline diagram of the proposed layout of the robots and conveyor. When the simulation is run, the progress of circuit boards through the system can be watched, and the build-up of bottlenecks or the robots being starved of work quickly recognized. More important, the *reasons* for poor performance become apparent by careful attention to what is happening on the screen.

Other pictures show a range of comparative statistics for the current run and previous runs. These include robot utilization and work-in-progress.

INTERACTIONS   Interactive routines are provided to allow the user to vary all model parameters. These include conveyor speed, the speed of each robot and the size of its input and output buffers, the product mix, batch size and time between batches.

EVOLUTION   The model started life as a very simple simulation. After the first few runs, it became apparent that additional detail was required, especially in the areas of robot input and output buffers, batch size and time between batches. After many runs the results formed the basis for a decision to invest in a particular set of robots and the connecting conveyor system.

However, before this decision could be made, a separate, very detailed,

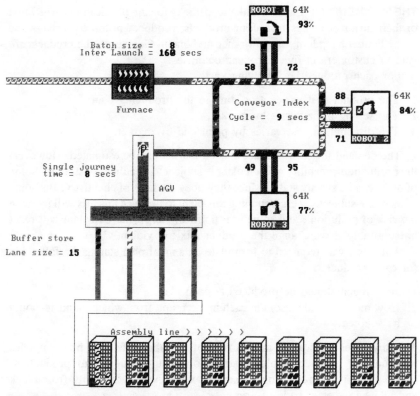

Note: AGV = Automatic guided vehicle

Figure 15.2   Proposed layout

model had to be developed for investigating the allocation of component types to each robot, looking microscopically at the carousel system for supplying individual components to the robots. Only in this way could management gain sufficient confidence to proceed.

Strategic planning

The final example shows the use of VIM in assisting the more strategic types of decision often made in companies. It refers to a multinational company with plants in different countries, trying to satisfy different markets with different products. Previously, market constraints meant that each local plant manufactured all products for its local markets. These constraints were then relaxed, and the question was raised as to whether certain plants should concentrate on certain products for supply to all markets.

THE PROBLEM   CF Limited make feedstocks for the plastics industry. Most of their turnover comes from four products, produced at three plants — one in the United Kingdom, one in France and one in Germany. The products are sold to customers in five European countries.

For each product the following vary:

1. The product cost varies according to the producing plant.
2. The selling price varies by market.
3. The distribution cost varies by plant and by market.

The demand for each product in each market can be estimated. However, the production capability at each plant is subject to peculiar constraints. Some of these can be strictly stated, since they obey the laws of chemistry. But some of them are subjective, e.g. 'running this plant to produce this mix will increase the risk of pollution'; and some are 'political', e.g. 'the UK plant will react unfavourably if we change the product mix too violently'.

A method was required to formulate an annual plan stating the following for each product:

1. How much should be produced at each plant.
2. How much should be sold in each market, and from which plants it should be sourced.

The key objective was to maximize profit — the difference between sales revenue and production plus distribution cost — subject to production, transportation and marketing constraints which varied in clarity from black and white to a pale shade of grey.

THE PICTURE   Figures 15.3 and 15.4 are largely self-explanatory. The left-hand half of the screen shows demand and supply information. The right-hand half of the screen can be switched to show either cost and revenue data (Figure 15.3) or the table of allocations (Figure 15.4). This latter picture is required when interacting.

Figures 15.3 and 15.4 show the model in an early stage of development. There are three producing plants and three markets. More importantly, the production constraints cover only total production for each plant. Pictures to show the subtle complexities of production constraints were developed later. Nevertheless, all the data needed by the decision-maker is presented in an easily accessible form. For example, a single keystroke switches between Figures 15.3 and 15.4.

INTERACTIONS   The main interaction allows the user to specify the quantity of each product to be supplied from each producing plant to each market. Whenever a change is made the corresponding numbers are updated.

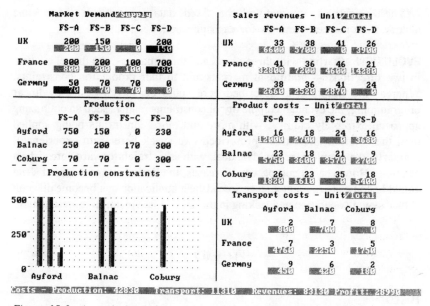

Figure 15.3 Annual plan information — demand/supply and revenue

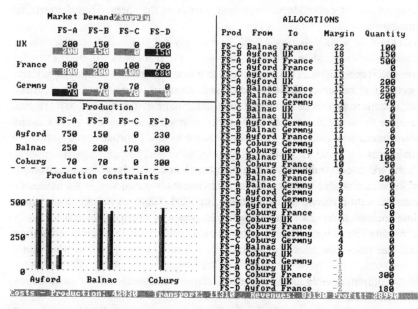

Figure 15.4 Annual plan information — demand/supply and allocations

The user can also interact with the 'fixed' data, i.e. the cost and revenue data and the market demands for each product.

EVOLUTION   Starting with three plants and three markets, the model evolved in two directions — additional markets and further production constraints. Whereas the simple case described here could be solved easily by linear programming, the eventual complexity of constraints renders such an optimizing approach extremely clumsy, with more and more constraints being applied until the solution is virtually prescribed (we speak here from experience). Similarly, the simple case could be dealt with as a straightforward spreadsheet example. However, as complexity increases, the limitations of a spread sheet would be too constraining: a large spreadsheet application can become difficult to use, slow in operation and lacking in the appropriate pictorial representation.

HOW?

History

Visual interactive modelling, as an approach to problem-solving, started in the late 1970s with the technique of simulation. Models built using the earliest VIM software tools made an immediate impact on the client. They demystified simulation.

These early models, once built, were easy for the non-computer-literate manager to experiment with, but they were far from easy to build, even for computer specialists. This was because a knowledge of a language such as Fortran was required. However, managers aware of the power of the approach became more and more interested in building their own models. Furthermore, because 'what if? computing by pictures' seemed a natural way to look at and learn about *any* problem, they wondered why the approach was limited to simulation.

An additional problem was that a Fortran-like environment imposed a strait-jacket on the model-builder when it came to adapting a model — we have seen that adaptability is one of the hallmarks of VIM. Changes in logic took a long time to implement and thus model evolution was not truly interactive.

Meanwhile, developments in the technology of microcomputers and colour graphics continued apace. Computers proliferated among people who would never otherwise have become involved with computing. Furthermore, microcomputers were achieving processing speeds previously attainable only on mainframes.

All these forces created a demand for more user-friendly VIM software tools, using 'higher-level' methods of representing the model to the computer.

Eventually, over the space of ten years, a new generation of VIM software tools evolved.

Somewhat surprisingly, even the computer experts who had become skilled in first generation VIM software rapidly took to the new tools. This was because of the following:

1. The vastly increased speed of building and adapting models.
2. The much greater width of application of the approach.
3. A considerable improvement in ease of use, without the usual attendant reduction in flexibility and power.

These will now be discussed.

Speed and adaptability

A vital requirement of VIM is that a first-shot model can be up and running quickly — perhaps taking a few hours or days, depending on the application. It must then be easy and quick to adapt any aspect of the model, whether it is 'data', 'logic', 'pictures' or 'parameters'. This adaptation time-scale is measured in *minutes* — fast enough to keep up with the ideas generated by the previous run of the model. It is like playing darts; if you throw three darts in quick succession you stand a better chance of hitting the required target than if you are forced to wait a few hours between throws.

Full adaptability also means that there should be no annoying constraints on the size or complexity of the eventual fully fledged model.

These requirements have now been met by available VIM software tools.

Width of application

Visual interactive modelling software has suffered to some extent from its historical beginnings in simulation, but is now much more widely applicable. Good VIM software will provide a 'core' of visual interactive facilities which can be used to build *any* visual interactive model. Examples of these facilities include pictures which can be shown on screens by means of windows, icons, menus, tables, variables, logic units and so on. Then additional sets of facilities ('extensions') can be provided for particular application areas, such as simulation, scheduling, allocation, vehicle route planning, strategic planning, distribution and so on. The core is the power tool, and the extensions can be seen as 'add-on' attachments.

It is also essential that the software can communicate with other systems (especially company databases, etc.). As a particular example of this requirement, it is often necessary to interface a visual interactive scheduling system with a materials requirements planning (MRP) system, often because MRP systems cannot produce a meaningful schedule against the finite capacities of the production processes (although they do a very good 'administrative' job in handling complex material requirement calculations).

Ease of use

There seems to be general agreement that current VIM software is easier to use than its forbears, but there is no reason to suppose that it cannot be made even easier. Unfortunately, there is a logical fact which prevents a would-be modeller from simply saying 'compute' to the computer — a complex piece of logic requires a correspondingly flexible language to express it. Given the requirement to represent a range of logic from simple to complex, the software must include an editor for model logic which leads the modeller by the hand and prevents him from making errors. Furthermore, specialized editors for the creation and amendment of pictures, interactions, etc., must be supplied — it is unacceptable to ask the modeller to write computer code for such purposes.

Also important is the rate at which familiarity with the software is gained. In the case of many first-generation packages, an extensive training period was necessary before any useful work could be contemplated. Current software has removed the need for detailed knowledge of a general-purpose language, and this significantly reduces the learning time required.

There is an unquenchable market demand for easier to use software. Ease of use normally means loss of power and generality, and this can be a cause for concern. The underlying question is 'how can a generalized VIM package handle all the problem-specific features found in real life?' There would seem to be two ways of approaching this question:

1. Add more and more facilities, each dealing with a particuilar feature. This tends to produce a very cumbersome package.
2. Allow an 'escape route' to a lower-level language.

There is no clear evidence that one of these is better than the other, especially in this age of growing computer literacy.

Conclusions

This chapter has attempted to explain the nature of the visual interactive approach to problem-solving, and why it came into being. It has briefly given some examples of its use.

VIM software has changed out of all recognition from its beginnings in the late 1970s. It is now possible for people with only moderate computing skills (and sometimes none at all) to develop visual interactive models. Also, the range of management problems on which it can be used has expanded considerably.

The philosophy behind the approach starts with the recognition that a complex management problem cannot be parcelled and predefined. One's perception of it, and insight into it, follows a lurching process, in which each step in conceptual thinking is followed by experiment. A child was once observed trying to erect a folded deck-chair. He pulled it by one corner and watched what happened: each further experiment was followed by a further period of thought, and the chair was soon erected. It probably never would have been erected if all steps to the successful conclusion had had to be determined before the chair was touched. VIM parallels such a discovery process, and one in which the problem-owner can participate fully.

It has often been said that the real power of VIM becomes apparent only when a traditional non-visual approach has been used first and a visual interactive model created later. There is certainly a growing army of VIM builders and users. Among their number are very few indeed who would revert to a non-VIM approach for solving an ever-increasing range of management problems.

– 16 –

Working on problems using cognitive mapping

C. EDEN

What is a cognitive map and what is it supposed to do?

A cognitive map is designed to help give *structure* to a problem. It is an organized representation of the way in which a client *believes* a problem has come about. The client may, of course, be the cognitive mapper. Most often the mapper is an operations researcher trying to understand a client; however, there is no reason why the process described should not be used to help sort out a problem that belongs to the mapper.

A cognitive map includes both a description of a problem situation and an understanding about what can and cannot be done about a problem. Thus a problem is taken to be something that includes within its definition the practical problems of getting something done. These aspects of the problem are not left until the end of the so-called problem-solving activity. They are taken to be a significant part of the way in which each of us sees a problem. Indeed, the problem we face is often that of 'how to get something done'.

The system of beliefs, captured by a cognitive map, gives an indication of *why* the situation is problematic. The mapping process helps identify the sense of direction ('goals'), or disappointment about current direction ('not-goals'), embedded in statements made about the situation. It does not assume that a problem-owner knows what his or her objectives are, or how to proceed towards solution. The problem-owner is not expected to describe the problem in any set order or structure, indeed the presumption on the part of the cognitive mapper is that the problem may exist partly because there is doubt about the relevance of some aspects of the situation, because there may be conflicting goals and because there are uncomfortable ramifications of possible actions.

The added value that comes from undertaking the formal business of developing and analyzing a cognitive map is the process of providing clues as to the way in which the complexity within a problematic situation can be managed. These clues may be: an understanding of the nature of the goal *system*; a sense of how different parts of the situation interrelate; suggestions about the most important options identified by implication; and an understanding and identification of the 'nub of the issue'. Essentially, building a cognitive map is about *structuring the problem.*

> When approaching a business problem, don't try to come up with the answers . . . Focus on what the problems are . . . If you get the wrong answer to the right question, you usually have a chance to fix it . . . But if you get the right answer to the wrong question, you're sunk . . . And business does altogether too much of that (Peter Drucker).

When is it worth building a cognitive map?

Many OR techniques involve considerable investment in modelling the problem. This means that a user of the modelling technique has to make an a priori judgement about benefits likely to accrue from the activity. In the case of cognitive mapping this decision is usually simpler because mapping can be undertaken, at one extreme, as a 'doodle' about the problem in order to get a feel for its nature, or, at the other extreme, as a serious exercise in understanding a complex issue involving a number of participants and subsequently as a method for providing group decision support (Eden and Radford, 1990) or guidance for major quantitatively based OR projects. In the first instance the map may be constructed by the problem-owner, contain about 25 concepts, be on the 'back of an envelope' and analyzed by visual inspection. In the second case it might involve extensive interviews with several stakeholders, the construction of a computer model with 2,000 concepts, the use of the model in a group workshop and the use of extensive techniques for analyzing a cognitive map.

What this means is that maps can be constructed on an incremental basis with a quick evaluation of benefit at each 'milestone'. A major decision about use does not necessarily have to be made in advance. Nevertheless, there are some characteristics of problems that make mapping particularly appropriate:

1. If the problem relates to a situation where it is described predominantly by qualitative notions then mapping is an excellent starting point. Sometimes there is an expectation that a qualitative problem will at some future time become more numerical. The process of problem *structuring* is often particularly critical in these cases.
2. If there are likely to be a number of important and different perspectives

on the problem then mapping is likely to be a good way of drawing together this richness and negotiating a new vision of the problem that all interested parties can work on together.

3. If the problem is strategic in nature, and therefore involves consideration of subjective views of the future, then mapping is an appropriate way of developing, testing and managing the anticipated future.

4. If the situation under consideration involves identifying a number of related projects that different working parties can address as if they were independent, mapping is likely to provide a sound way of identifying them.

Building up a cognitive map in an interview

The key element of the process of mapping a client's understanding of his problematic situation derives from asking 'why is he/she telling me this?' Thus assertions about the nature of the world are taken seriously as if they had action implications by asking, 'so what?' (not necessarily explicitly). The client is treated as if he or she were a 'scientist' attempting 'to make sense of' (Kelly, 1955), or unravel, the situation they face. Thus if the client says 'Joe's office is too large' then we can be reasonably certain that the statement implies action to 'make Joe's office smaller' by, for example, 'moving Joe' or 'changing the size of his current office'.

In cognitive map format this would look like:

Joe's office too large
... make Joe's office smaller

Move Joe ...   Change the size of Joe's current office ...

Note that the ellipses (three dots) are read as 'rather than' and separate the first (emergent) phrase and its contrast or 'opposite pole'; the negative sign on the end of the arrow signifies that the emergent phrase of one concept leads to, or is explained by, the contrasting phrase of the other concept. Thus it is often the case that the *contrasting phrase* represents a future situation, in contrast to the present or past; or alternatively the present in contrast to past or future. Similarly the contrasting phrase often signifies the nature of a solution.

It is easy to presume the above *possible* actions because the original statement was evaluative (included the word 'too' in it) and implied a sense of direction which needs to be made explicit ('what would be good and/or bad about 'Joe's office being smaller'?'). However, a person will often make non-evaluative statements that are made as if an objective fact were being stated. Thus 'Joe's office is large' does not say whether this is good or bad, and so prompts an attempt to discover why the statement is being made. This can be done by discovering the *evaluation* of the 'fact' and/or identifying the action implications — 'there is a debate about values and about facts *and about their relationship one to another* . . . because any assertion about the nature of the world is seen as having action implications *for disturbing the social order* [amongst members of an organization]' (Eden, 1989).

For example if a client says 'we are losing at least a quarter of our potential production each week', it is delivered as a fact and we do not know how it is being evaluated. *Non-verbal* aspects of this statement may clearly indicate that the client is not happy about this predicament. That is, the client may have said it with a despairing tone and body movements which make it clear that the situation is discomforting to him. If this is so then we can presume that some opposing circumstance might relieve this unhappiness, such as 'production at 90 per cent of potential would be OK'. Note how this contrast has elements of 'satisficing'. Mapping is designed to capture the realistic expectations of the client rather than what 'should or ought' to be the case. Mapping, as a problem construction tool, is not intended to be normative but '*descriptively* prescriptive' and suggestive of action.

In order to give more meaning to statements made, we would also want to elicit, or at the very least guess, what the outcome of a stated circumstance might be *for the client*. In relation to the statement above, we might simply ask 'so what?' and so elicit the reply that 'it's not good enough' implying that the current circumstances is a bad thing *per se* — it is not optional, but is *evaluated* as bad and thus of a value or *goal status*. The answer may alternatively be 'deliveries are becoming poorer', which again begs the question 'so what?' and the possible answer 'our best customers are losing their trust in us'. In this way we are *carefully* bulding up a chain of personally viewed causes and effects, means and ends.

The cognitive map of this problem, as described, would be as shown in Figure 16.1. The process looks obvious, but many of the assertions about the world, made by clients, do not have obvious reasons for being stated and so are ignored by the consultant as if they were simply background irrelevances or 'red herrings' and therefore a waste of the consultant's time. Alternatively, the consultant sees them as so obvious in their importance that a presumption is made incorrectly about why the statement has been made. Experience in problem structuring using maps suggests that it is often these so-called 'asides' that can be crucial to identifying possible actions.

For example, if the client says something like 'we're a nice organization to work in', it sounds like a throw-away line. But if we always presume that every statements has a purpose until proven otherwise, then the requirement in the mapper is to note the concept and attempt to understand the *meaning*

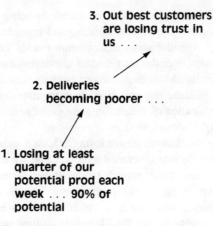

3. Out best customers
are losing trust in
us . . .

2. Deliveries
becoming poorer . . .

1. Losing at least
quarter of our
potential prod each
week . . . 90% of
potential

Figure 16.1

of the statement in terms of *action* consequences. Thus with prompting or
energetic listening it may be followed by the assertion that 'I can't understand
why the labour force won't accept the changes.'

All of this is tantamount to good interview technique designed to find out
where the client 'is coming from'. However, if the process is converted into
a cognitive map, it becomes the basis for problem construction *and also* efficient
interviewing (see Eden and Simpson, 1989, for further exploration of the role
for cognitive mapping). A map drawn 'on the hoof' signals potential misunderstandings and encourages the client to make explicit elements of the
problem that have hitherto remained unsaid or in the subconscious. A part
of the skill of the good interviewer is to draw out the experience and wisdom
of the client as it is related to the problem situation (Eden *et al.*, 1983, Chapter
3).

The nature of cognitive map

To demonstrate the features of a cognitive map, let us try building a cognitive
map from scratch. The example I will use comes from an attempt at
understanding a problem I faced recently while waiting for my return flight
from London Heathrow airport to Glasgow.

I do the trip regularly and had become increasingly frustrated at spending
almost as much time in a queue waiting to have my hand baggage checked
by the X-ray machine as I spent in the air. I had already written to the managing
director of British Airports Authority complaining, and he had replied arguing
that the problem could not be solved until more labour was available. However,

on this particular occasion, a couple of months later, I had suffered again and subsequently missed my flight. Being an operations researcher, I reckoned that there must be something that could be done about what seemed, on the face of it, to be a queueing problem. But I first wanted to reflect on the nature of the problem *as I, a naive but frustrated passenger, saw it.* I sat in the lounge, pencil poised over a clean, unlined A4 sheet of paper and started building my map.

My problem label 'extensive queues at X-ray' starts the map (concept 1 on Figure 16.2 — the concepts are numbered in the order they were written down). This label is the emerging pole of the concept and obviously represents the current circumstance as I saw it. The first prompt to myself arises from the encouragement mapping provides for making explicit the contrasting pole. In this case the prompt question was, what do I reckon would be acceptable? — 'three minutes or less of a queue' (contrasting the future with the present and suggesting a characteristic of the solution). My next prompt, why am I exercised by this situation? — 'high level of axiety about missing flight' (2) (I had just missed one) rather than 'viewing X-ray checks as routine checks'. I also saw the situation as promoting an 'increase in total journey time' (3) and additionally realized that it was not only anxiety about missing flights but also actually 'missing flights' (4) that worried me. The final first thought about why the situation was a problem *to me* reflected previous experiences of 'flights being held up by late passengers' (5) arriving at the gate but with baggage already checked into the aircraft hold (meaning the flight must be held).

(Note that it is interesting that I did not elaborate this latter argument onto the map, and yet the process of explaining it to a reader has now alerted me to an option available to me which would ensure that I would not miss the flight in future! This demonstrates the need to elaborate the detail in maps rather than be tempted to use them as summary statements. It is the detailed theories about why the situation is as it is that lead to good problem structuring and so to more imaginative, robust and practical solutions.)

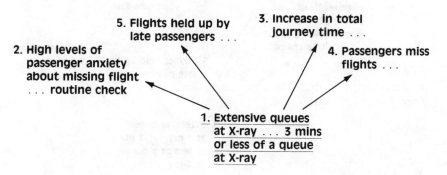

Figure 16.2

So the initial picture of the *problem* (why it matters, concepts 2—5) rather than a *situation* (label, concept 1) looked like Figure 16.2. I then started elaborating the nature of the problem by following the consequences of the outcomes already identified by tracking my personal experience and understanding of air travel. Late passengers (5) (Figure 16.3) mean that 'all passengers arrive at their destination late' (6) and 'flight runs off schedule' (7). Although flights running off schedule did not matter to me *per se*, I immediately noted my overriding *not-goal* of 'passenger frustration with air travel' (8).

(Note that I would not express 'no frustration with air travel' as a *goal*, whereas the negative outcome matters a great deal to me.)

I went on to link 'flight off schedule' (7) through 'air traffic delays increase' (9) to 'arriving late' (6) and also link directly 'flights off schedule' (7) to 'arriving late' (6).

(Note that this was done without noting the intermediate explanation — my belief that when flights run off the schedule then there is a greater likelihood that they will move further off schedule. This omission is bad practice. If I were interviewing I would always ask the client to elaborate any link which exists in parallel to another link between the same concepts. This ensures that the 'short cut' link is a different set of theories from another path of argumentation.)

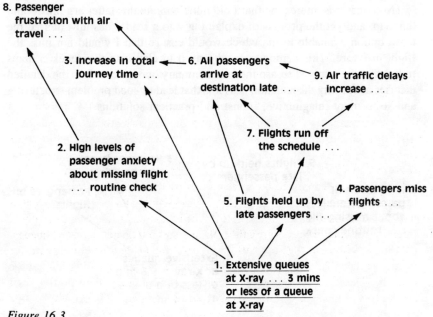

8. Passenger frustration with air travel . . .

3. Increase in total journey time . . .

6. All passengers arrive at destination late . . .

9. Air traffic delays increase . . .

2. High levels of passenger anxiety about missing flight . . . routine check

7. Flights run off the schedule . . .

4. Passengers miss flights . . .

5. Flights held up by late passengers . . .

1. Extensive queues at X-ray . . . 3 mins or less of a queue at X-ray

Figure 16.3

Figure 16.3 shows the current version of the map, and reflects a 'minimum' version of the problem; that is, it has recorded at least one *goal* or *not-goal*. Next I thought it might help me if I were to try and understand the situation from the point of view of the British Airports Authority (Figure 16.4). I had always been led to believe that the main income to BAA came from selling things (duty-free, food, etc.) to waiting travellers; thus it seemed likely that 'X-ray queues' (1) would lead to 'reduced time in shopping malls' (10) and thus 'reduced revenue from shops' (11). However, it also seems possible that they might be worried about their 'reputation for inefficiency' (12) which could result from 'passengers missing flights' (4) and 'passenger anxiety' (2), and more importantly that their 'reputation for safety might begin to suffer' (13).

This represents the first stab at looking at the problem from the point of view of two stakeholders, (myself and BAA). (The map currently shows three 'heads' (concepts 8, 11 and 13). A 'head' is a concept with no further consequences. Concepts 8 and 13, one for each stakeholder, seem to be of a genuine *goal* or *not-goal* status. However, concept 3 is also of *goal* status for myself with concept 2 almost certainly a *not-goal*; in other words I cannot imagine arguing for 'routine checks' as a goal but the ramification of 'high anxiety' is, for me, a bad thing *per se*. Similarly, it seems likely that the contrasting pole of concept 12 is a *goal* for BAA. Thus I have already begun the process of implicitly identifying a *goal system* as it relates to this particular problem situation.)

Glancing around the map led to my noting that 'flights off schedule' (7) (Figure 16.5) means 'extra fuel used' (14) with 'increased cost to airlines' (15) and thus 'increased fares' (16) (the contrast of 'decreased fares' being a goal for me) and so more 'frustration with air travel' (8).

(There are now three paths of argumentation from 'queues' (1) to 'frustration' (8), two representing relatively obvious short-term consequneces and this latter path representing a less obvious long-term consequence that I would be less likely to have attributed to 'queues at the X-ray machines'.)

With 'sensible' looking *goals* for the two major stakeholders it seemed worth exploring the most obvious options for reducing queues. However, before doing so I added my previously stated belief about 'flights held up by late passengers' (5) being the consequence of 'passengers check in baggage before X-ray' (17).

The solution which had been mentioned by the managing director was to 'deploy more staff' (18) (Figure 16.6), but this would inevitably mean a higher likelihood of 'staff standing idle' (19). But on the other hand, if BAA could 'identify the rate of queue growth' (20) and so 'anticipate increased queues' (21) then they could 'deploy staff on demand rather than without regard for queue length' (22) and so reduce the likelihood of 'staff standing idle (at the machines)'. Nevertheless 'deploying staff on demand' (22) still means that 'staff are waiting around (in a waiting room) to do something' (23). An implication of 'deploying more staff' is that 'more X-ray machines' (24) would be needed.

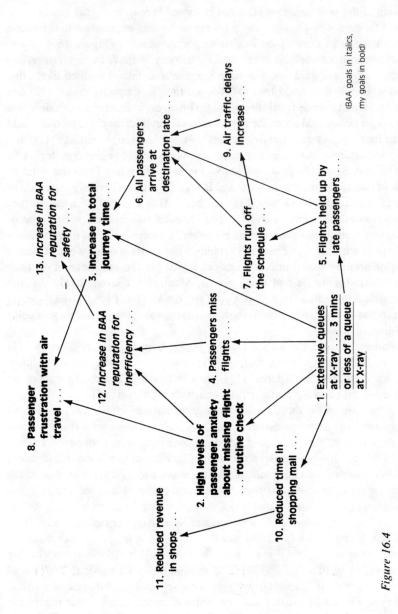

(BAA goals in italics, my goals in bold)

1. Extensive queues at X-ray . . . 3 mins or less of a queue at X-ray

2. High levels of passenger anxiety about missing flight routine check

3. Increase in total journey time . . .

4. Passengers miss flights . . .

5. Flights held up by late passengers . . . .

6. All passengers arrive at destination late . . .

7. Flights run off the schedule . . . .

8. Passenger frustration with air travel . . . .

9. Air traffic delays increase . . .

10. Reduced time in shopping mall . . . .

11. Reduced revenue in shops . . . .

12. Increase in BAA reputation for inefficiency . . . .

13. Increase in BAA reputation for safety . . . .

Figure 16.4

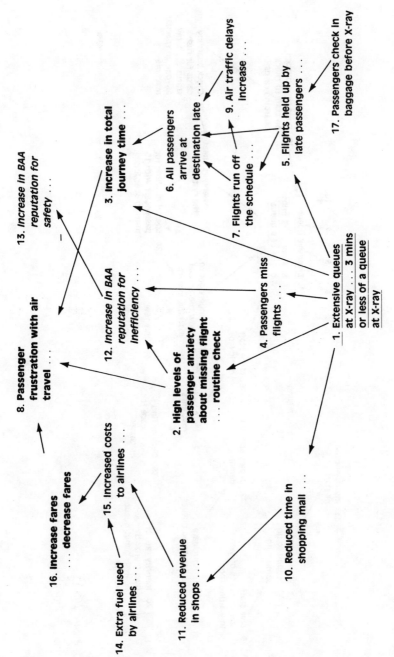

Figure 16.5

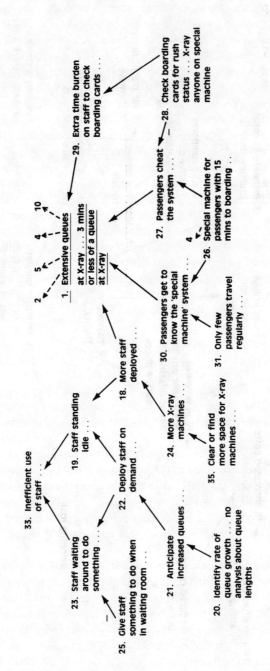

Figure 16.6

(Note that implications *for* action are mapped as *supporting* options, not as consequences of the action. Concept 24 is subordinate to 18. In order for 18 to be acted upon other options would be needed including the one identified. Adhering to the rule that an option *leads to* a desired outcome, a means leads to a desired end, is important if the map is to be used analytically rather than as a scratch pad. The importance of this role is a reflection of the use of mapping for problem-solving instead of self-reflective modelling (Eden *et al.*, 1979) and is discussed further below.)

Having 'staff waiting around' (23) to be called 'on demand' (22) seemed to be a 'silly' ramification which could be countered by 'providing staff with something to do when they are in the waiting room' (25). Other options appear on Figure 16.6 as concepts 26–31, 33 and 35.

(Note that a number of options have ramifications to outcomes that are consequences of 'extensive queues' (1). For example, using a 'special machine for passengers with 15 minutes to boarding' (26) acts as a way of stopping 'passengers missing flights' (4). Yet it is also seen as having ramification for 'queues' (1) because 'passengers cheat the system' (27) which would require consideration of the option of 'checking boarding cards for rush status rather than X-raying anyone on the special machine' (28). Thus consideration of one option generates others as well as suggesting ramifications that may be *not-goals*.)

The map shown in Figure 16.7 took me about twenty minutes and contains thirty-seven concepts. Concept 32 is another major reason for flights running off schedule and concept 34 is a direct consequence of concept 11. Concepts 36 and 37 appear as detailed elaboration of the links between concepts 1 and 3 and concepts 1 and 13 respectively. Note that these elaborations occurred because as I reviewed the map I had forgotten the reasoning behind each of these beliefs! I was then forced to elaborate, to myself, the reasoning and so inserted the extra two concepts. This process of elaboration through detailed arguments is often seen as discouraging, because it makes the problem more complex. It is, however, absolutely crucial to the process of effective problem-solving. For example, by introducing concept 37 it raises the possibility of exploring other ways of making 'passengers believe checkers are more thorough' other than 'extensive queues', thus attacking a BAA goal (concept 13).

The map is only the beginning of problem-structuring, for it is clearly only a sketch of the problem. In addition the concepts have been written in a short-hand manner — many of the concepts are incomplete in the sense that they have not specified the 'actor' responsible (for example concept 1 does not make it explicit that it is passengers who are the actors in the queue), the contrasting pole is rarely specified, the object of the action is often unclear, and some concepts are expressed as assertions rather than as a call to action. Although the map is 'improper' — not following in full the guidelines for cognitive

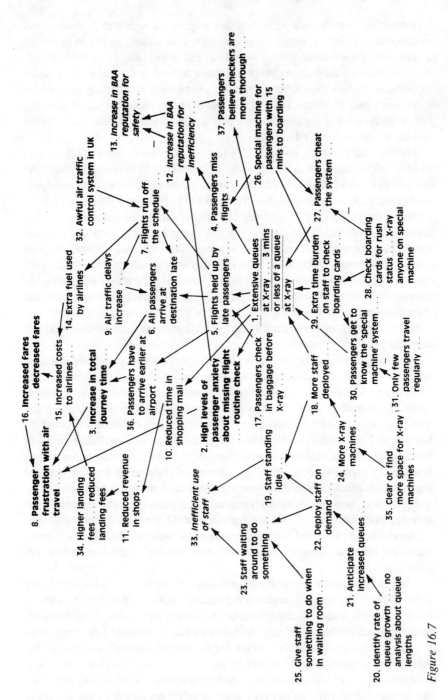

Figure 16.7

mapping (Ackermann *et al.*, 1990) it still provides a basis for exploring the features of a map that can help in understanding the problem and identifying options within the problem.

Detecting the emerging features of a cognitive map

The methodology for constructing a cognitive map aims to follow from a theoretical framework that guides understanding about the characteristics of problems and 'problem-finishing' (Eden, 1986). The primary characteristic of a map is that it is *hierarchical*, representing the view that problems derive from a wish to make a situation better, or less bad, than it currently seems to be. The top part of the hierarchy suggests the direction of despair to be alleviated or the desires to be met. The bottom represents the circumstances that are believed to cause the situation and therefore might be changed — a potential portfolio of actions to 'finish' with the problem.

Because the map as a hierarchy forms the key structural feature, coding the map into a hierarchical format is an important and non-trivial activity. As the mapper is listening to the client's beliefs, he or she is attempting to understand accurately the directionality of the belief — which of two concepts matters most — the desired outcome — and which is the means to attaining the desired outcome.

Directionality is determined by considering the belief from the standpoint of action or intervention, in other words which element in a belief is the option for action and which is the desired outcome. The decision derives from consideration of 'desire' or goal. Thus the statement that 'aircraft are often late when airports are overcrowded' could be interpreted as 'aircraft being late' (implying an option to act to 'avoid lateness') may *lead to* 'airports being overcroweded' as the not-desired outcome. Alternatively, it may be interpreted as 'airports being overcrowded' (implying the option of acting to 'avoid overcrowding') may lead to 'aircraft being late' as the not-desired outcome. It is important that the hierarchical relationship is clarified with the client.

It is the hierarchical form of a cognitive map that, for the most part, is the basis for analyzing the nature of the problem. For example the top, bottom and middle of a map can usually be taken to represent different features of the problem. If many concepts at the top of the map are accorded the status of 'goal' or 'not-goal' then the problem is *likely* to be more complex to work on. It will be more difficult to find a small number of actions that will create overall satisfaction. It is not unusual to find that some clients talk about their problem in such a way that the map is dominated by goals/not-goals and has little content that describes the situation itself. In other cases the map reflects a simple apex with one or two goals/not-goals, in which case analysis can more easily focus upon creatively identifying actions. It is also possible that a problem-owner has no conscious view of goals and that the map is dominated by a description of a situation which is simply regarded as bad, but without any clear understanding why it might be seen that way.

The nature of the map, in the terms identified above — dominance or otherwise of goals/not-goals — obviously indicates something of significance about the problem-owner and his or her attitude to the situation. It thus provides some clues about the way in which a consultant might tackle the problem. For example, if people define their problems through a dominance of not-goals then their anxiety is likely to be dominated by a view of the situation which requires the removal of 'pain'. This view is in contrast to the person whose problem is dominated by goals, and who has a problem about changing the situation into a vision of something better (proactive problem-solving), rather than something less bad (reactive problem-solving). Similarly the person for whom the emergent poles are negative descriptions of the world is more likely to be a 'reactive depressant' and responding to pressures from elsewhere rather than from him or herself (they have been convinced of the problem by someone else). A combination of reactive depressant with someone who has alluded to neither goals or not-goals is likely to mean that the person has little ownership of the problem — they have been told there is a problem rather than persuaded of it.

These are obviously generalizations but they provide clues about how a consultant/mapper or the problem-owner/mapper can tentatively reflect on the interaction between the situation and the person describing it. However, the hierarchical nature of a map also enables many other meaningful analyses of the structure to be conducted. These will be discussed below within the context of theories about the nature of problems.

The analysis of cognitive maps

'Problems can be broken down into a number of related and interacting parts' — cluster analysis. This is a commonly held view, and given the designed structural nature of a cognitive map it is possible to consider a number of ways of identifying these parts and the nature of their interaction with one another. Each method serves a different analytical purpose and reflects a particular understanding of unravelling the complexity of problems.

The most obvious way of 'breaking the problem down' is by forming the concepts into clusters, where each cluster represents a manageable number of concepts that are well-linked to one another but relatively unlinked to other clusters. In this analysis the links are taken to be directionless and a concept does not appear in more than one cluster. The analysis is seeking to minimize the number of 'bridges' (arrows) between each cluster. Thus the 'perfect' cluster is one which has no links to any other cluster — it is an 'island' and therefore represents a part of the problem which may be considered without reference to other parts. The cluster analysis may be undertaken formally by computationally drawing together, into the same cluster, concepts that have the most similar links. Clusters are formed by continually drawing together similarly linked concepts, and can be tested for the extent of 'bridging' between clusters. The extent to which differentiation is significant provides a measure of robustness of the clusters in relation to small changes in links. It is also possible, with relatively small maps (less than fifty concepts), to identify clusters by visual inspection.

In the BAA example above, a cluster analysis reveals that there is no successful way of breaking the problem into parts. This conclusion is not as unhelpful as it might appear — it suggests that the problem, as defined, is very well 'knitted together' and that any approach to solution must take account of all aspects that have been acknowledged in the map. (This suggests that the British Airports Authority should not, in the view expressed by my map, disaggregate the problem into apparently tractable parts!)

An alternative way of clustering derives from consideration of the hierarchy, and so the direction of the links. The analysis presumes that each goal/not-goal will need a solution strategy related to it, and so each goal/not-goal will prescribe the formation of a cluster that is made of all concepts subordinate to it. Concepts can thus appear in any number of clusters.

In the above model the goals and not-goals for both BAA and myself were as follows:

For myself:

2	high level of passenger anxiety (not-goal)
3	decrease in total journey time (goal)
8	passenger frustration with air travel (not-goal)
16	decreased fares (goal)

For BAA (as seen by myself):

12	increase in BAA reputation for inefficiency (not-goal)
33	not inefficient use of staff (goal)

The clusters formed by this method are listed below. Each group of concepts or hierarchical cluster is a possible part of the overall issue and the extent to which the parts are separable is indicated by the degree of overlapping membership of the groups (in this case very high, matching the results of the non-hierarchical clustering) — the groups/clusters are as follows (the goal/not-goal which formed the group is marked with an asterisk, and the size of the group is noted in brackets).

GROUP 1   subordinates of concept 2 (eleven concepts)

  1 Extensive queues at X-ray . . . 3 mins or less of a queue at X-ray
*2 High levels of passenger anxiety about missing flight . . . routine check
18 More staff deployed
24 More X-ray machines
26 Special machine for passengers with 15 mins to boarding
27 Passengers cheat the system
28 Check boarding cards for rush status . . . X-ray anyone on special machine
29 Extra time burden on staff to check boarding cards
30 Passengers get to know the 'special machine' system
31 Only few passengers travel regularly
35 Clear or find more space for X-ray machines

GROUP 2   subordinates of concept 3 (eighteen concepts)

  1 Extensive queues at X-ray . . . 3 mins or less of a queue at X-ray
*3 Increase in total journey time
  5 Flights held up by late passengers
  6 All passengers arrive at destination late
  7 Flights run off the schedule
  9 Air traffic delays increase
17 Passengers check in baggage before X-ray
18 More staff deployed
24 More X-ray machines
26 Special machine for passengers with 15 mins to boarding
27 Passengers cheat the system
28 Check boarding cards for rush status . . . X-ray anyone on special machine
29 Extra time burden on staff to check boarding cards
30 Passengers get to know the 'special machine' system
31 Only few passengers travel regularly
32 Awful air traffic control system in the United Kingdom
35 Clear or find more space for X-ray machines
36 Passengers have to arrive earlier at airport

GROUP 3   subordinates of concept 8 (one concept)

*8 Passenger frustration with air travel

GROUP 4   subordinates of concept 12 (twelve concepts)

  1 Extensive queues at X-ray . . . 3 mins or less of a queue at X-ray
  4 Passengers miss flights
*12 Increase in BAA reputation for inefficiency
18 More staff deployed

24 More X-ray machines
26 Special machine for passengers with 15 mins to boarding
27 Passengers cheat the system
28 Check boarding cards for rush status . . . X-ray anyone on special machine
29 Extra time burden on staff to check boarding cards
30 Passengers get to know the 'special machine' system
31 Only few passengers travel regularly
35 Clear or find more space for X-ray machines

GROUP 5   subordinates of concept 13 (twelve concepts)

  1 Extensive queues at X-ray . . . 3 mins or less of a queue at X-ray
*13 Increase in BAA reputation for safety
18 More staff deployed
24 More X-ray machines
26 Special machine for passengers with 15 mins to boarding
27 Passengers cheat the system
28 Check boarding cards for rush status . . . X-ray anyone on special machine
29 Extra time burden on staff to check boarding cards
30 Passengers get to know the 'special machine' system
31 Only few passengers travel regularly
35 Clear or find more space for X-ray machines
37 Passengers believe checkers are more thorough

GROUP 6   subordinates of concept 16 (twenty concepts)

  1 Extensive queues at X-ray . . . 3 mins or less of a queue at X-ray
  5 Flights held up by late passengers
  7 Flights run off the schedule
10 Reduced time in shopping mall
11 Reduced revenue in shops
14 Extra fuel used by airlines
15 Increased costs to airlines
*16 Increased fares . . . decreased fares
17 Passengers check in baggage before X-ray
18 More staff deployed
24 More X-ray machines
26 Special machine for passengers with 15 mins to boarding
27 Passengers cheat the system
28 Check boarding cards for rush status . . . X-ray anyone on special machine
29 Extra time burden on staff to check boarding cards
30 Passengers get to know the 'special machine' system
31 Only few passengers travel regularly
32 Awful air traffic control system in the United Kingdom

34 Higher landing fees . . . reduced landing fees
35 Clear or find more space for X-ray machines

GROUP 7   subordinates of concept 33 (ten concepts)

18 More staff deployed
19 Staff standing idel
20 Identify rate of queue growth . . . no analysis about queue lengths
21 Anticipate increased queues
22 Deploy staff on demand
23 Staff waiting around to do something
24 More X-ray machines
25 Give staff something to do when in waiting room
*33 Inefficient use of staff
35 Clear or find more space for X-ray machines

'Potent' options

Group 3 contains no concepts because it is superordinate to three other concepts, each of which is a goal/not-goal in its own right. However, each of the other groups contains some similar concepts, indeed concepts 18, 24 and 35 are in all six possible groups. These concepts must therefore be *potent* in their potential impact on the goal system; they may be good or bad options but they are certainly significant. But concepts 24 and 35 are subordinate to 18 and have no other consequences, thus option 18 is a particularly noteworthy potent option. Similarly concepts 26 and 28 are each in five groups and have slightly different ramifications and so are each likely to be *potent*.

Potent options are worth identifying because they provide one indication of the options that must be evaluated in the search for a portfolio of actions. Further evaluation in relation to content and the 'power' of the beliefs (arrows) may reduce their potency, but they are, nevertheless, a good starting point.

Key options

The previous section introduced the notion of 'potent' options — those that have a large number of ramifications for goals/not-goals. In addition we can identify options that act as 'gates' to the goal system. If the model is totally pyramidal, where any concept has only one consequential route to the most hierarchical concept, then the single key option is the 'head' of the map. A key option is a concept as close to the top of the model as possible and which does not exclude any possible ramifications. Thus in our model, concepts 28 and 26 are key options because they both have more than one consequential path, whereas concept 22 is also a key option for the same reason but it is not a 'tail'. In this way a portfolio of options is identified in such a way that, unless the identified option is attrctive, then any subordinate options need not be considered. The process of identifying 'key options' thus provides for the efficient evaluation of options. In effect it means that any subordinate concepts can be temporarily concatenated into the key option and only considered if the key option looks promising.

The 'nub of the issue': significant or core concepts

When a map is drawn certain concepts seem to be central because they have lots of explanations and lots of consequences (in our map concept 1 is, not surprisingly, the most obvious). It is usual for the problem label (concept 1) to be central; however, it is also likely that other concepts emerge as central to the definition of the problem, and these are usually worth noting. For the BAA map concept 1 has four ins and six outs, with concept 7 the next highest total of two ins and three outs, and concepts 5 and 6 having two ins and two outs, and three ins and one out respectively. These 'central' concepts with a high local domain count are often clues to the 'nub of the issue' and are worth noting as such.

The above domain analysis tends to overplay local characteristics and miss holistic features, such as amount of argumentation supporting and consequential to a concept, and the extent of elaboration of the arguments. Thus it is usually worth considering the centrality of concepts along these more complicated dimensions. In the BAA map such an analysis reveals that concepts 1, 7 and 5 are once again significant, but that in addition concepts 18, 27 and 30 are also important, for example:

concept 18   has one path of argument supporting it — 35 > 24 > 18;
eleven paths of argument that are ramifications;
twenty-three concepts are encompased by explanations and consequences;
the mean length of a path of argument is five concepts.

whereas concept 5   has seven paths of argument supporting it;
four paths of argument that are ramifications;
nineteen concepts are encompassed by explanations and consequences;
the mean length of a path of argument is four concepts.

An index of centrality may be created which combines these four characteristics. Clearly there is no absolutely best way of calculating the index; the results should, therefore, be treated as indicative and taken alongside a domain measure of centrality.

Thus we may consider concepts, 1, 5, 7, 18 and 27 to be possible *key concepts*.

Summarizing the problem through analysis

A useful summary of the problem is often released by using a combination of goals/not-goals, key concepts, and key options, and the cluster analysis. The summary, by its nature, *invites attempts at developing a portfolio of actions*. The actions are developed by evaluating the options as if they were capable of implementation and then elaborating the map in the form of identifying further explanations for the option being considered. By building subordinate concepts, each explanation becomes a possible action in itself which supports the original option.

For the BAA problems this description would be as follows:

1. [Problem label] The problem of 'extensive queues at the X-ray machine' (1) is important because:
2. [Goals/not-goals] 'passengers are becoming increasingly frustrated with air travel' (8) because they 'are suffering high levels of anxiety' (2), and would like to see 'decreased fares' (16) and 'a decrease in journey time' (3) but fear the opposite; in addition BAA would like 'no increase in their reputation for inefficiency' (12) and an 'increase in their reputation for safety' (13).
3. [Key concepts] significant elements of the problem relate to 'flights running off schedule' (7), their being 'held up by late passengers' (5), 'passengers cheating systems' (27) and the possible need for 'more staff to be deployed' (18).
4. [Key options] for consideration are: 'deploying staff on demand' (22), avoiding 'staff waiting around to do something' (23), 'checking boarding cards for rush-status' (28), and devoting a 'special machine for passengers with 15 mins to boarding' (26).

In addition the cluster analyses suggest that it is important to deal with this problem as a whole, for breaking the problem into components could mean missing important ramifications.

The key concepts indicate that any further consideration of the problem (more problem construction) would probably be most efficiently devoted to these areas of the problems. Obviously such a conclusion is a 'rule of thumb' and is fraught with dangers about the apparent arbitrariness of the completeness of the current map, but nevertheless, given such choices have to be made, it is usually indicative. Thus my time is likely to be best spent considering further the avoidance of flights running off schedule, how to stop flights being held up by late passengers, stopping passengers cheating the sysem and finding ways of deploying more staff, in such a way that the consequences are positive for goals and negative for not-goals.

A strategy for devising a solution is suggested as: 'deploy staff on demand' by 'avoiding their waiting around', introduce the 'checking of boarding cards for risk-status' with a 'special machine'. Each option can be explored in turn (but within the context of a portfolio of action). The immediate consequences must be explored and the detailed actions (explanations) evaluated. In addition the map provides the basis for understanding the role of each option with respect to each goal/not-goal.

The role of technical operations research

The above material has described the process of *problem construction* and *problem structuring*. The process of problem structuring often reveals a robust solution to the problem by following the approach outlined above. 'One implication of acting/thinking cycles is that action is often part of defining the problem' (Isenberg, 1989) and so it is also likely that the *act* of building a cognitive map releases a portfolio of actions.

However, it is very likely that problem-structuring enables the problem to be described in manageable chunks, each of which can be dealt with relatively independently. The map may, therefore, reveal characteristics that are amenable to analysis as a technical OR problem. For example, concepts 18, 19, 20, 21, 22, 23, 24, 25, 33 and 35 suggest a simulation model set against criteria for success of 'inefficient use of staff' and 'extensive queues'. The operational definition of 'extensive' is contained by 'time in shopping mall' (10), 'levels of anxiety' (2), number of 'fights held up by late passengers' (5), 'passengers' belief about checkers being more thorough' (37), and the extent to which 'passengers arrive earlier' (36) — in other words problem resolution is defined by the direct 'out-domain' of concept 1.

The 'out-domain' which defines the criteria for success for the simulation model tests also suggests a tractable market research project (links 1>2, 1>37), designing tracking between queues and missing flights (link 1>4), and a study of the relationship between queue lengths and flights being held up (link 1>5).

The results of these technical studies can subsequently be set within the broader qualitative aspects of the problem which are defined by the map. Typically each cluster (in a larger problem) can be related to an identifiable OR study.

Cognitive mapping software: using COPE

The model constructed in this example is comparatively small (many maps are several hundred concepts) and so the map can be presented graphically and analyzed visually. As maps become larger it is helpful to use specially designed software (COPE) (Ackermann, 1990) to store the map, to represent parts of it on a VDU or printer (the software was used to lay out all the maps displayed in this chapter), and more important to analyze and to classify parts of the map and particular concepts. The software is designed to run on the lowest common denominator of PC hardware (DOS-driven IBM PC compatible) so that it can be used by OR analysts on the desktop computers available to their clients. Although this constraint has serious consequences on the form of the display (prescribed by an IBM character set), it nevertheless permits the widest possible use. The software is command driven and passive. Successful use of the software depends on, and allows, creativity on the part of the user in relation to the specific benefits sought with respect to problem and to client.

Group decision support systems and strategy development

This chapter has considered the role of cognitive mapping for problem construction in relation to a single client, where the client or an OR consultant may be the mapper. By definition, a cognitive map relates to a single person, for a map that does not relate to a person has nothing to do with cognition (a person's thinking) about a problem. The intention of the chapter has been to demonstrate how mapping can be useful as a problem-solving aid in its own right, and also as a method for defining OR projects that relate to the needs of the client.

However, as noted in the list of circumstances appropriate for cognitive mapping at the beginning of the chapter, cognitive maps are a powerful way of dealing with problems that involve several different perspectives. Thus by implication cognitive maps are helpful in aiding a group or team in creating solutions to a problem that will: (a) fully utilize the wisdom and experience of all members of the group, and (b) facilitate high levels of commitment to the solution devised by the group. In this context cognitive mapping is used as a core technique within a group decision support system (GDSS) known as SODA (strategic options development and analysis; Eden, 1989b). In this instance the cognitive maps of each member of the team are aggregated into a single 'strategic' map. This aggregate map is analyzed using the same methods as those identified above, and the conclusons of the analysis used to design a SODA workshop which is guided by 'on-the-hoof' use of the computer software (COPE). The computer drives a large monitor and a 'slave' screen so that the participants can use the model to guide their deliberations and a facilitator can record and analyze in real time on the slave screen (Ackermann, 1990).

In this form the technique of cognitive mapping combined with the computer-based tool COPE, set within the context of SODA as a designed GDSS, acts to help groups work on major strategic problems and develop and review strategy (Eden and Huxham, 1988). Similarly, aggregated cognitive maps can be used to develop an understanding of qualitative interview data.

Acknowledgements

I am indebted to my colleagues Fran Ackermann and Dr Steve Cropper for the major part they have played in developing many of the ideas discussed in this chapter, and to ICL who have sponsored much of the research we have undertaken.

References

Ackermann, F. (1990) 'The role of computers in group decision support', in C. Eden and J. Radford (eds) *Tackling Strategic Problems: The role of group decision support*, Sage.

Ackermann, F., C. Eden and S. Cropper (1990) *'Guidelines for Cognitive Mapping'*, Working Paper, Department of Management Science, University of Strathclyde.

Eden, C. (1986) 'Problem solving or problem finishing', in M.C. Jackson and P. Keys (eds) *New Directions in Management Science*, Gower.

Eden, C. (1989a) 'Operational research as negotiation', in M. Jackson, P. Keys and S. Cropper (eds) *Operational Research and the Social Sciences*, Plenum.

Eden, C. (1989b) 'Strategic options development and analysis — SODA', in J. Rosenhead (ed.) *Rational Analysis for a Problematic World*, John Wiley.

Eden, C. and C. Huxham (1988) 'Action-oriented strategic management', *Journal of the Operational Research Society*, **39**, 889–99.

Eden, C. and J. Radford (1990) *Tackling Strategic Problems: The role of group decision support*, Sage.

Eden, C. and P. Simpson (1989) 'SODA and cognitive mapping in practice', in J. Rosenhead (ed.) *Rational Analysis for a Problematic World*, John Wiley.

Eden, C., S. Jones and D. Sims (1979) *Thinking in Organizations*, Macmillan.

Eden, C., S. Jones and D. Sims (1983) *Messing About in Problems*, Pergamon.

Isenberg, D.J. (1989) 'How senior managers think', in W.H. Igor (ed.) *Intuition in Organizations*, Sage.

Kelly, G.A. (1955) *The Psychology of Personal Constructs*, Norton.

–17–
Putting operations research to work

S.L. COOK and M.F. SHUTLER

Introduction

Up to now in this book we have covered the background history of OR, the basic idea of its method and approach, a fair range of techniques that have proved useful and examples of their application. In this last chapter, we turn again to a more general issue, that of how we can 'get it all together' and make it work in our various organizations.

In spite of the many applications listed in these pages, there are difficulties and there have been all too many examples of studies which started in high hope and ended with no successful on-going implementation of a solution to the original problem. This question of 'implementation' has been the subject of considerable research in recent years, and in the ensuing pages we shall discuss some of the most important of these issues.

Of course, no two organizations are exactly alike — they have different sizes, shapes, purposes and styles, and they are made up of unique mixes of unique, individual, human beings. Prescriptions and aphorisms are no substitute for experience, common sense and human understanding. We hope the discussions and suggestions of these final pages will be read in that spirit.

Roles and responsibilities

There are two main issues in organizing the application of OR: the strength of professional support available and the accountability for success of the project. The number of possible combinations is too great to enumerate them all. When discussing the manager 'having a go by himself' we had in mind a situation of little or no professional support; an opposite possibility is where a very strong OR team is given executive responsibility for the project. Both of these possible arrangements have their strengths and uses, but, for reasons of space, we must concentrate here on the more usual situation where there is substantial OR support available, and responsibility is shared in some way between the OR team and the manager.

In the traditional 'line and staff' relationship, the manager retains full authority to make decisions, but listens to the advice of the 'staff' person, who also has communication channels to higher management through his staff functional links. This is a bureaucratic concept which can work well or badly; in some circumstances both manager and operational researcher may be anxious about their own authority and responsibility. Peter Drucker (1960) sought to resolve this dilemma by recognizing the complete authority of the line manager, who must 'carry the can', the staff man being merely an adviser to the manager. Unfortunately this solution recognizes neither the amount of interaction needed between operations researcher and manager in an OR project, nor the degree of commitment to results essential to a good operations researcher. An alternative, increasingly acceptable in modern organizations and strongly recommended by many OR men, is to recognize a collective responsibility for the project. A team manager and representatives from OR and many other departments are chosen. Operations research will contribute with all the others to the final outcome. It becomes an 'ours' project, not a 'his', 'hers' or 'theirs'. However, we have noted some caveats on pp. 29–30.

There is certainly evidence that natural and effective co-operation of this kind has sometimes been discouraged by over-emphasis on the line manager's authority. However, there is little doubt either that attempts to increase the authority of the operations researcher through his functional links to higher management can be even more destructive of effective collaboration. The partnership needs to be natural, not imposed.

Thus the manager needs to be able to feel that his partnership with the OR team is one of equals, for the duration of the project. In the end he will have to carry executive responsibility for operating the system. In Chapter 2 we recommended a formal handover process.

Modern professional operations research function reviewed

In this section we review what an OR function ought ideally to cover, as a sort of yardstick against which efforts in a particular organization might be measured. We do this by grouping the various aspects of OR into five basic 'elements': classical, technical, contextual, dynamic and integrative.

The 'classical' element

The 'classical' element, as its name implies, is the original base from which the eminent founders of OR worked — the base of science, scientific method and the research approach. It implies curiosity, leading to exploration; the imaginative creation of hypotheses, followed by their ruthless criticism in open debate; intellectual honesty and objectivity (Ackoff, 1962; Magee, 1973).

The classical element brings to a problem a basic mental approach, with certain skills in structuring and handling ideas, including classification and quantification. It also brings an interdisciplinary approach, in which models from a wide range of disciplines may provide analogies which may prove useful in modelling the problem situation. It does not bring any knowledge considered to be specially relevant to the problem situation, but rather an 'open mind' about what is and what is not important.

The 'technical' element

The 'technical' element is defined as the skilled application of specific logical and mathematical techniques which can aid problem-solving — a list including all those quantitative techniques described in this book, and many more. Whilst complementary to the classical element in terms of effective OR, it unfortunately demands rather different qualities, temperament and training for its development. This poses problems of balance in the training of the individual in the composition of the group. For example, 'classical' abilities are best developed through experience in a wide range of different problem situations; repeated experience in one problem area is likely to compromise the open mind. Technical abilities, on the other hand, are best developed by repeated experience of using each technique in different, but related, problem areas.

To some extent, it would be possible to have operations researchers, and OR groups, of deliberately different emphasis in order to be suited for different types of work. The emphasis would be on classical OR for unstructured problems of types not yet successfully solved, and 'technical' for relatively standard types of problem. But it is not as simple as that. Even with relatively standard problems, it is often desirable to take a fresh look at the problem; while with unstructured problems, progress can especially be made by separating out parts of the problem which are amenable to standard techniques in order to reveal more clearly the essential kernel of the problem for attack by the more 'classical' approach. So the two elements are very much complementary in good OR and must be developed in the same group and as far as possible in the same individuals.

A most important skill is the ability to generate and develop new techniques (logical and quantitative) needed by many problems. This skill is perhaps on the borderline between the classical and the technical elements.

The 'contextual' element

The 'contextual' element is defined here as the application of relevant existing theory and of relevant practical experience, from areas of knowledge specific to the context of the problem. This contrasts with both the classical and the technical elements. The emphasis of OR has always been to study the problem as it is, in its context, from what can be measured and observed in that context. Relationships built into the model have, as far as possible, been derived from observation of the problem context, rather than inferred from general theory.

But there have always been exceptions to this. In the earliest OR, where a problem involved natural science or engineering phenomena, technological relationships based on theory were often incorporated as, for example, in the early U-boat studies. Even where the knowledge is of a very empirical kind — such as experience of success and failure of particular practices in a field such as, say, traffic management — it can provide useful guidelines in approaching a problem. Many applications' areas, particularly in physical distribution, are now susceptible to common standard approaches (see Collcutt, 1980).

The 'dynamic' or 'change agent' element

The three elements described so far have been concerned with selecting the best or most appropriate solution to the stated problem, i.e. with deciding upon the desirable new state of the system. This is a 'static' concept, but successful implementation involves moving from the present to the new state — a dynamic process. However desirable the proposed new state to all concerned, the road to it from the present state may be unacceptably rough, or it may need special navigational aids.

Some of the issues involved in successful implementation of OR results have already been discussed on page 30. These were mainly the issues of manager/ scientist collaboration which is part of the problem. With any major change there are much broader issues of acceptability to all concerned — workers, customers, citizens; and here managers and scientists alike may need help, not to manipulate people into acceptance, but to set up the kinds of genuine participation in problem-solving that can lead naturally to acceptance.

Here we can draw on some of the ideas, approaches and experience of those behavioural scientists who have been concerned with programmes of social change in organizations, and who have influenced the soft OR discussed in Chapter 16 (e.g. Kelly, 1955). It seems likely that in the future the soft OR approach will be expanded and thus all OR scientists will need change agent skills.

The 'integrative' element

Finally, we come to the integrative element in OR; not just the ability to combine ideas and concepts from various disciplines, or the ability to combine theory with action — both of these are implied in other elements — but the ability to combine the activities to achieve a result in line with the needs of the situation; cost, timeliness, perhaps even style. We are concerned with the skills of the project leader and project manager in achieving the right balance of effort within and between the other four elements. Experience is especially important here. There is little doubt that in this element, art predominates over science, although there are some semi-scientific aids to project management that can be usefully applied.

It must be very clear by now that no operations researcher can be a self-contained 'jack of all trades'. That would be hard enough to achieve even within one of the elements, let alone across the five. All we can hope for in the individual is a degree of special competence in some parts of some of the elements and a general awareness of the remainder. Thus, a problem of any complexity needs to be tackled by a team of interactive individuals who together have a reasonable level of ability in the most important aspects; the project team needs to be backed up by a well-balanced OR group, backed up in turn by the profession as a whole and by the whole network of relevant knowledge and skills.

This, then, is the 'ideal' role of modern operations research, although not all organizations will find it necessary to exploit the full scope of OR.

Identifying worthwhile projects and selecting appropriate techniques for their solution

In this chapter we have discussed so far the roles of managers and of operations researchers in applying OR, the conditions for successful implementation of solutions and the nature of an effective OR group. We must leave for another place the problems of how to fit the group into the organization structure and how to manage and control OR work within the organization. One question remains to be tackled here: what should the group actually do? More precisely, how are possible projects identified, and how is it decided what techniques to use for a project?

Projects can be identified and selected for study in a wide variety of ways. When one new OR group was set up, the newly appointed manager made a six-week tour of the seven operating divisions, discussing the main problems being faced with general managers and their middle managements. From this came a list of twenty-four possible problems for OR. In discussion with the managing director's advisory committee, four of these were selected for study. Of these, three yielded good cash savings, two of them very substantial; the fourth was unsuccessful. Overall, the savings directly attributable to the OR work represented a return of about 200 per cent per annum on the total project costs; the best projects reached a figure of 500 per cent per annum. As a result, the group was expanded and a rule of thumb was devised that in future no 'bread and butter' projects would be taken on unless there was clear scope for at least a 500 per cent saving. It was recognized that some of the most important OR projects would have intangible benefits or very uncertain outcomes, and that these must be exempted from this calculation. As a safeguard, however, there should always be enough 'bread and butter' projects to yield tangible returns that can more than pay for the group's total activity.

Once a group is successfully launched, there is usually no point in further general surveys for potential projects — they will arise continually and the problem will be selecting those to be undertaken. Sometimes an urgent call for short-term help from management may lead to results revealing scope for major studies (one ten day emergency study led to a two year project yielding improvements worth £200,000 per annum). Conversely, a six-man-year investigation requested by the managing director to assist the board with long-range strategic decisions, led also to a series of worthwhile operational improvements and a major computer scheme.

Quite often, successful completion of an OR study in one section of an organization will lead to studies in neighbouring parts; for example, a stock control study for finished goods may lead forward to marketing or back into production control problems. And yet another source of profitable OR work, paradoxically, can be a survey of the opportunities to apply a particular technique, perhaps newly acquired within the group, which catches the imagination of the managers. Normally, 'technique-orientation' should be avoided like the plague — the focus should be on the problem and the technique should be incidental. But when some years ago one group set one of its newly recruited scientists to explore the scope for using linear programming to reduce iron- and steel-making costs, hitherto unrecognized problems were identified and very considerable benefits achieved first in one division and then in two others. An occasional technique-oriented exercise like this, carried out by a clearly problem-oriented group can thus be very effective.

In most projects, the problem will be identified and the study commenced before any attempt is made to consider which techniques will be relevant. However, a choice of technique has to be made in due course, and students and new practitioners often ask 'how do you decide what techniques to use?' The question is unfortunately almost impossible to answer. There is not much that can replace a gradual acquisition of experience and of the art of OR problem-solving. Clearly, a study of past case histories can help speed up this acquisition, whilst, given a particular case, discussion with others who have successfully tackled similar problems can help. In some cases the choice may be obvious; in others it may pay to explore different technique options in parallel before deciding which to use.

As a very general guide, however, we can set out roughly the extent to which groups of techniques have been used with success in industrial OR groups over the past thirty years. These groups are listed in descending order of frequency of use, of the group as a whole, judged on a very approximate subjective basis. In each group, elementary techniques are mentioned first, then more advanced ones (which may be used relatively infrequently). The dotted line represents a rough cut-off point below which it can be said that the techniques, whilst they may give useful insight, are only rarely instrumental in solving a real-world problem:

1. Cost models, relating cost in money terms algebraically to various physical and behavioural variables: from 'standard costing' representations to cost effectiveness and cost benefit analysis. All use spreadsheets as vehicles (Collcutt, 1980).
2. Statistical methods: from sampling and correlation and regression to statistical quality control, design of experiments and time series.
3. Interactive modelling in which the manager can interrogate the computer in real time (Chapter 15).
4. Simulation (representing interacting events in a complex system through time): from simple activity analysis charts to probabilistic computer representations to real-time interactive simulations or operational exercises where there is human intervention within the computer run; also 'systems dynamics' (non-probabilistic computer representation of very complex systems with internal feedbacks), e.g. world modelling.
5. 'Soft' OR, e.g. the involvement of OR scientists as facilitators in a decision process with many actors, each with his or her own personal goals; and the use of expert systems in which the OR scientist trains a computer to aid a human decision-maker using other humans' expertise.
6. Mathematical programming: from linear programming to non-linear (e.g. quadratic, integer, dynamic and goal-programming) (Collcutt, 1980).
7. Network methods: from critical path analysis and resource allocation for optimal project control and completion to vehicle routeing and graph theory (Collcutt, 1980).

8. Inventory theory: from simple rules for re-order level and re-order quantity to complex probabilistic models with automatic updating of parameters, specification of review procedures, demand forecasting and smoothing, etc. (see also 2 above and Moroney, 1958).
9. Decision analysis: from simple deterministic decision trees to probabilistic ones (Collcutt, 1980), weighting of outcomes, maximization of utilities.
10. Reliability theory (timing of machine replacements; Collcutt, 1980).
11. Queueing theory (used for simple queueing situations; Collcutt, 1980).
    . . .
12. Game theory, conflict analysis, conflict resolution.
13. Search theory — useful at sea, for oil exploration and in military applications.

This list should of course be taken only as a very rough guide; and there are considerable overlaps between some of the categories, as well as some omissions. As the OR staff develop some experience, that experience will take over in guiding their choice of techniques and for them a list of this kind will have little purpose.

Epilogue

This last chapter has tried to select a few pointers towards the establishment of a worthwhile OR function in an organization. As with most activities there is a limit to the value of prescription; trial and error is unavoidable. Perhaps we could just emphasize in a few words the qualities needed in a good OR group. In addition to intellectual competence, they should have (and should be encouraged by the organization to have) enthusiasm, curiosity as to how the organization ticks, intellectual honesty, an achievement orientation, a healthy scepticism of accepted ideas and practice and a deep commitment *both* to science and to the organization.

After this emphasis on the setting up of a formal OR function, perhaps we could return finally to the point we made in Chapter 1. This book is addressed mainly to managers and potential managers as individuals rather than to organizations. Individual managers may be in no position, as yet, to influence the setting up of an OR group in their organizations; or there may already be one there, but not available in their particular divisions. We hope this book may have given them some support for doing some OR themselves. If they do, we hope the book will also encourage them to keep in touch with the OR community, and perhaps even suffer vicariously from its failures and enjoy its successes as it continues to try to expand its competence and its applications in the world at large.

References and further reading

Ackoff, R.L. (1962) *Scientific Method: Optimising applied research decisions*, John Wiley.

Burns, T. and G.M. Stalker (1961) *The Management of innovation*, Tavistock.

Churchman, C.W. and A.H. Schainblatt (1965a) 'The researcher and the manager; a dialectic of implementation', *Management Science*, 11, 1369–87.

Churchman, C.W. and A.H. Schainblatt (1965b) 'Commentary', *Management Science*, 12, p. 132.

Collcutt, R.H. (1980) *Successful Operational Research: a selection of case studies for managers*, Operational Research Society.

Drucker, P. (1960) *The Practice of Management*, pp. 262–6, Heinemann.

Kelly, G. (1955) *The Psychology of Personal Constraints: A theory of personality*, Norton.

Likert, R. (1961) *New Patterns of Management*, McGraw-Hill.

Magee, B. (1973) *Popper*, Fontana.

Moroney, M.J. (1958) *Facts from Figures*, Penguin.

Appendices

— Appendix 1 —

Area under the normal density function: a table of

$$\Phi(x) = \frac{1}{\sqrt{(2\pi)}} \int_{-\infty}^{x} e^{-\frac{1}{2}y^2} \, dy$$

x	0.00	0.01	0.02	0.03	0.04	0.05	0.06	0.07	0.08	0.09
0.0	0.5000	0.5040	0.5080	0.5120	0.5160	0.5199	0.5239	0.5279	0.5319	0.5359
0.1	0.5398	0.5438	0.5478	0.5517	0.5557	0.5596	0.5636	0.5675	0.5714	0.5753
0.2	0.5793	0.5832	0.5871	0.5910	0.5948	0.5987	0.6026	0.6064	0.6103	0.6141
0.3	0.6179	0.6217	0.6255	0.6293	0.6331	0.6368	0.6406	0.6443	0.6480	0.6517
0.4	0.6554	0.6591	0.6628	0.6664	0.6700	0.6736	0.6772	0.6808	0.6844	0.6879
0.5	0.6195	0.6950	0.6985	0.7019	0.7054	0.7088	0.7123	0.7157	0.7190	0.7224
0.6	0.7257	0.7291	0.7324	0.7357	0.7389	0.7422	0.7454	0.7486	0.7517	0.7549
0.7	0.7580	0.7611	0.7642	0.7673	0.7704	0.7734	0.7764	0.7794	0.7823	0.7852
0.8	0.7881	0.7910	0.7939	0.7967	0.7995	0.8023	0.8051	0.8078	0.8106	0.8133
0.9	0.8159	0.8186	0.8212	0.8238	0.8264	0.8289	0.8315	0.8340	0.8365	0.8389
1.0	0.8413	0.8438	0.8461	0.8485	0.8508	0.8531	0.8554	0.8577	0.8599	0.8621
1.1	0.8643	0.8665	0.8686	0.8708	0.8729	0.8749	0.8770	0.8790	0.8810	0.8830
1.2	0.8849	0.8869	0.8888	0.8907	0.8925	0.8944	0.8962	0.8980	0.8997	0.9015
1.3	0.9032	0.9049	0.9066	0.9082	0.9099	0.9115	0.9131	0.9147	0.9162	0.9177
1.4	0.9192	0.9207	0.9222	0.9236	0.9251	0.9265	0.9279	0.9292	0.9306	0.9319

z	0.00	0.01	0.02	0.03	0.04	0.05	0.06	0.07	0.08	0.09
1.5	0.9332	0.9345	0.9357	0.9370	0.9382	0.9394	0.9406	0.9418	0.9429	0.9441
1.6	0.9452	0.9463	0.9474	0.9494	0.9495	0.9505	0.9515	0.9525	0.9535	0.9545
1.7	0.9554	0.9564	0.9573	0.9582	0.9591	0.9599	0.9608	0.9616	0.9625	0.9633
1.8	0.9641	0.9649	0.9656	0.9664	0.9671	0.9678	0.9686	0.9693	0.9699	0.9706
1.9	0.9713	0.9719	0.9726	0.9732	0.9738	0.9744	0.9750	0.9756	0.9761	0.9767
2.0	0.9772	0.9778	0.9783	0.9788	0.9793	0.9798	0.9803	0.9808	0.9812	0.9817
2.1	0.9821	0.9826	0.9830	0.9834	0.9838	0.9842	0.9846	0.9850	0.9854	0.9857
2.2	0.9861	0.9864	0.9868	0.9871	0.9875	0.9878	0.9881	0.9884	0.9887	0.9890
2.3	0.9893	0.9896	0.9898	0.9901	0.9904	0.9906	0.9909	0.9911	0.9913	0.9916
2.4	0.9918	0.9920	0.9922	0.9925	0.9927	0.9929	0.9931	0.9932	0.9934	0.9936
2.5	0.9938	0.9940	0.9941	0.9943	0.9945	0.9946	0.9948	0.9949	0.9951	0.9952
2.6	0.9953	0.9955	0.9956	0.9957	0.9959	0.9960	0.9961	0.9962	0.9963	0.9964
2.7	0.9965	0.9966	0.9967	0.9968	0.9969	0.9970	0.9971	0.9972	0.9973	0.9974
2.8	0.9974	0.9975	0.9976	0.9977	0.9977	0.9978	0.9979	0.9979	0.9980	0.9981
2.9	0.9981	0.9982	0.9982	0.9983	0.9984	0.9984	0.9985	0.9985	0.9986	0.9986
3.0	0.9987	0.9987	0.9987	0.9988	0.9988	0.9989	0.9989	0.9989	0.9990	0.9990
3.1	0.9990	0.9991	0.9991	0.9991	0.9992	0.9993	0.9992	0.9992	0.9993	0.9993
3.2	0.9993	0.9993	0.9994	0.9994	0.9994	0.9994	0.9994	0.9995	0.9995	0.9995
3.3	0.9995	0.9995	0.9995	0.9996	0.9996	0.9996	0.9996	0.9996	0.9996	0.9997
3.4	0.9997	0.9997	0.9997	0.9997	0.9997	0.9997	0.9997	0.9997	0.9997	0.9998
3.6	0.9998	0.9998	0.9999	0.9999	0.9999	0.9999	0.9999	0.9999	0.9999	0.9999

— Appendix 2 —
Demand analysis/forecasting worksheet (Chapter 6 exercises)

		60	70	65	75	75	60	75	65	70	77	60		
1 Current demand value	d_t													
2 Forecast	u_{t-1}	70*												
3 Error	$e_t = d_t - u_{t-1}$													
4 Cumulative error	Σe_t													
5 Squared error	e_t^2													
6 Cumulative squared error	Σe_t^2													
7 $\alpha \times$ error	αe_t													
8 $(1-\alpha)$ past smoothed error	$(1-\alpha)\bar{e}_{t-1}$	0*												
9 Current smoothed error	$\bar{e}_t = \alpha e_t + (1-\alpha)\bar{e}_{t-1}$													

10 $\alpha \times$ absolute error	$\alpha|e_t|$									
11 $(1-\alpha)$ past MAD	$(1-\alpha)\text{MAD}_{t-1}$	10*								
12 Current MAD	$\text{MAD}_t = \alpha|e_t| + (1-\alpha)\text{MAD}_{t-1}$									
13 Currend std dev.	$1.25 \times \text{MAD}_t$									
14 Tracking signal	$T_t = \bar{e}_t/\text{MAD}_t$									
15 Exponential weighting constant for forecast† (see below)	A									
16 $A \times$ current demand	Ad_t									
17 $(1-A) \times$ past forecast	$(1-A)u_{t-1}$									
18 Next month's forecast	$u_t = Ad_t + (1-A)u_{t-1}$									

* Estimate or guess.
† Simple exponential smoothing $A = \alpha$, adaptive response rate forecasting $A = |T_t|$, delayed adaptive response rate forecasting $A = |T_{t-1}|$.

— Appendix 3 —
Answers to exercises

Chapter 3

1. (a) LCF solution (Figure A.1(a)), total cost £136. (There are many ties; the following solution is obtained by choosing a higher row in preference to a lower one, and a left-hand side column in preference to a right-hand one.)

(b) The VAM solution (Figure A.1(b)) is optimal and may be obtained in one step from the LCF solution above. It is not unique; alternative optimum obtained by introducing asterisked cell.

(c) £2.

(d) £2 per unit at either 1 or 2.

2. (a) Take the cheaper of road and rail costs and put an arbitrary cost figure of 1,000 for infeasible routes. The VAM solution shown is also optimal, total cost £3,507 per week. Shadow prices calculated by setting $u_3 = 0$.

(b) Increasing capacity at pit 4 and reducing purchases at pit 3 changes costs by $£(-16-3) = -£19$ per 100 tonnes, hence pay up to £19 extra per 100 tonnes on additional supplies.

(c) Shifting requirements from works 3 to works 2 saves £22 per 100 tonnes.

3. (a) Consider the initial stock and months of purchase as origins and the months of usage and closing stock as destinations. A dummy destination represents unused supplier's capacity. Since it is not possible to use cartons purchased in a previous month, the costs will be infinite in the lower left triangle of cells. For the other cells the cost will be equal to the basic price of £100 per thousand less supplier's price discount less present value discount of £2 for each month after September, as calculated in Table A.1. Note that cost depends only upon month of purchase and not upon month of usage. There are no further cash outflows for stocks initially held (the first row), nor for unused supply capacity (the dummy column) (Figure A.3).

(b) Neither LCF nor VAM produces an optimal solution, but a variant of LCF (take months of use in turn and choose cheapest source) yields the optimal

(a) LCF solution

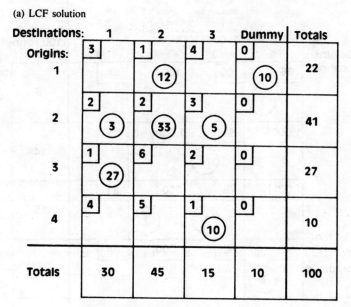

Destinations: 1 2 3 Dummy | **Totals**

Origins:	1	2	3	Dummy	Totals
1	3	1 (12)	4	0 (10)	22
2	2 (3)	2 (33)	3 (5)	0	41
3	1 (27)	6	2	0	27
4	4	5	1 (10)	0	10
Totals	30	45	15	10	100

Total cost is £136

(b) VAM solution

Destinations:

Origins:	1	2	3	Dummy	u_i
1		(22)			−1
2	(3)	(23)	(5)	(10)	0
3	(27)		*		−1
4			(10)		−2
v_j	2	2	3	0	

Total cost is £126

Figure A.1

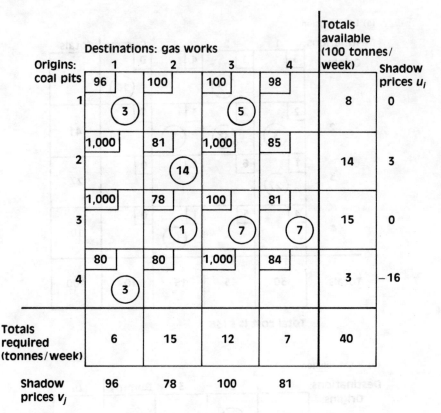

Figure A.2

		Table A.1		
Month of purchase	Supplier's price discount	Present value discount	n.p.v. of cost	
September	£6	—	£94	
October	£3	£2	£95	
November	—	£4	£96	
December	—	£6	£94	
January	£5	£8	£87	
February	£6	£10	£84	

solution shown. There are three alternative optima obtained by introducing cells with asterisks.

(i) Delaying production for one month saves nothing in carton purchasing costs in September or October, £1 per thousand in November, £7 in December and £3 in January;

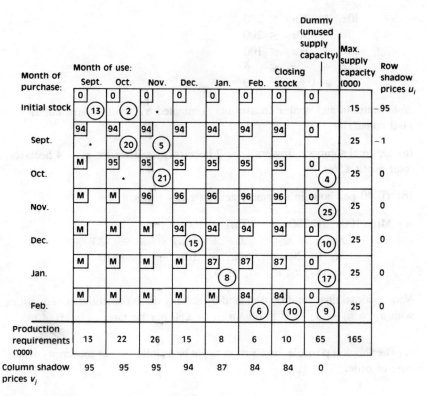

Figure A.3

(ii) Increasing supply capacity would save £1 per thousand in September but nothing in subsequent months. (All calculations in present value terms.)

Chapter 4

1. $62\frac{1}{2}$ hectares wheat, 35 hectares potatoes, $2\frac{1}{2}$ hectares fallow. Solving dual constraints

$$
\begin{aligned}
u_1 + 6u_2 \quad &= 90 \\
u_1 + 3u_2 + u_3 &= 60
\end{aligned}
$$

where shadow price of land $u_1 = 0$ yields value of labour $u_2 = 90/6 = £15$ per hour; value of quota $u_3 = 60 - 3(£15) = £15$ per hectare.

2. Max. $80x_1 + 100x_2$

s.t. $10x_1 + 10x_2 \le 100$

$$40x_1 + 20x_2 \leq 200$$
$$0x_1 + 50x_2 \leq 200$$
$$10x_1 + 10x_2 \leq 100$$
$$x_1 + x_2 \leq 6$$
$$x_1 \geq 0, \ x_2 \geq 0$$

Note: autumn and winter constraints dominated by spring constraint and by land constraint.

(a) Optimal solution: flowers $x_1 = 2$ hectares, strawberries $x_2 = 4$ hectares, total profit £560.

(b) £0.40 per hour in summer, zero at other times.

(c) Min. $100u_1 + 200u_2 + 200u_3 + 100u_4 + 6u_5$
  s.t. $10u_1 + 40u_2 + 0u_3 + 10u_4 + u_5 \geq 80$
  $10u_1 + 20u_2 + 50u_3 + 10u_4 + u_5 \geq 100$
  $u_1, u_2, u_3, u_4, u_5, \geq 0$

Note: optimal dual solution obtained by solving these constraints as equalities with $u_1 = u_2 = u_4 = 0$ to obtain $u_5 = $ £80 per hectare, $u_3 = $ £0.40.

3. The simplest possible formulation might be as follows. Let subscript j denote type of order, $j = 1, \ldots, n$.

Let x_j = number of orders type j scheduled
  p_j = priority score for order j
  a_j = time required on assembly line for order j
  A = total time available on assembly line
  b_j = number of engines type j available.

$$\max \sum_{j=1}^{n} p_j x_j$$

$$\text{s.t.} \sum_{j=1}^{n} a_j x_j \leq A$$

$$0 \leq x_j \leq b_j, \ j = 1, \ldots, n$$

As a matter of fact, this simple model could be solved by hand by ranking orders j in decreasing order of ratio p_j/a_j, and setting in turn to maximum limits b_j until available time A is fully utilized.

If there is only one order of each type, the problem is one of integer programming ($x_j = 0$ or 1). In practice, additional constraints are imposed.

Chapter 5

1. Either LP1:

Maximize
$$
\begin{bmatrix}
0 & 0 & \ldots & 0 & 0 & 1 \\
\lambda_1 & \lambda_1 & \ldots & \lambda_{29} & \lambda_{30} & w
\end{bmatrix}
$$

Subject to
$$
\begin{bmatrix}
7.300 & 6.600 & \ldots & 5.400 & 4.900 & 0 \\
5.744 & 3.725 & \ldots & 4.105 & 2.887 & 0 \\
0 & 0 & \ldots & 0 & 0 & 0 \\
13.2236 & 9.0976 & \ldots & 15.2188 & 12.3599 & -7.7975 \\
6.983 & 5.246 & \ldots & 3.459 & 2.475 & -1.426 \\
17.757 & 13.734 & \ldots & 28.738 & 26.599 & -19.286
\end{bmatrix}
\begin{array}{l}
\leq 2.900 \\
\leq 1.606 \\
\leq 4.64 \\
\geq 0 \\
\geq 0 \\
\geq 0
\end{array}
$$

$\lambda_j \geq 0, \; j = 1, 2, \ldots, 30.$

Or LP2:

Minimize
$$
\begin{bmatrix}
0 & 0 & \ldots & 0 & 0 & 1 \\
\lambda_1 & \lambda_2 & \ldots & \lambda_{29} & \lambda_{30} & z
\end{bmatrix}
$$

Subject to
$$
\begin{bmatrix}
7.300 & 6.600 & \ldots & 5.400 & 4.900 & -2.900 \\
5.744 & 3.725 & \ldots & 4.105 & 2.887 & -1.606 \\
0 & 0 & \ldots & 0 & 0 & -4.64 \\
13.2236 & 9.0976 & \ldots & 15.2188 & 12.3599 & 0 \\
6.983 & 5.246 & \ldots & 3.459 & 2.475 & 0 \\
17.757 & 13.734 & \ldots & 28.738 & 26.599 & 0
\end{bmatrix}
\begin{array}{l}
\leq 0 \\
\leq 0 \\
\leq 0 \\
\geq 7.7975 \\
\geq 1.426 \\
\geq 19.286
\end{array}
$$

$\lambda_j \geq 0, \; j = 1, 2, \ldots, 30$

2. Assuming that the managing director does not want to know anything about LP, the table could be explained along the following lines:

> The inputs and outputs of the Zennor shop are listed in the last column, and compared to a 'composite' shop which has been constructed by taking 0.146 times the Cardiff shop plus 0.056 times the Dover shop, plus 0.314 times the Paisley shop, plus 0.279 times the Yeovil shop. This composite has been chosen from all thirty shops (by the DEA procedure) to have at least as much sales of each kind as Zennor, with the least use of inputs in the same relative proportions as Zennor. The composite shop uses only 0.984 times as much of each input as Zennor, and actually has higher sales of the second type of output, women's clothing.

3. After standardizing each DMU to, say, an output level of 100, the following isoquant (Figure A.4) can be drawn. DMU$_4$ is inefficient by comparison with DMUs 1 and 6; DMU$_5$ is inefficient by comparison with DMUs 1 and 7.

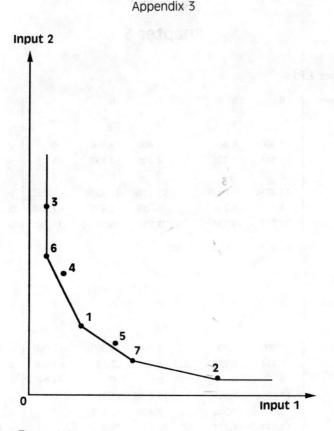

Figure A.4

DMU_3 would come out of the DEA computation with 'efficiency = 1', since there is no combination of the other DMUs which can produce more output than DMU_3 without using more of input 1, but it is obviusly using more of input 2 than DMU_6, and it is important that the DEA output draws attention to this anomaly, and ensures that DMU_3 is duly compared to DMU_6. This situation is obvious for the mini-problem, but needs also to be taken into account for a multi-dimensional case, either by the use of a special-purpose computer package, or by a modification of the objective function of the LP.

4. By plotting the outer 'envelope' of the five points (Figure A.5), and again making the assumption that proportionate outputs can be obtained along the rays from the origin, we can see that DMU_4 is inefficient by comparison with DMUs 1 and 4, and DMU_2 is inefficient by comparison with DMUs 1 and 5.

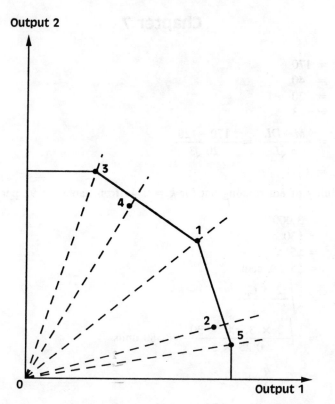

Figure A.5

Chapter 6

1. No. Because the forecast is more responsive with a value for α of 0.5; at no time does the tracking signal exceed 0.7.

2. $\alpha = 0.5$ is best because this value minimizes the mean squared error (MSE = 173).

3. Not for this set of data. The MSE of the delayed adaptive response rate forecast is 178. The MSE for the simple exponentially weighted forecast with $\alpha = 0.5$ is 173.

Chapter 7

1. $M = 170$
$D = 40$
$\sigma = 20$
$L = 3$

$$k = \frac{M - DL}{\sigma \sqrt{L}} = \frac{170 - 120}{20 \sqrt{3}}$$

$$k = 1.44$$

Probability of not running out for $k = 1.44$ from tables = 92 per cent.

2. $A = 3,000$
$C_o = £30$
$C_m = £5$
$i = 25$ per cent

$$Q_o = \sqrt{\frac{2 A C_o}{i C_m}}$$

$$= \sqrt{\frac{2 \times 3,000 \times 30}{0.25 \times 5}} = 380 \text{ units}$$

$$C = i C_m \frac{q}{2} + \frac{A}{q} C_o$$

$$= 0.25 \times 5 \times \frac{380}{2} + \frac{3,000}{380} \times 3$$

$$= 237.5 + 236.8 = 474$$

Cost of storage and ordering = £474 per annum.

3. For $k = 1.44$, $E(k) = 0.033$, $\sigma = 20$, $L = 3$, $Q = 380$

$$P' = 1 - \frac{E(k)\sigma \sqrt{L}}{Q}$$

$$P' = 1 - \frac{0.033 \times 20 \times \sqrt{3}}{380}$$

$$P' = 1 - 0.003 = 0.997$$

Customer service level = 99.7 per cent.

4. $D = 40$
$\sigma = 20$
$L = 3$
$R = 12$

For VSL of 94 per cent from tables $k = 1.55$.

$$S = D(R+L) + k\sigma \sqrt{(R+L)}$$
$$= 40(12+3) + 1.55 \times 20 \times \sqrt{(12+3)}$$
$$= 600 + 120 = 720 \text{ units}$$

Maximum stock level = 720 units

Shortage per annum = no occasions × average shortage

$$= \frac{52}{R} E(k)\sigma \sqrt{(R+L)}$$

Hence

$$(1-P')A = \frac{52}{R} \times E(k)\sigma \sqrt{(R+L)}$$

$$P' = 1 - \frac{52}{AR} E(k)\sigma \sqrt{(R+L)}$$

For $k = 1.55$ $E(k) = 0.026$

$$P' = 1 - \frac{52}{3,000 \times 15} \times 0.026 \times 20 \times \sqrt{(15+3)}$$

$$P' = 1 - 0.0025 = 0.997$$

Customer service level = 99.7 per cent.

Chapter 9

2. (a) See Figure A.6.

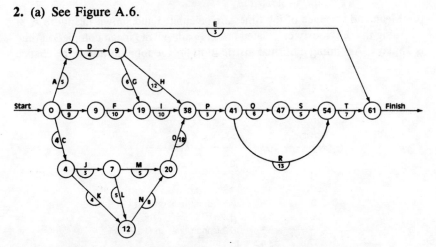

Note: to simplify the figure, numbers inside nodes are early start times, *not* node labels

Figure A.6

(b) The critical path comprises activities CJLNOPRT. Minimum completion time is 61 days.

(c) Earliest start time for M is day 7, latest is day 15 (= 20 − 5).

(d) No change since F not on critical path.

(e) By 1 day, and critical path now routed via CKN.

3. (a) See Figure A.7.

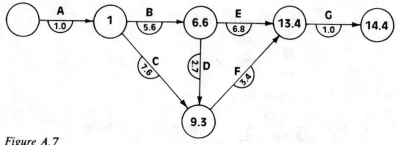

Figure A.7

(b) Using usual time estimates (as shown), critical path is ABEG, with estimated completion time (1.0 + 5.6 + 6.8 + 1.0) = 14.4 days.

Total float of 1.3 days on C, 1.3 days on D and 0.7 days on F, subject to conditions noted. See Table A.2.

(c) Mean and variance of job times are calculated and shown in Figure A.8.

Along the previously calculated critical path ABEG mean completion time is 15 days. Assuming a normal distribution for the total duration, the chance

—— **Table A.2** ——

Activity	ES	LS
A	0	0
B	1.0	1.0
C	1.0	2.3 (conditional on F at LS)
D	6.6	7.3 (conditional on F at LS)
E	6.6	6.6
F	9.3	10.0 (conditional on D at ES)
G	13.4	13.4

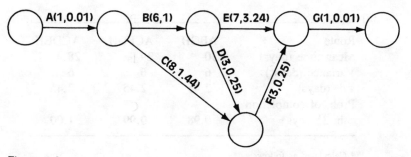

Figure A.8

of exceeding the mean is exactly 50 per cent. There are two other possible routes with the following characteristics:

Route	ABDFG	ACGF
Mean time	14 days	13 days
Variance	1.52 days^2	1.71 days^2
s.d.	1.23 days	1.30 days

From the table in Appendix 1 the probability of route ABDFG meeting 15 days is 79 per cent, as this represents $(15-14)/1.23 = 0.813$ standard deviation units beyond the mean. For route ACFG the probability is 94 per cent $[(15-13)/1.30 = 1.54$ s.d. units]. Hence probability of all paths being complete within 15 days is

$$0.50 \times 0.79 \times 0.94 = 0.37 \text{ or } 37 \text{ per cent}$$

(assuming complete independence of routes) i.e. a rather poor chance of meeting the 15 day deadline.

4. See Figure A.9.

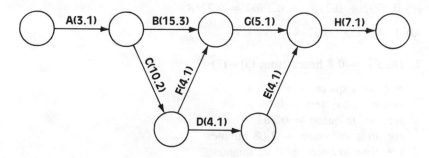

Figure A.9

(a)

Route	ABGH	ACFGH	ACDEH
Mean time (days)	30	29	28
Variance (days^2)	6	6	6
s.d. (days)	2.45	2.45	2.45
Prob. of completion in 35 days*	0.98	0.99	1.00

* Calculated as follows:
$(35-30)/2.45 = 2.04$ s.d. units hence 98 per cent probability, etc.

Overall probability of completion in 35 days is:

$0.98 \times 0.99 \times 1.00 = 97$ per cent for the single project.

(b) Probability of completing all five projects on time $= (0.97)^5 = 86$ per cent.

(c) (i) If the means all increased by 10 per cent the probabilities of completing one project on time would be $0.79 \times 0.90 \times 0.96 = 68$ per cent, hence $(0.68)^5 = 15$ per cent for all; (ii) if all variances double then probability of completing one project on time is $0.925 \times 0.958 \times 0.978 = 86.5$ per cent, hence $(0.865)^5 = 48.5$ per cent for all five projects.

Chapter 10

1. From Table 10.1 with $\lambda = 2$

(a) 0.1353

(b) 0.1804

(c) $0.2707 + 0.2707 + 0.1804 = 0.7218$

(d) $1 - 0.1353 - 0.7218 = 0.1429$.

2. Here $\mu = 0.8$ hence from $(3)-(7)$

prob. of a queue $= \rho = 0.4$
ave. no. in system $= 0.66$
ave. no. in queue $= 0.26$
ave. time in system $= 2.08$ minutes
ave. time in queue $= 0.83$ minutes.

3. If $\mu = 0.4$ then

$$\text{ave. time in queue} < 3 \text{ mins for } \frac{\lambda}{0.4-\lambda} \times \frac{1}{0.4} < 3$$

or

$$\lambda < 0.22 \text{ arrivals per minute}$$

4. Use the formula in question 6. Suppose the switchboard cannot hold waiting calls, hence maximum queue length $q = 0$. Syski's formula reduces to

$$P_n \begin{cases} \dfrac{\rho^n}{n!} P_0 & n \le c \\[2ex] \dfrac{\rho^n}{c!\, c^{n-c}} P_0 & n > c \end{cases}$$

where

$$1/P_0 = \sum_{n=0}^{c} \rho^n/n!$$

The probability of a free line is the probability of less than c calls in the system:

$$\sum_{n=0}^{c-1} P_n = 1 - P_c = 1 - \frac{\rho^c}{c!} P_0$$

Now $\lambda = 40/60 = 0.67$ calls per minute, $\mu = 0.5$ calls per minute and $\rho = \lambda/\mu = 1.34$. Table A.3 shows values of relevant parameters for different numbers of operators c. Evidently, three operators are required to achieve a 90 per cent probability of at least one free line.

5. Here $\lambda = 2$ per hour, μ_1 (without gauge) $= 4$ per hour, μ_2 (with gauge) $= 5$ per hour. Total annual cost of machine idle time $= 1/(\mu - \lambda)$ hours down

—— Table A.3 ——

c	1	2	3	4	5
$\rho^c/c!$	1.34	0.89	0.39	0.17	0.04
$1/P_0$	2.34	3.23	3.62	3.79	3.83
P_0	0.43	0.31	0.28	0.26	0.26
P_c	0.57	0.27	0.10	0.04	0.01
$1 - P_c$	0.43	0.73	0.90	0.96	0.99

per machine $\times$ λ machines per hour $\times$ 8 $\times$ 5 $\times$ 50 $\times$ £5 per hour = £10,000 for μ_1, £6,667 for μ_2. Thus, annual savings of £3,333 more than justify purchase of gauge.

6. For $c = 2$ and $q = 1$

$$1/P_0 = 1 + \rho + \frac{\rho^2}{2!} + \frac{\rho^3}{3!2}$$

Assume $\lambda = 0.8$, $\mu = 1.0$ hence $\rho = 0.8$ (*Note*: the instructor needs to supply these or alternative assumptions.) Then

$$1/P_0 = 1 + 0.8 + 0.32 + 0.04 = 2.16$$

so
$$P_0 = 0.46$$
$$P_1 = \rho P_0 = 0.37$$

$$P_2 = \frac{\rho^2}{2} P_0 = 0.15$$

$$P_3 = \frac{\rho^3}{3!2} P_0 = 0.02$$

Chapter 13

1.

	$P(G) = 0.40$	0.75	0.95
Option 1	5.00	5.00	5.00
Option 2	9.00	3.75	0.75
Option 3	5.01	3.25	1.74

Thus as the quality of the software trapping increases from poor (probability of a trap = 0.40) through the probable value ($P(G) = 0.75$) to very good ($P(G) = 0.95$) we see the optimal decision changes as follows:

Probability	Optimum
0.40	Option 1
0.75	Option 3
0.95	Option 2

It has to be said that when the $P(G) = 0.40$ the decision is only marginally in favour of option 1 against option 3.

2. Calculation of conditional probabilities (Figure A.10).

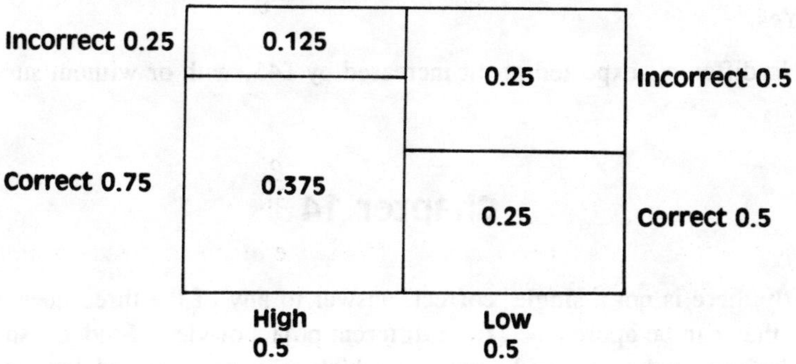

Incorrect 0.25
0.125
0.25
Incorrect 0.5
Correct 0.75
0.375
0.25
Correct 0.5
High
0.5
Low
0.5

Figure A.10

Evaluation of survey option (£'000) (Figure A.11).

Survey
£59.96
0.625
Predict
high
Build
(£95)
0.60
£235
Forecast correct
0.40
−£115
Incorrect
0.375
Predict low
Build
(£1.55)
0.667
−£115
Correct
0.33
£235
Incorrect
Not build
−£15

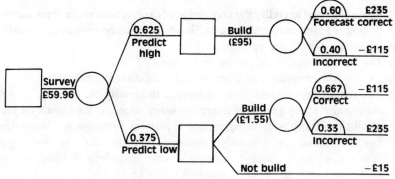

Figure A.11

Note that the survey is so unreliable that even if a low demand is predicted, it is still more profitable to take the risk of building.

Overall evaluation (Figure A.12).

Build
(£75)
0.5
High
£250
0.5
Low
−£100
Survey
£60
Not build
£0

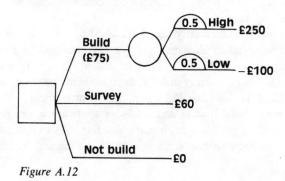

Figure A.12

(a) No: the survey has no information value.

(b) Yes.

(c) No different; expected profit increased by £45, with or without survey.

Chapter 14

Clearly there is not a single 'correct' answer to any of the three questions, since they can be approached from different points of view. Students should also be expected to apply knowledge which they have gained from other chapters.

1. The answer should include the following points at least:

(a) There is a need to codify the knowledge of experts who are in short supply, or simply to improve operational efficiency compared with using manuals.

(b) Training of staff can be improved.

(c) The time of specialists can be better used.

(d) Distinguish between goal-directed and data-driven applications.

(e) The role of the non-technical manager is to identify the need for an ES. He can also set up groups of interested users, to assess the impact on staff and their relations with managers, and to perform a strategic and integrating function. Finally, it is usually a non-technical manager who is going to take the decision about investment in any ES which replaces human expertise which has a large potential effect on profits.

2. The following application areas among others can be thought of as fitting the bill:

(a) Stock control, because one is dealing often with routine decisions and routine forecasts covering many thousands of items. Many argue that the automated decisions flowing from a stock control model are better than those taken by human beings.

(b) The allocation of different types of crude oil to refineries in order best to meet final product demands from many sources. In this case the relationship between decision variables and profit is very well known. Decisions have to be taken even daily, there are many hundreds of equations needed and it is the final 0.25 per cent improvement which counts. Programming blast furnaces and feed-mix applications are similar.

(c) The allocation of products from particular factories to particular depots so as to minimize transport costs is another routine and frequently well-specified area for the application techniques. There can be more argument about vehicle scheduling.

(d) Queueing problems: often the applications are fairly simple, but important for quality of service to the customers. If one cannot solve the equations for a particular situation, one can resort to simulation.

(e) Project management: the prime requirement of the project manager is a system which will enable him to control his project to time, cost and technical performance. Critical path methods do this very well. Runs of the models have to take place frequently and objectives can be quantified fairly easily.

3. The role of OR practitioners in ES could include the following:

(a) Acting as users of intelligent front ends to OR packages, e.g. simulation.
(b) Acting as users of aids to the computer programming part of an OR model and of AI software generally.
(c) Acting as users of ES packages to assess their applicability.
(d) Acting as users of ES applications to assess their usefulness in the company.
(e) Acting as developers of ES generally because of the ability of OR workers generally to
   (i)   abstract systems from the real world;
   (ii) perform knowledge acquisitions;
   (iii) operate with microcomputing technology;
   (iv) integrate various types of IS (as in a decision support system).
(f) Acting as developers of A1 systems which gain from 'OR' involvement (see pages 216−17).
(g) Acting as developers of mathematical models that are called upon within an ES.
(h) Acting as developers of visual interactive models (as front ends to ES).
(i) Acting as developers of time-handling facilities.

Specific techniques or application areas could be simulation/visual interactive modelling (Chapters 12 and 15) and production control and performance comparison; equally the student could speculate about the potential of ES in combination with less promising techniques such as linear programming. Also base the answer on pages 214−15.

— Index —

293